ENERGY IN LATIN AMERICA AND THE CARIBBEAN

THE CURRENT AND FUTURE ROLE OF CONVENTIONAL ENERGY SOURCES IN THE REGIONAL ELECTRICITY GENERATION

LATIN AMERICAN POLITICAL, ECONOMIC, AND SECURITY ISSUES

Additional books in this series can be found on Nova's website
under the Series tab.

Additional e-books in this series can be found on Nova's website
under the e-book tab.

ENERGY SCIENCE, ENGINEERING AND TECHNOLOGY

Additional books in this series can be found on Nova's website
under the Series tab.

Additional e-books in this series can be found on Nova's website
under the e-book tab.

ENERGY IN LATIN AMERICAN AND THE CARIBBEAN

THE CURRENT AND FUTURE ROLE OF CONVENTIONAL ENERGY SOURCES IN THE REGIONAL ELECTRICITY GENERATION

JORGE MORALES PEDRAZA

nova
publishers
New York

For permission to use material from this book please contact us:
Telephone 631-231-7269; Fax 631-231-8175
Web Site: http://www.novapublishers.com

NOTICE TO THE READER

The Publisher has taken reasonable care in the preparation of this book, but makes no expressed or implied warranty of any kind and assumes no responsibility for any errors or omissions. No liability is assumed for incidental or consequential damages in connection with or arising out of information contained in this book. The Publisher shall not be liable for any special, consequential, or exemplary damages resulting, in whole or in part, from the readers' use of, or reliance upon, this material. Any parts of this book based on government reports are so indicated and copyright is claimed for those parts to the extent applicable to compilations of such works.

Independent verification should be sought for any data, advice or recommendations contained in this book. In addition, no responsibility is assumed by the publisher for any injury and/or damage to persons or property arising from any methods, products, instructions, ideas or otherwise contained in this publication.

This publication is designed to provide accurate and authoritative information with regard to the subject matter covered herein. It is sold with the clear understanding that the Publisher is not engaged in rendering legal or any other professional services. If legal or any other expert assistance is required, the services of a competent person should be sought. FROM A DECLARATION OF PARTICIPANTS JOINTLY ADOPTED BY A COMMITTEE OF THE AMERICAN BAR ASSOCIATION AND A COMMITTEE OF PUBLISHERS.

Additional color graphics may be available in the e-book version of this book.

Library of Congress Cataloging-in-Publication Data

Energy power in Latin America and the Caribbean : the current situation and the future role of conventional energy sources for the generation of electricity / editor, Jorge Morales Pedraza.
  p. cm.
  Includes bibliographical references and index.
  ISBN 978-1-62081-899-2 (hbk.)
  1. Energy development--Latin America. 2. Energy development--Caribbean Area. 3. Electric power production--Latin America. 4. Electric power production--Caribbean Area. 5. Energy policy--Latin America. 6. Energy policy--Caribbean Area. I. Pedraza, Jorge Morales.
  HD9502.L32E556 2012
  333.793'2098--dc23
                                                                    2012020018

Published by Nova Science Publishers, Inc. † *New York*

CONTENTS

PREFACE

It is certain that energy production and, particularly the generation and sustained growth of electricity, constitute indispensable elements for the economic and social progress for any country. Energy, undoubtedly, constitutes the motive force of civilization and it determines, to a high degree, the level of the future economic and social development of a country. To ensure adequate economic and social growth it is vital, that all available energy sources are used in the most efficient and economic manner for electricity generation.

Electricity generation using fossil fuels is a major and growing contributor to the emission of carbon dioxide to the atmosphere, gas that produces a significant change in the world climate. These changes are affecting, in one way or another, almost all countries in all regions. However, renewable energy sources for the generation of electricity, including the use of nuclear energy need not produce CO_2 and would have no negative impact on the world climate. However, all approved plans for the use of nuclear energy for electricity generation in the coming years are under deep revision in several countries after the nuclear accident in the Fukushima nuclear power plant located in Japan in March 2011. As a consequence of this accident, some countries have already decided to suspend expansion of their current nuclear power programs; others have suspended the introduction of a nuclear power program for electricity generation, while others have decided to shut down all operating nuclear power plants in the coming years.

One of the main problems that the world is facing is how to satisfy the increase in electricity demand using all available energy sources in the most efficient manner and without increasing CO_2 emission.

The preparation of a national energy policy, in which priorities and preferences are identified, should be one of the main governmental responsibilities. Every country's energy mix should involve a range of national preferences and priorities in order to satisfy the foreseable increase in electricity demand without affecting the climate. These national policies and strategies should balance between expected energy shortages, environmental quality, energy security, energy cost, public attitudes, safety and security, and production and service capabilities.

Keywords: Energy policy; energy strategies; energy reform; Oil; natural gas; liquid natural gas; coal; pipelines; refineries; electricity generation; oil reserves; gas reserves; coal reserves

ACKNOWLEDGMENT

During the preparation of the present book different professionals assisted me in the compilation of relevant information regarding the current and future role of fossil fuels in the region electricity generation. Master Juan Carlos Portal, from Ceiba Investment Ltd, UK, assisted me in the preparation of the different sections dedicated to the current use of different fossil fuels for the electricity generation in Cuba.

My lovely daughter MSc. Lisette Morales Meoqui has been an extremely helpful assistant in collecting the necessary information and reference materials used in the preparation of the book, in addition of her own Doctorate studies on Economics, and her current job as Head of Finance in the Austrian firm Zeno Track GmbH. My dear son Jorge Morales Meoqui, now Doctor in Economics has been also extremely helpful in the revision of some of the initial materials used during the preparation of the book.

Without any doubt, the present book is a reality thanks to the valuable support of my lovely wife, Aurora Tamara Meoqui Puig, who had assumed other family responsibilities in order to give me the indispensable time and the adequate environment to write the book.

INTRODUCTION

Preparation of a book, which has an objective to ensure the survival of the humankind, is certainly a complex task. Providing a stable and secure supply of energy is a great challenge for governments seeking to achieve sustainable development goals, since the main energy sources providing economic growth and social development are present in the Earth only in specific locations and in limited quantities.

Energy is, undoubtedly, an important element in the struggle of any country to alleviate poverty, promote economic growth and foster social development. But as the world consume more and more energy, stress is placed on current level of energy reserves and the environment at national, regional and international levels. The world should work together to safeguard the environment without slowing socioeconomic development. Third World countries should look for adequate technological solutions in order to change present unsustainable patterns of consumption and production in developed countries and to seek the low-hanging fruit and the win-win solutions that provide the least costly ways of achieving sustainable development goals.

The present book has five Chapters and complements my other book entitled "Energy in the Latin American and the Caribbean Region: The Current and Future Role of Renewables and Nuclear Energy in the Region Electricity Generation", to be published by Nova Science at the end of 2012.

Chapter I provide a general overview of the current and future role of conventional energy sources in the region electricity generation. According to IEO (2010) and the World Energy Council (2008), the Latin American and the Caribbean region have 10% of the world's oil reserves, 5% of the world's natural gas reserves, and 1.6% of the world's coal reserves.

The Western Hemisphere is roughly self-sufficient in energy. The USA and the Southern Cone[1] are the two principal centers of heavy and increasing energy consumption and energy external dependence, while Canada, the Gulf of Mexico, and the Andean zone are the principal hydrocarbons producers and net exporters. The USA consumed in 2009 around 19 070 million barrels of oil per day, which represents between 22% and 23% of world's oil

---

[1] Southern Cone includes the following four countries: Argentina, Chile, Uruguay, and Paraguay.

total consumption. In the Latin American and the Caribbean region nine countries produce today oil and/or gas in sufficient volumes to ensure their self-sufficiency and, in some cases, to be or become significant exporters of hydrocarbons in the near future. These countries are Venezuela, the country with the highest oil reserves confirmed in the world in 2011 (296,500 billion of barrels), and with an oil production in 2012 of 2 480 000 barrels per day; Mexico with oil reserves of 11 692 million barrels in 2010, and with an oil production of 2 910 000 barrels per day; Brazil, with oil reserves of 12 857 million barrels in 2010, and with an oil production of 2 055 000 barrels per day; Colombia with oil reserves in 2011 of 1.9 billion barrels, and with an oil production of 786 000 barrels per day; Argentina with oil reserves of 2.587 billion barrels in 2010, and with an oil production of 642 000 barrels per day; Ecuador with oil reserves of 7 062 million of barrels in 2010, and with an oil production of 486 000 barrels per day; and Trinidad and Tobago with oil reserves of 728.3 million of barrels at the end of 2010, and with an oil production of 151 000 barrels per day.

Chapter II includes updated information on the current and future role of oil in the region electricity generation during the coming years. Mexico and Central and South American countries delivered nearly 14% of world's oil production in 2005. In 2008, the region produced 8.8% of the world's oil production, representing a reduction of 5.2% respect to 2005. Latin American production of crude oil[2] averaged 7.15 million barrels per day in 2003, and it is expected to increase this production to almost 12 million barrels per day by 2030; this represents an increase of 4.75 million barrels per day or 68% respect to 2003. However, this goal will be achieved only if Venezuela, Mexico, and Brazil, among a limited number of other countries in the region, increase their oil production in a significant manner in the coming years. Oil production is dominated at present by the following countries: Mexico, Venezuela, Brazil, Ecuador, Colombia, and Argentina. Venezuela and Mexico are, at the same time, the most important oil exporter's countries in the Latin American and the Caribbean region. Brazil, Colombia, Ecuador, and Argentina are important destinations for foreign investment, and helpfully produce enough oil to meet their own domestic needs, particularly in the case of Brazil. Within the region, only Mexico, Brazil, and Venezuela produced in 2010 more than two million barrels per day.

It is important to stress that all countries in the Central American sub-region depend on oil and by-product imports for electricity generation. The level of oil dependency by country is the following: Panama (66%), Costa Rica (52%), Honduras (50%), Nicaragua (44%), Guatemala (42%), and El Salvador (21%).

The Andean region accounts for almost 27% of South American oil consumption, which has been on the increase, especially in Venezuela in recent years. Venezuela is the country with the highest forecast oil demand in the region until 2018, followed by Colombia, Ecuador, Peru, and Bolivia. The oil demand in the Andean region is expected to increase from around 750 000 barrels per day in 1990 to around 2.5 million barrels per day in 2018; this represents an increase of 333%.

---

[2] The average world' oil production in 2011 reached 88.5 million barrels per day. The average world's oil consumption in that year reached 89.1 million barrels per day, exceeding the oil production in 0.6 million barrels per day. The deficit between the oil production and consumption is due to an increase in the demand of China, India, and some other countries in the Asia and the Pacific region.

Chapter III provides updated information on the current and future role of natural gas in the region electricity generation during the coming years. In 2003, Latin American and the Caribbean's proven natural gas reserves amounted to 7.5 trillion m^3, which represents 5% of the world's total natural gas reserves. In 2004, the regional's natural gas reserves registered a slight descent of 0.02%, reaching the amount of 4.98% of the world's total. In 2005, the regional's natural gas reserves were estimate in around 4.4% of the world's total; this represents a further decrease of 0.6% respect to 2004. The countries with the largest natural gas reserves in the region are Venezuela, with 4.97 trillion m^3, very far from Bolivia, the second country with the largest natural gas reserves in the region.

According to EIA sources, Latin American and the Caribbean's natural gas production in 2009 was 6,720 billion m^3. In 2008, the level of consumption in the whole region (excluding Mexico) was 4,706 billion m^3, an increase of 2.75% in comparison to 2007. The level of consumption in Central and South America represent 4.27% of the world's total. Production of natural gas in the Latin American and the Caribbean region is expected to expand significantly over the next three decades, reaching 516 billion of m^3 in 2030. The share of offshore production is expected to climb from the current 20% to 32% in 2030; this represents an increase of 12%. Domestic demand is expected to grow fast from 101 billion of m^3 in 2001 to more than 370 billion of m^3 in 2030; this represents an increase of 266%. Demand in the power generation sector will account for more than half of this increase, spurred by a need in many countries to reduce dependence on hydro power for electricity generation. Brazil is expected to lead the growth with 7% annual average demand growth over the next thirty years; this country will account for 20% of the region's gas demand in 2030, and will play a pivotal role in the region's gas infrastructure evolution. As a whole, for the twenty six OLADE countries, natural gas consumption accounted in 2003 for 19% of the region's primary energy mix. Starting from this point, natural gas consumption could be expected to increase from 192 109 m^3 per day in 2000 to about 422 109 m^3 per day in 2010; this represents an increase of 119.7%.

With respect the future of natural gas it is important to stick out the following: Energy demand in most countries is expect to continue to outrun economic growth with elasticity in the range 1 to 1.1. Therefore, economic growth in most countries of the Latin American and the Caribbean region will require a substantial increase in energy needs, and consequently provide a large potential for natural gas market development. The decision adopted by some Southern Cone countries to refurbish oil-fired-power plants to gas-fired-power plants in order to reduce the participation of oil in their energy balance will increase the use of natural gas for electricity generation in the region.

Chapter IV includes updated information about the current and future role of coal in the region electricity generation during the coming years. In 2010, the Latin American region has proven recoverable coal reserves of 16 billion tons, which represent between 1.6% and 2% of the world's coal reserves. According to BP Statistic report 2010, Brazil has 7.06 billion ton of coal reserves, which are the highest in the region, followed by Colombia with 6.82 billion tons, Mexico with 1.2 billion tons, and Venezuela with 0.48 billion tons. Recoverable coal reserves by type in Central and South America, excluding Brazil, are the following: Hard coal: 8.5 billion tons; Sub-bituminous: 2.2 billion tons, and lignite: 0.1 billion tons.

Central and South American countries consumed 0.9 quadrillion Btu of coal in 2007. Brazil, with the world's ninth-largest steel production in 2007, accounted for 51% of the region's coal demand, while Chile, Colombia, Argentina, and Peru accounted for most of the remainder. Coal consumption in Central and South American countries is expect to increases by 0.8 quadrillion Btu from 2007 to 2035, with most of the increase in Brazil, primarily for coke manufacture and electricity generation. Overall, South America's imports of coking coal—driven primarily by demand in Brazil— will grow from about 0.4 quadrillion Btu in 2008, to 1.1 quadrillion Btu in 2035; this represents an increase of 175%. Brazil and Chile account for most of the increase in thermal coal imports to South America through 2035.

Chapter V includes a summary of the main conclusions reached about the participation of conventional energy sources in the region electricity generation during the coming years.

Chapter I

GENERAL OVERVIEW

Worldwide, energy[3] concerns have been transformed in an important issue for the future of the humankind. For this reason, governments are adopting comprehensive energy policies in order to use, in the most effective and economic manner, all available energy sources[4] for the production of electricity[5]. According to British Petroleum Statistical Review of World Energy (2010), as result of these policies world primary energy consumption – including oil, natural gas, coal, nuclear and hydro power – fell by 1.1% in 2009, the first decline since 1982 and the largest decline (in percentage terms) since 1980.

Energy poses a formidable challenge for governments seeking to achieve sustainable development goals, because some of the main energy sources that can be used to achieve these goals can be found in the Earth only in limited amounts and in specific locations. Energy is an important element in the fight to alleviate poverty, promote economic growth, and foster social development. But as the world consume more and more energy, stress is placed on the current level of energy reserves and on the impact on the environment at national, regional and international levels. The world should work together to protect the environment without slowing socioeconomic development, particularly in developing countries, and to look for technological solutions in order to change unsustainable patterns of consumption and production prevailing in industrialized countries.

Current estimates indicate that 1.6 billion people are without access to electricity and that 2.4 billion people have no access to modern fuels for cook their food. This means that approximately one third of the world's population live in the dark, eat uncooked or semi-cooked food and/or are exposed to hazardous indoor air pollution on a daily basis. In the specific case of Latin American and the Caribbean countries, around 34.1 million of peoples have no access to electricity in 2008. Expanding energy access to this group of people is essential for alleviating poverty. Improving energy access for the alleviation of poverty also means promoting small and medium-scaled businesses, industrial development and better transportation networks in a general effort to improve socio-economic well-being. All of this

---

[3] When the term "energy", is used in the present book, is to refer to heat and power.

[4] When the term "energy sources" is used in the present book, is to refer to the different types of energy used as the input to generate electricity or heat.

[5] When the term "electricity" is used in the present book means an energy carrier with a very wide range of applications. Electricity is used in almost all kinds of human activity ranging from industrial production, household use, agriculture, commerce, for running machines, lighting and heating of houses, among others.

will require greater energy use. To achieve these goals with minimal adverse effects on the environment is a basic goal of sustainable development (IAEA-UN, 2007).

For the above reasons, energy–related issues dominate the discussion inside government's officials as well as the debates in parliaments, academia, business, and private and public industries, multilateral organizations, the civil society, non-governmental organizations (NGOs), among others. Potential confrontations over oil and gas supplies, energy reserves and transportation networks have become geopolitical flashpoints. The extension in the use of oil, carbon and large hydro power plants are now sensitive political issues in many countries due to the opposition of environment groups to increase the use of these types of energy sources for electricity generation, bearing in mind its negative impact in the environment. On the other hand, energy security has become a more important factor than military capability, diplomatic strategy, and even political stability (Arriagada, 2006).

It is important for policy makers to understand the implications and impacts of different energy programs, alternative policies, strategies and plans in shaping economic and social development within their countries, and the feasibility of making development sustainable over time. The use of energy indicators, when properly analyzed and interpreted, can be useful tools for communicating data relating to energy and sustainable development issues to policy makers and to the public, and for promoting institutional dialogue. Energy indicators can be used to monitor progress of past policies, and to provide a "reality check" on strategies for future sustainable development. This cannot be done, however, without critical analysis of the underlying causal and driving factors (IAEA-UN, 2007).

SUSTAINABLE MANAGEMENT OF ENERGY

Sustainable management of energy is a key element of economic and social development and must take account of the environmental dimension (climate change and implementation of the Kyoto Protocol, among others). In view of the poor performances of Latin American and the Caribbean energy systems as a whole, national administration should be provided with expertise in the form of aid for pooling experiences and knowledge. OLADE has aggregated the key issues on "sustainable energy management" into a program called "Integration and Sustainable Development." The program comprises the following objectives:

a) To contribute to mitigate contaminating emissions from energy production and use based on the European experience, while not neglecting the growing demands of development in the Latin American and the Caribbean region, and prioritizing attention to the least protected sectors of the population;

b) To support the creation of an appropriate environment for regional energy trade through the harmonization of laws, regulations and standards, and the identification of energy integration projects in order to better utilize the natural resources of the region and reduce the environmental impact of energy activities;

c) To satisfy the cross-cutting information requirements of the OLADE's member countries, the Secretariat and the program as a whole, in a timely and properly updated manner;

d) To train the human resources of the region's energy sector for the new challenges inherent in the liberalization of the sector and the integration of regional energy markets.

The Western Hemisphere is roughly self-sufficient in energy. The USA and the Southern Cone[6] are the two principal centers of heavy and increasing energy consumption and energy external dependence, while Canada, the Gulf of Mexico and the Andean zone are the principal hydrocarbons producers and net exporters. The USA consumed, in 2009, around 19 070 million of barrels of oil per day, which represents between 22% and 23% of world's oil consumption. Today, nine Latin American and the Caribbean countries produce oil and/or gas in sufficient volumes to ensure their self-sufficiency, and, in some cases, to be or become significant exporters of hydrocarbons in the near future. These are the cases of Venezuela, the country with the highest oil reserves confirmed in the world in 2011 (296,500 billion of barrels) and with an oil production in 2012 of 2,480,000 barrels per day; Mexico with oil reserves of 11 692 million barrels in 2010, and with an oil production of 2 910 000 barrels per day; Brazil with oil reserves of 12 857 million barrels in 2010, and with an oil production of 2 055 000 barrels per day; Colombia with oil reserves in 2011 of 1.9 billion barrels in 2011, and with an oil production of 786 000 barrels per day; Argentina with oil reserves of 2.587 billion barrels in 2010, and with an oil production of 642 000 barrels per day; Ecuador with oil reserves of 7 062 million of barrels in 2010, and with an oil production of 486 000 barrels per day; and Trinidad and Tobago with oil reserves of 728.3 million of barrels at the end of 2010, and with an oil production of 151 000 barrels per day. Brazil exports petroleum and over the medium-term it could become a very important oil exporter. Colombia and Peru may also become influential petroleum exporters in the future. Argentina produce sufficient gas to satisfy its internal demand but the amount of natural gas exported to other countries, particularly Chile, has been declining since 2001.

THE DEVELOPMENT OF THE ENERGY SECTOR

During the 1980s, under a severe economic crisis experienced by most countries in the Latin American and the Caribbean region, the model used for energy development showed its shortcomings and collapsed. The main problems were, among others:

a) The political interference in State-owned enterprise management and sector policies;
b) A weak regulatory framework;
c) A lack of separation of policy making, regulation, and ownership roles of the States;
d) Wide-spread subsidies in electricity tariffs;
e) A lack of incentives for improving efficiency.

These problems, complemented by high inflation and devaluation rates, led to a deterioration of State-owned enterprises finances, poor performance of State-owned enterprises, bad investments, worsening of reliability and quality of service, and difficulties in financing expansion plans. The final result was that, in most countries of the region, the

---

[6] Southern Cone covers the following four countries: Argentina, Chile, Uruguay, and Paraguay.

power sector became a major drain of public finances, including high level of corruption, and a constraint for economic and social development.

Major efforts were made during the 1980s by several Latin American and the Caribbean countries to improve the performance of State-owned enterprises by implementing rehabilitation programs of infrastructure, management, and finances. However, most of these efforts failed as they were not supported by any substantial institutional reform.

In the 1980s and early 1990s, many countries in the region made efforts to improve the performance of State-owned enterprises through programs that did not involve major sector restructuring, mainly financial and operational rehabilitation, technical assistance and contract-plans. However, these programs have proven to be ineffective in most cases. In the early 1990s, it was clear that the poor condition of the power sector in the region was related to structural factors and that the prevailing institutional arrangements in most countries were not satisfactory for the future provision of a reliable and efficient electricity service. According to Dussan (1996), the main factors were:

a) State-owned enterprises operated with little autonomy as State's offices with conflicting mandates to invest and operate efficiently and, at the same time, to meet unclear government's social and political goals. The lack of autonomy and the government's interference in day-to-day operations has not resulted in a better control for good performance. On the contrary, it has contributed to a lack of management accountability and the weakening of performance targets;

b) State-owned enterprises operated in many cases under a weak regulatory framework characterized by a lack of clear rules and objectives. Regulation of State-owned enterprises was usually informal and carried out through direct government influence or self-regulation, in accordance with State-owned enterprises interpretation of their own statutes. Usually, price regulation was based on political and macroeconomic considerations and resulted in the application of tariff subsidies that were not transparent nor focalized, distorted price signals and encouraged inefficient consumption, resulted in tariff levels that were not sufficient to cover costs, and were regressive for they usually benefit medium income customers;

c) State-owned enterprises usually held a legal monopoly position, served a captive market and faced no threats from potential competitors and, therefore, did not have incentives to focus on customers' needs or to improve its efficiency;

d) The investment decision process used in the 1980s relied on a centralized and sometimes inflexible organization designed to implement a least-cost plan, valid for a set of assumptions on the behavior of key variables and generally comprising relatively large power generation plants requiring long preparation and construction periods. In many cases, expansion plans lacked flexibility to adapt to changing conditions and the decision process was too slow to respond to unexpected changes. Furthermore, central planning was used in many cases to please special interests and meet not clear government objectives, resulting sometimes in the development of large and costly generation projects;

e) Governments allocated a major share of public funds and public debt to finance new investment in the energy sector;

f) The indiscriminate application of tariff subsidies and the inefficient operation and control of State-owned enterprises have required periodic financial rescue operations with huge transfers from national budget. In general, these operations have been carried out with little planning and poor results: Resources are transferred but without significant structural associated with these transferences; temporarily, tariffs are adjusted and performance is slightly improved; the same conditions prevailing before the operation surface once again and the cycle starts over.

The development of the power sector in the Latin American and the Caribbean region will be critical for the region's economic growth over the coming decades. The economic and social development of the region over the past forty years has been supported by a widespread program of electrification that has greatly increased the provision of electricity services to households, commerce, and industry.

Over the coming decades, the supply of electric power will need to be expanded further in order to meet the growing demand for electricity and to reduce the current number of families living without electricity but how the production and use of electricity develops will have broad ramifications for the diverse economies and societies of the different countries.

Despite the favourable economic situation of the region, it is facing a severe energy crisis and this situation constitutes an important impediment to the economic and social development of the region as a whole. The crisis stems from the mismanagement of energy resources, lack of investment, and the absence of effective energy integration. Despite efforts made by a group of countries in the past years in trying to move forward several energy integration schemes, the crisis affecting the energy sector has not been solved yet.

The lack of regional integration is due to the lack of political will of several governments to undertake energy integration in a more effective manner, the inadequacy of normative mechanisms to regulate the integration process, the lack of incentives to the private sector to support regional energy integration, the lack of sufficient resources to finance some of the energy integration proposals submitted by some governments, particularly in the past decades, and the ineffectiveness of international organizations to stimulate energy integration in the region, among other factors.

On the other hand, it is important to know that less than 1% of the Americas' primary energy demand is met with wind, solar, and various forms of ocean power −as opposed to nuclear energy, hydroelectric, biomass, and low-carbon energy sources. For this reason, traditional fossil fuels[7] continue to dominate (over 80%) the Hemisphere's primary energy mix, and will continue to do so well into the future, if the region's energy scenario is not radically transformed (Isbell, 2009).

From Figure 1, the following can be stated: Fossil fuels are the type of energy dominant in the whole Latin American and the Caribbean region, with the exception of Central America. In that sub-region, renewable energy sources are the dominant type of energy used for electricity generation.

The use of renewable energy sources for electricity generation, as a real substitute of fossil fuels has become, in recent years, an important component of the energy balance in several countries.

---

[7] Fuel is any substance burned as a source of heat or power. The heat is derived from the combustion process in which carbon and hydrogen in the fuel substance combine with oxygen and release heat. The provision of energy as heat or power in either mechanical or electrical form is the major reason for burning fuels. Fuels can be produced in a large diversity of ways: deep mine for coal, offshore platform for oil, forest for fuel-wood, etc.

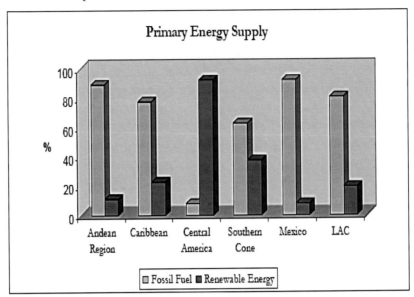

Source: OLADE- SIEE, 2005.

Figure 1. Primary energy supply.

However, there are some limitations in the use of renewable energy sources for this electricity generation in some Latin American and the Caribbean countries, mainly due to the opposition of the public opinion. For example, the construction of more large dams to generate electricity is facing strong public opposition in Venezuela, Chile, and Brazil. These countries have already a large production of electricity using hydro energy sources and the public has the perception that there is very little what can be done to increase the use of hydro power for the production of electricity in the future, without affecting the environment. The use of solar and wind energy for electricity generation ís today very limited in several countries of the region, and it is expected that this situation will not chnage significantly in the near-term.

The provision of adequate and reliable energy services at an affordable cost in a secure and environmentally benign manner and in conformity with social and economic development needs is an essential element of sustainable development. Energy is vital for eradicating poverty, improving human welfare and raising living standards (UNDP, UNDESA and WEC, 2000). However, most current patterns of energy supply and use are considered unsustainable (UN, 2001). Many areas of the world have no reliable and secure energy supplies, and hence no energy services, which limits economic and social development. In other areas, environmental degradation from energy production and use inhibits sustainable development.

Adequate and affordable energy services have been critical to economic and social development and for the transition from subsistence agricultural economies to modern industrial and service-oriented societies. Energy is central to improved social and economic well-being, and is indispensable for industrial and commercial wealth generation. But, however, essential it may be for economic and social development, energy is only a means to an end. The end is a sustainable economy and a clean environment, high living standards, prosperity, and good health (IAEA-UN, 2007).

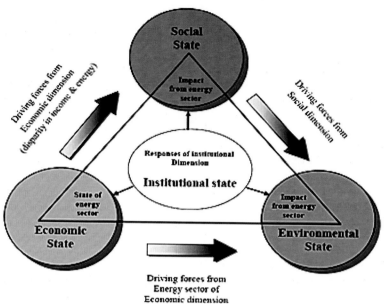

Source: IAEA/IEA (2007).

Figure 2. Interrelationship among sustainability dimensions of the energy sector.

In relation to energy instability it is important to be aware of the following: The Latin American and the Caribbean region is an important but somewhat instable world player in energy matters. This instability is due in part to the region's frequent political disturbance as well as to comparably slow economic performance compared with other developing regions, particularly Asia and the Pacific, which have led to power production below the region's potential. This situation can change in the coming years, if Latin American and the Caribbean governments have the political will to do so.

TECHNOLOGIES AVAILABLES IN THE ENERGY SECTOR

In the Latin American and the Caribbean context around 73% of the power plants operating in the region have nominal outputs less than 50 MW, 23% are in the range of 50 MW to 400 MW, and 4% are in the range of 400 MW and 1 000 MW. In the region, the main types of fossil-fuel-fired power plants are plants with conventional steam or gas turbines. Gas turbines account for 27%; steam turbines for 56%; gas-combined-cycle plants contribute 7%; and diesel engines 6% of the power generation. The balance of 4% is made up by geothermal and nuclear power plants. Coal actually plays no major role in the Latin American and the Caribbean power sector, although large coal reserves are present in Brazil, Colombia, and Mexico.

Adequate power technologies for large scale power generation corresponding to the Latin American and the Caribbean power market needs comprise gas and steam turbine power plants, as well as combined-cycle power plants running on natural gas. Options for the longer term (more than twenty years) include pulverized coal combustion and integrated gas combine-cycle power plants, for the time when the oil and gas reserves of the region start to deplete. For small-to-medium-power outputs (up to approximately 30 MW), a diesel generator power plant can be a genuine alternative. On short-to-medium term (less than fifteen years) new installations of power generation will be mainly based on natural gas and corresponding power generation technologies.

For the fossil-fuel-fired power sector there are three main technology options that can be considered for the electricity generation in the short-to-medium-term. These are the following: a) Combined-cycle gas turbine technology (CCGT); b) Refurbishment of oil to gas-fired-power plants; and c) Retrofitting of emission reduction facilities.

Summing up the following can be stated: Fossil-fuel-fired power generation in the Latin American and the Caribbean region heavily relies on gas and oil utilization and corresponding power generation technologies, such as gas and oil fired gas turbines and boilers with steam turbines. For decentralized power supply in remote areas, diesel engines are suited best, as long as the power interconnection network and the local power distribution network do not provide the requested coverage. It is, however, a clear political objective of the region to expand the power interconnection network, as well as the gas pipeline network in the current decade, in order to match the growing power demand foreseen of industry and population. Huge progress can already be recorded concerning the power coverage in densely populated areas, where the supply of electricity almost covers more than 97% of the population in several countries. However, in 2008, the power coverage of the whole region was 93% due to the limited coverage of rural areas (70%).

THE ENERGY REFORM

In the second half of the 20th century, the reform of the structure of the energy sector in the Latin American and the Caribbean region was implemented with great speed. The pioneer country in the region in applying an energy reform was Chile. In 1982, the country was the first in the world in de-regulate and privatize the electric sector. Between 1992 and 1996, a group of countries followed the Chilean example taking advantage of the lesson learned with the aim of using their own models. Brazil carried out energy reform in 1996. A second deep energy reform in Brazil was carried out during 2004, with the purpose of incentivizing the development of their hydroelectric potential. Another group of countries carried out similar energy reforms until the year 2000.

Two groups of countries with success results can be identified associated with the implementation of energy reforms. The first group includes countries that have a wide energy demand with space for the competition, and, for this reason, a model of free market was chosen by them. This group of countries reflects satisfactory results in reducing energy losses, in improvement of reliability, and in producing a substantial improvement in the image of the energy public sector.

The second group includes countries where the reduced size of the energy demand does not justify a competition and a free market model, and, for this reason, they opted for unique buyer's structure. This group also obtains satisfactory results in the analyzed indicators and in the reception of private investments. However, in a limited number of countries such as Cuba, Haiti, Paraguay, and Suriname, the energy sector still is under the control of the State.

The economic and fiscal crisis in the 1980s, the poor performance of the State-owned enterprises, and the international trend toward deregulation, competition and privatization, prompted most of the governments in the region to consider reforming their electric power sectors. In general, the reform programs were designed to meet the following basic objectives:

a) To ensure the long-run development and provision of electricity service in the most effective manner and in the lowest cost possible. This requires: i) That the utility is remunerated or compensated sufficiently to cover its operating costs and meet its cost of capital, so that required expansion can be financed; ii) That projects required to meet demand are commissioned on time and on cost; and iii) That the technical capacity to provide the service is developed and maintained;

b) To achieve economic efficiency in the provision of services and use of electricity through least-cost expansion, operation and efficient management, and cost-reflective pricing;

c) To secure social and national objectives. This includes, among other things, improvements in service penetration, security and reliability of supply, environmental goals and provision of electricity service to low income consumers, among others;

d) To reduce the role and intervention of the State in the energy sector, through the concentration of their activities in the field of energy regulation;

e) To attract private capital;

f) To introduce competition and price deregulation, wherever feasible;

g) To regulate the residual monopoly areas, in a manner that maximizes the benefits and reduces the costs of intervention.

The situation only got worse in the beginning of the 1990s. In spite of the increasing demand for electricity, which amounted to 2 500 MW per year on average during 1991-1994, the expansion of generating and transmission capacity was only 1 080 MW per year. Several utilities that embraced ambitious expansion plans during the 1970s and 1980s were not able to pay the loans contracted. Others companies lacked more professional management and had high running costs that also could not be met with their revenues. The prevailing institutional and regulatory framework was also not adequate at the time to solve financial transactions within generating and distributing companies, and the huge debt that was accumulated by them (De Martino Jannuzzi, 2004).

To avoid another energy crisis in the future, several Latin American and the Caribbean countries started, at of the beginning of the 1990s, an energy reform with the purpose of:

a) Improving further the energy balance in each country;

b) Reducing the use of fossil fuels for electricity generation;

c) Increasing the participation of renewable energy sources available in the region in the energy mix;

d) Adopting of new institutional and regulatory arrangements in order to reduce the role and intervention of the States in the energy sector;

e) Introducing competition and price deregulation, wherever feasible;

f) Promoting the participation of the private capital in the energy sector;

g) Expanding on-going nuclear power programs for electricity generation in a limited group of countries, in order to reduce the CO_2 emissions to the atmosphere;

h) Diminishing the cost of the production electricity using the most cost effective and efficiency energy sources.

In general, on the energy reform programs the following can be stated: The energy reform programs carried in several countries of the Latin American and the Caribbean region were adopted with the aim of addressing the failure of existing institutional arrangements to meet the above objectives, by introducing competition and private capital as major instruments to achieve economic efficiency and by clarifying the role of the State in the energy sector[8]. These programs are based on the following basic principles:

a) Separation of the policy making, regulatory and commercial functions of the State;

b) Creation of a competitive wholesale power market and price deregulation in countries where competition in the market is feasible;

c) Establishment of a clear, stable and non-discriminatory regulatory framework;

d) Participation of private capital in the provision of public services, according to comprehensive laws and regulations in force (Dussan, 1996).

The main policy elements that a government has to keep in mind to design an effective energy reform program in the energy sector are, among others, the following:

a) The scope and degree of competition;

b) The market structure;

c) The ownership structure.

According to Bacon and Besant-Jones (2002), the main principles that should be followed to implement successfully an energy reform are the following:

1. Obliging electricity enterprises to operate according to commercial principles. This obligation extends to State-owned entities that undertake one or more of the basic functions in the supply chain, namely generation, transmission, system control, distribution, and supply services to users of electricity;

2. Introduction of competition in order to improve sector performance in terms of efficiency, customer responsiveness, innovation, and viability. Competition can be developed in the generation and supply service segments but in most cases is not feasible in the network segments (transmission, distribution, and system control) because these functions are natural monopolies;

3. Restructuring of the electric power supply chain due to the introduction of competition. This involves breaking up (unbundling) the incumbent power utility

---

[8] It is important to stick out the following: The Southern Cone was the sub-region where the first market opening and liberalization reforms of the electric sector structure over the past decades were introduced, replacing organizations based on vertical integration and on State monopolies by a vertical and horizontal unbundling of the industry. Electricity markets were established both at wholesale and retail level and State companies were privatized (World Energy Council, 2008).

into multiple generators and distributors of power that trade with each other in a competitive wholesale power market;

4. Privatization of the unbundled electricity generators and distributors under dispersed ownership, because competition is unlikely to develop properly between entities that are under common ownership—whether State or private. In developing countries, furthermore, private investors and operators are expected to bring in financial resources and technical and managerial expertise that will rectify the prevailing low standard of electricity supply by State-owned power utilities;

5. Development of economic regulation of the power market that is applied transparently by an agency that operates independently from influence by government, electricity suppliers or consumers. In the wholesale market, the focus of regulation is to prevent anticompetitive abuses of market power. In the retail market, the focus of regulation should be on balancing the interests of suppliers with the interests of their captive customers;

6. Focusing of government's role on policy formation and execution while giving up the roles of operator and investor with divestiture of State ownership in generation and distribution.

However, taking into account the peculiarities of the energy power system, the political climate, the country endowments and situation limiting the scope of these sector policies, the question to be answered is the following: How much competition can be introduced and which are the different options available for changing the market and ownership structures? Generally, there is a trade off in the choice of policy elements, as they are interrelated and have to be reconciled to achieve the objectives of an energy reform program. Competition is introduced to achieve economic efficiency but may increase the investor risk, and the cost of capital required to finance expansion.

A market structure, with vertical and horizontal separation of generation, transmission, and distribution activities facilitates competition, but increase transaction costs, and may represent a loss in economies of scale and scope. Privatization will raise new financial resources, but the maximization of assets value may require conditions that would constraint competition, like take or pay power purchase agreements for generation plants or monopoly rights over specific distribution areas.

It is important to single out that prior to the energy reform carried out in several Latin American and the Caribbean countries in the 1990s, the whole energy sector in Cuba (since the 1960s), Suriname, Haiti and Paraguay was in the hands of the public sector. In several other countries, however, private investors are shareholders of energy companies with additional participation of the States among them[9].

There are also a few wholly State-owned companies particularly in, Jamaica, Ecuador, Mexico, Trinidad and Tobago, Honduras, Costa Rica, Grenada, Guyana, Uruguay, Venezuela, Colombia, Brazil and Nicaragua, but in some cases they participate only partially in the energy sector. In some other countries such as Argentina, Bolivia, Guatemala, Panama, Barbados, Chile, El Salvador, Peru, and Dominican Republic, the electrical system is predominantly under private ownership.

---

[9] In general, there has been strong resistance to electricity privatization in several Latin American countries. The resistance was relative weak in Argentina, Brazil and Chile.

Table 1. Summary of the electricity market structure in the South Cone

Segment	Argentina	Chile	Paraguay	Uruguay
Generation	Private companies. State share: 26%	Private companies	State company ANDE	TEP and private companies
Transmission	Private companies	Private companies	ANDE	TEP
Distribution	Private companies, some concessions controlled by the State	Private companies	ANDE	TEP
Regulator	SE-ENRE	CNE/SEC	-	URSEA

Note: SE (Secretary of Energy); ENRE (State regulator); CNE (National Energy Commission); TEP (National Administration of Power Plants and Electricity Transmission; ENDE (State regulator and provider).

Source: World Energy Council (WEC).

During the 1990s, several Latin American and the Caribbean countries liberalized their regimes in the treatment of investments, as well as their service sectors. In the energy sector, these reforms meant the elimination of obstacles to national and international private firms being able to operate at all levels of the energy industry, from exploration and production of natural gas and oil, to distribution and sales of petroleum products. Even though most of the countries in the region modified their normative frameworks in the energy sector, the degrees of liberalization were different. In many cases, the modifications were limited due to different precepts established in their respective constitutions; in others, it was determined that this was a strategic sector and, for this reason, should stay in the public sector. Others have a mixture of ownership. Nevertheless, the foreign investment laws implemented by the majority's of the countries in the region seek to assure that investments, particularly in the energy sector, find no roadblocks in elements currently in effect in the respective national laws.

It is important to stress that, despite of the willingness of several countries to implement energy reforms, it have not been completed in some of them for different reasons. One of them is the lack of the necessary resources to implement such reforms. During the implementation of a reform in the energy sector the following elements, among others, should be taken into account. First, elements of any energy reform such as competition, privatization, changes in market structure, and regulation, are not goals by themselves but instruments to achieve sometimes conflicting objectives like attracting private capital to finance sector investment, and promoting economic efficiency. Second, the peculiarities of the power system, the socioeconomic conditions and the political climate in each country are relevant factors that determine the pace and scope of the reform. Third, the reform is an evolutionary process, and, for this reason, it is important to have an orderly transition to implement the new institutional and regulatory arrangements.

In the course of the energy reform, the adoption of environmental legislation demanding environmental impact assessment studies prior to any power sector investment project to be carried out by any State of the region, has become a key element of any energy policy and strategy. At the same time, not all countries in the region have updated regulations in force on CO_2 and other gases emission reduction from power generation. The reason is the following: The contribution of the Latin American and the Caribbean region to the world's CO_2

emissions is around 8%, and since the region has received the classification of "developing country" status in the Kyoto Annexes, it is not obligated to reduce existing emissions level[10].

Finally, it is important to know the following: The reform of the energy sector could be constrained by political climate, socioeconomic conditions, and economic considerations, among others. In many cases, the scope and timing of the reform will be determined by special political and economic circumstances that create a window of opportunity for reforming the sector as part of the reform of the States (Dussan, 1996).

Based on what has been said before, the following can be stated: There is a great diversity in the characteristics, stage of development, endowments, and prospects for the energy reform in the Latin American and the Caribbean countries. Therefore, the elements of the energy reform will also be different across countries, and there is not a single instrument or model of regulation that should be endorsed as the best alternative for all countries of the region. However, the experience in the elaboration and implementation of energy reforms in different countries of the region could be used as reference by others during the elaboration and implementation of its own energy reform.

The different energy reforms implemented by a selected group of countries in the Latin American and the Caribbean region are briefly described in the following paragraphs.

The Energy Reform in Argentina

In the early 1990s, the Argentinean government unbundled and privatized its electricity generation and transmission sectors. Distribution companies, mostly owned by provincial governments, were privatized shortly afterwards. In August 1989, the Law of State Reform (Law 23.696) was adopted, setting the basis of the privatization program to be conducted by the government during the upcoming years. This Law specified which State-owned companies would be subject to privatization, and determined the rules and restrictions to be applied to foreign capital participation in the process.

Law 24.065, published in 1991, set the basis for the reform of the electricity sector and introduced dramatic changes in the industry structure. The vertically integrated State-owned utilities were divested into three main businesses: generation, transmission and distribution. According to the Law, generation was considered to be a competitive activity, and therefore the State would impose virtually no regulation (neither price, nor entry-related) in this business (apart from an authorization for exploration of natural resources, in the case of hydro generators).

Transmission and distribution, on the other hand, were considered activities of public interest. Tariffs in these two sectors would be regulated by the State, and the distribution companies would have the responsibility of meeting total demand in their operating areas, and would be subject to penalties in case of failure. Entry in these businesses would also be severely regulated. The regulatory role in the distribution and transmission businesses was assigned by law to ENRE – the national regulator, who would approve the tariffs, grant concessions, and establish penalties. The establishment of an electric market, and a

---

[10] Twenty six countries from Latin American and the Caribbean region have signed the Framework Convention on Climate Change; twenty three have signed the Kyoto Protocol; and in twenty countries the respective National Authorities for the Clean Development Mechanism was established.

marketplace for wholesale electricity transactions in August 1992, changed the whole nature of competition in the generation business. Generators, distributors and large consumers - but not transmission firms - are allowed to negotiate electricity in the free market (Alves Ferreira, 2002).

In 1995, the government established a policy for the provision of off-grid electricity for lighting and social communications (radio and television) to the dispersed rural population and to provincial public services, such as schools, health centers, and police stations. The Federal Secretariat of Energy set up a program, called "Program for the Electricity Supply to the Rural Population in Argentina (PAEPRA)," to promote electricity supply within six years to 314 000 rural households and 6 000 public services in sixteen provinces—all distant from power distribution grids. Wherever practical, PAEPRA was supposed to give preference to renewable energy systems for electricity production. PAEPRA's mandate was to articulate policy; the provincial governments were to fund the projects. To help steer funding to off-grid projects, the World Bank provided resources with the aim of covering the implementation of projects in eight of these provinces over six years. The project, called "Project of Renewable Energy in the Electric Rural Market," aims to provide electricity to about 70 000 households and 1 100 public services. The project cost around US $120 million. The World Bank provided US $30 million on loan; the Global Environment Facility provided US $10 million grant; Argentina's Electricity Development Fund for provincial projects allocated US $26 million; the concessionaires provided US $44 million and the customers US $10 million.

In Argentina, after the success of the model in the formative years, there was evidence that some regulatory issues should be the objects of second generation reforms in order to optimize investment in the generation and transmission segments. After a long economic recession, during which there was a failed attempt in 2001 by the Congress to introduce reforms that would increase the market mechanisms in the electricity sector, an economic crisis gave rise to a transition period starting in 2002 within the framework of the Economic Emergency Law. This, together with the withdrawal of the flow of private capital for investment in electricity generation in developing countries at the end of the 1990s, led to stagnation of investment and to difficulties in meeting the high power demand growth. Since 2003, the State is reprising the role of developer and investor – without excluding private investment – to achieve a capacity expansion in generation and transmission.

In September 2006, the Secretary of Energy launched the Energy Plus Program with the objective of increasing generation capacity and meeting the rising demand for electricity. The Program applies for consumption levels above those for 2005. In this new de-regulated market, only energy produced from new generation plants will be traded. The aim of the Program is twofold. On one hand, it seeks to guarantee supply to residential consumers, public entities, and small and medium enterprises. On the other hand, it aims at encouraging self-generation by the industrial sector and electricity cogeneration.

In December 2007, the government launched the National Program for the Rational and Efficient Use of Energy (PRONUREE, Decree 140/2007). This Decree declared the rational and efficient use of energy to be in the national interest and is also part of the energy sector strategy to counter supply/demand imbalance. The PRONUREE, under the responsibility of the Secretary of Energy, aims to be a vehicle for improving energy efficiency in the energy-consuming sectors and acknowledges that energy efficiency needs to be promoted with a long-term commitment and vision. It also acknowledges the connection between energy efficiency and sustainable development, including the reduction of greenhouse gas emissions to the atmosphere. The program also recognizes the need for individual behavioral changes to be promoted with an educational strategy, with the public sector setting the example, by assuming a leadership role in the implementation of energy conservation measures in its facilities.

PRONUREE includes short and long-term measures aimed at improving the energy efficiency in the industrial, commercial, transport, residential and service sectors and public buildings. It also supports educational programs on energy efficiency, enhanced regulations to expand co-generation activities, labeling of equipment and appliances that use energy, improvements to the energy efficiency regulations, and broader utilization of the Clean Development Mechanism to support the development of energy efficiency projects. The objective of the program is to reduce electricity consumption by 6%, according to public sources, including the press.

One of the first activities defined under PRONUREE is the national program to phase out incandescent bulbs by 2011 in Argentina. The Program, financed by the government, aims to replace incandescent bulbs with energy efficient compact fluorescent lamps in all households connected to the electricity grid and selected public buildings. The Program, which has initially undergone a pilot phase and expects to replace 5 million incandescent lamps in the next six months, foresees the distribution of 25 million lamps overall. Staff from the distribution companies will visit each household to replace the incandescent lamps and to inform residential users on the advantages of replacing the bulbs and of the efficient use of energy in general.

In March 2008, the government approved Resolution 24/2008, which created a new natural gas market called "Gas Plus" to encourage private investment in natural gas exploration and production. The Gas Plus regime applies to new discoveries and to tight gas fields. The price of the new gas, whose commercialization will be restricted to the domestic market, will not be subject to the conditions established in the Agreement with Natural Gas Producers 2007-2011 but will be based on costs and a reasonable profit. Experts believe that, if the Gas Plus regime is successful, it could stimulate new investments in electricity generation plants under the Energy Plus Program as it could ensure fuel supply to the new power plants.

Energy Reform in Bolivia

In 2002, the government established Bolivia's Rural Electrification Plan (PLABER) with the objective of contributing to the socio-economic development of rural areas through access to electricity and its efficient and productive uses. The short-term goal of the program was to make 200 000 new connections within five years (increasing electricity access in rural areas from 38% to 45%). It had been estimated that, by the end of the program, PLABER would have reached its goals by 70% of the initial objective.

However, the model established by this program did not have significant effects in increasing coverage, expanding infrastructure and improving service quality in rural and isolated areas. For this reason, a new Rural Electrification Decree (Supreme Decree No. 28567) was approved in 2005. This new Decree aims at increasing rural access through the extension of electric networks, development of renewable energy for electricity generation, and a change in the energy mix (substitution of diesel by natural gas, biomass, and other renewable energies) and an increase in distribution capacity. The Rural Electrification Decree and its associated regulatory framework encourage stakeholders in the energy sector to establish partnerships with other government agencies to implement the rural electrification plan. An agreement between the Ministry of Public Works, Services and Housing and the Ministry of Education will allow for the installation of solar photovoltaic systems in rural areas. Under the pilot phase, 500 solar panels are expected to be installed.

In 2006, the government presented a new electricity program called "Electricity for a Decent Living". The program has been designed to improve both rural and urban electrification. The short-term goal (2006-2010) of the program is to increase rural electrification to 53% (connection to the grid of 210 000 new households) and urban electrification to 99% (connection to the grid of 460 000 new households). The medium-term goal (2010-2015) is to achieve universal access in urban areas and a 70% access in rural zones. In the final phase in 2020, rural access should reach 87%, and universal coverage should be reached by 2025. The Law also mandates de creation of a Common Fund for Universal Access to Public Electricity Service and creates a co-financing mechanism of the national government with prefectures, municipalities and the private sector with the purpose of financing the implementation of the program at all levels.

The Energy Reform in Brazil

Brazil started its power sector reform in the mid of the 1990s, implementing changes in the management, organization, ownership, and decision-making of its electricity sector. Privatization was one of the initial steps of the process, which aimed to attract private investments and create competition within the industry. As these changes have taken place, it was observed that public interest activities related to energy efficiency, research and development undertaken in the past by State-owned utilities also changed. Traditionally, the country has shown support towards energy efficiency and energy research and development with the creation of research center for the power sector in the 1970s, and a national electricity conservation program, PROCEL, in the mid of the 1980s. These initiatives were mostly financed and managed within the structure of the large State-owned Eletrobras.

As reform started in Brazil, these initiatives suffered a discontinuation, budget cuts and re-definition of roles due to different political and economic factors. At the same time, new regulatory measures and the creation of a national public interest fund have helped to maintain and potentially enhance the country's effort to promote energy efficiency and investments in energy research and development.

The cornerstone of the Brazilian electricity sector reform was implemented in 1993, with the suppression of the tariff equalization system between regions, and the implementation of the National Electric Transmission System, which gave independent power producers open access to the transmission electricity grids. In 1995, the federal government launched an intensive privatization process that focused mainly on distribution utilities, allowing the States and federal governments to use cash proceeds from the asset sales to pay down debt (Mendonça and Dahl, 1999).

In late December 1996, the Brazilian Congress passed a law creating the Electric Power National Agency (ANEEL). Until then all utilities being privatized were regulated only by the terms of the contract at the time of the sale of assets by the public utility. This new agency has been entrusted with regulatory oversight of the restructured Brazilian electric industry.

ANEEL is responsible for setting up the regulatory regime necessary to provide the right signals to the market and other measures, in accordance with national energy policies adopted by the government. ANEEL regulates the power sector, sets guidelines for tariffs and rate-making, approves tariffs, and has the authority to grant concessions to service providers. Such an authority resembles a licensing or authorization power to grant a private agent the right to use public resources to generate, transmit, or distribute power. ANEEL is also charged with establishing competition among the actors, as well as reliability and cost effectiveness of service, including rural areas. ANEEL has decentralized its activities, transferring regulation oversight to some State Public Utility Commissions that are better positioned to monitor the performance of distribution utilities.

Two of the main results of the power sector reform are the creation of the National System Operator and the wholesale electricity market. The restructuring process started with the privatization of distributing utilities. By 2001, more than 80% of the electricity sold in the country was done by privatized distributing companies. This contrasts with the situation found in the generating side, which is still dominated by State-owned companies and only 30% of generating capacity is done by private enterprises. The new system re-defined the role of the public sector, which is no longer the main financial agent, but responsible for the indicative planning for generation and normative for transmission and regulator (De Martino Jannuzzi, 2004).

On August 2009, the President of Brazil presented to the Congress his proposed reform of the hydrocarbon regulatory framework. At the heart of his proposal, is the government's desire to control more the hydrocarbon sector. The State wants to maximize domestic value added of the oil and gas sector through an active industrial policy, and direct revenues to social development, such as poverty reduction, education, culture, the environment and science and technology, all of which have widespread implications for the private sector and for Petrobras.

The reform proposal, in effect, envisions a mixed regulatory regime. Previously signed contracts would be upheld, but the country would introduce production-sharing contracts for previously unlicensed areas and others that the State considers strategic. The government would be able to award contracts directly to Petrobras, or use a competitive licensing process to award them to companies offering the most profit oil to the State. These companies would bear exploration risk and, in the case of success, be reimbursed in "cost oil" for their expenses up to pre-established limits. Petrobras would be the operator of every production-sharing contract, with a guaranteed minimum 30% stake, and have the ability to participate in the bidding process for the remaining 70%.

One aspect of the proposal that seems to have taken many by surprise is the plan for the government to boost its stake in Petrobras and help fund Petrobras' investments in specific selected strategic areas. The bill allows the government to transfer the rights to 5 billion barrels of oil equivalent at a mutually agreed price that is preliminarily estimated at around US $50 billion. These changes underscore the growing role of the State and Petrobras, in Brazil's energy sector moving forward.

A decision that will cause unease within the energy sector is the proposed creation of a new State organ, Petrosal, who will administer production-sharing contracts on behalf of the Ministry of Mines and Energy (MME), manage sales of the State's share of oil and gas, and represent the State in all the proceedings. The implementation of such an organ, which will have an active role in project operational committees, could create potential unease with Petrobras, as the operator, opening up the possibility of operational uncertainties.

The proposed reform augments State control and strengthens the power of the Executive Branch in the hydrocarbon sector. It gives the federal government more discretion over the level of competition in the sector and weakens the role of the independent regulator, the National Petroleum Agency (ANP), in favor of the MME and National Energy Policy Council. Finally, even though the current decentralized revenue distribution system will remain, control of the revenues that do accrue to a new social fund—proposed to be funded by oil revenues from production-sharing contracts—may emerge as a potentially controversial topic. The new system is based on the premises that it should foster competition where possible (generation and commercialization of electricity) and regulate where necessary (transmission and distribution – monopolies with open access).

Brazilians of different political groups have long shared the goal of safeguarding Petrobras' dominance, so there is likely to be wide support for the initiatives that strengthen Petrobras. But the Brazilian government is facing a difficult balance between the desire for State control and providing sufficient regulatory certainty and reward to encourage private investment.

Finally, it is important to stress the following: In Brazil, energy policies and policy frameworks for sustainable development focus on guaranteeing universal access to energy, encouraging energy efficiency, and the use of renewable energy sources. Universal access to energy is being pursued through recently implemented programs like the Energy Program for Small Communities (PRODEEM), through the "Light for All Program" and through policy efforts practiced for decades, like subsidies for liquefied petroleum gas (LPG) used for cooking purposes and low cost electricity for low level consumers.

Energy efficiency has been officially promoted since 1985, which marked the creation of the National Electricity Conservation Program (PROCEL), and, since 1992, through the creation of the Brazilian National Program for Rationalization of Oil Products and Natural Gas Use (CONPET). These two programs have been reasonably promoted by the government and are well accepted by society, but they have yielded modest results, especially CONPET. Private participation is increasing through the flourishing of energy service companies, mainly since the establishment of a compulsory federal program requiring investments by utilities in energy conservation at the clients' facilities. The concept of electricity efficiency was tested during most of 2001, with considerable public engagement when electricity shortages affected most of the country's population.

Energy systems based on renewables were strongly facilitated by government initiatives in favor of hydro power and alcohol fuel promotion. The Brazilian Alcohol Program, the world's largest commercial renewable energy effort until today, was launched in 1975. Sugar cane ethanol is now competitive with gasoline without subsidies. Its importance has been increased by activities in the electricity supply market through the operation of thermal fired-power plants using sugar cane bagasse. These power units, initially designed to produce heat and power for sugar mills, are selling surplus electricity to the national grid.

Social acceptability and participation, as well as political support, have been important elements for the success of such renewable energy schemes. Nevertheless, since the 1990s public debate on large hydro power has increased and environmentalists have successfully slowed its implementation. Small hydro power is once again considered an option for electricity supply, but it is well understood by society that large hydro power plants might still be constructed, provided attention is paid to the displaced population. Recent government energy program - the Alternative Energy Sources Incentive Program - intends to address simultaneously the issues of universal access to energy and increased use of renewable sources.

The Energy Reform in Chile

Initial organizational reform in the energy sector took place in Chile at the beginning of the 1980s. Since that period, Chile's National Energy Commission (CNEC) has being promoting a sustainable development program in the field of energy. The four energy policy guidelines associated to this program are:

a)   Private investment will be the main source of capital for energy sector expansion, and the regulatory framework must be clear and stable to attract both local and international private investments in order to support such expansion;

b)   Policies must promote energy efficiency. Clean energy at the least cost is required to be competitive and to reduce the cost of energy for the nation's exporting industrial sectors;

c)   Energy development must ensure the protection of the environment. Prevention is critical and, for this reason, all new energy projects in Chile require an environmental assessment before been approved;

d)   Social equity must be an objective of sustainable energy development. Poverty can be overcome through employment in energy development and by providing basic energy services to the poorest sectors. To this end, Chile is implementing a rural electrification program. Renewable energy is an excellent tool to provide electricity to remote areas where the national electricity grid is inaccessible.

Chile's long range electric power capacity expansion plan released in April 2002 shows a growing dependence on gas-fired electric power generation. The CNEC foresees the development over the next decade of ten new combined-cycle gas-fired power plants and one new hydroelectric facility to be connected to its central interconnected system, the central region's grid serving 93% of Chile's population. Law No. 19 613 passed in 1999 gives the Superintendence of Electricity and Fuels the authority to monitor power companies and impose fines on them for failing to meet their contractual supply obligations to distributors and large customers. The Law was passed as a political response to Chile's power shortages, which began in November 1998. Article 99bis and Resolution 88 of the Electricity Law have been a source of contention in Chile's electricity sector[11].

In May 2002, fast track electricity legislation was sent before the Chilean parliament with the aim of changing the present regulations, above all in transmission. The bill modifies rates and tolls, defines and sets prices for complementary services, and modifies the rates system in

---

[11] Article 99bis requires generators to guarantee electricity supply in all circumstances, including during drought, under the threat of fines. Resolution 88 requires generators to sell electricity to distributors even without a contract.

the Aysén and Magallanes isolated grids. But it does not modify those aspects of the current legislation that have inhibited investment by generators - Article 99bis or Resolution 88.

Chile's energy sector is largely privatized, particularly the electricity industry. Chilean energy demand has been growing rapidly (averaging more than 7% annually) since 1992. A significant portion of this growth has come from increased power demand by the mining sector, the country's single largest industry, and by large urban areas such as Santiago, which alone contains almost 40% of Chile's population. The increase in the demand combined with scant fossil fuel resources make Chile a net importer of energy.

In Chile, the energy reform continued over the two decades after it began: The transmission segment was separated – it had been linked to generation – with a view of increasing transparency and competition in the setting of supply prices.

The Energy Reform in Colombia

Transition from a highly regulated economic regime to an unrestricted access market has been underway in Colombia since 1990. At that time, the Colombian government introduced several policies to spur economic development and promote private enterprise. In 1994, the government enacted Laws 142 and 143 that provide the current framework for the electricity sector. Law 142 established that "the provision of electricity, telecommunications, water, sewage, and bottled gas distribution, are essential public services that may be provided by both public and private entities". Law 143 encouraged greater private sector involvement in the power sector, and separated the electricity industry into separate generation, transmission, and distribution components.

The key governmental body involved in the energy sector in Colombia is the Ministry of Mines and Energy, which is responsible for the overall policy making and supervision of the electricity sector in the country. It regulates generation, transmission, trading, inter-connection, and distribution, and approves generation and transmission programs. The Ministry delegates supervisory authority over the electricity sector to a number of its agencies, specifically the Energy Regulatory Commission and the Union of Mineral and Energy Planning. The Commission regulates the transmission and distribution of electric power and gas and adjusts policies and procedures by which these services can reach the consumers and allow market competition between providers.

In Colombia, the energy reform went from State prevalence with participation of private investment, to mix property with private prevalence, to an open market. Since 1999, upstream sector initiatives include allowing foreign oil companies to own 100% stakes in oil ventures, the establishment of a lower, sliding-scale royalty rate on oil projects, longer exploration licenses, and forcing Ecopetrol, the national oil company, to compete with private operators.

Colombia still faces many challenges in its upstream oil sector, including a lack of proven oil reserves and steep decline rates at its largest oil fields. It is unclear if the recent investment flows can be maintained in the near-term due to the weakening global economy. As a result, IEA forecasts that Colombian oil production will decline at an average of 4% per year in the short-term.

Colombia's Congress passed, on June 2011, a key reform to spread billions of dollars in oil and mining royalties as it seeks to hike exports of oil and coal. Colombia, the world's No. 4 coal exporter has seen a boom in oil and mining investment since a 2002 crackdown on illegal armed groups, which has helped ramp up production of petroleum, thermal and metallurgical coal and minerals. However, it was not until 2001 that the Law 697, which promotes the efficient and rational use of energy and the alternative energies, was promulgated. The Law was regulated by the Decree 3683 issued in 2003 (Ruiz and Rodríguez-Padilla, 2006). So far, the program for rational and efficient use of energy developed by the application of the Law 697, has established labels and efficient standards (Altomonte et al., 2003).

President Juan Manuel Santos' reform plans to centralize how royalties are managed to more evenly distribute around US $3 billion a year nationwide and stamp out inefficiency and corrupt abuses of regional commodity resources. The constitutional reform has faced opposition by commodity-producing regions, which have balked at sharing more. According to government estimated up to 30% of the royalties will be saved, and the reform would gradually reduce the percentage that producing regions receive to 25% from the current 70%.

Colombia's energy and mining sectors have been a key factor for boosting economic growth in the last few years, drawing in billions of dollars in foreign direct investment and making up around half of all exports from the Andean nations. Infrastructure bottlenecks and deficiencies are seen as the main problem for the country as it seeks to nearly double coal production to nearly 150 million tons and more than one million barrels of oil per day over the next few years.

The Energy Reform in Cuba

The development of the energy sector since 1959 can be divided into three periods:

a) *The period between 1959 and 1989.* During this period a rapid growth in Cuba's energy sector occurred, facilitated by subsidized Soviet oil imports and other forms of financial support. The period included the country's largest buildup in energy generation infrastructure and highest rates of growth in consumption, based on oil and products imported from the former Soviet Union. During this period the government began the introduction and development of an important nuclear power program for electricity generation.

b) *The period 1990 to 1997.* During this period, domestic oil production was accelerated and Cuba began to use fuel oil in its seven large generation power plants. Unfortunately, domestic oil's high sulfur levels damaged the generation infrastructure severely, provoking an increase in maintenance services and an increase in the number of stop of these plants. The nuclear power program initiated in the 1970s was definitively cancelled in this period.

c) *The period 1998-2011.* This period is marked by Venezuelan support, the blackouts of 2004-2005, the Energetic Revolution of 2005-2006, and the independent power production arrangement with Sherritt, based on combined cycle gas turbines. While the sector is now significantly more stable than during the period of blackouts, the high proportion of generation that is based on liquid fuels results in extremely high costs and very high carbon emissions. The financial sustainability of the sector depends, in a significant manner, on the largesse of Venezuela. If support from

Venezuela is reduced or ended, the energy sector would enter once again in an extremely difficult period.

In Cuba, the last energy reform called "Energetic Revolution" has five main aspects:

a) Energy efficiency and conservation;
b) Increasing the availability and reliability of the national electric grid;
c) Incorporating more renewable energy technologies into the energy portfolio;
d) Increasing the exploration and production of local oil and gas;
e) Increasing international co-operation in the energy sector.

The objective on the current energy reform was not to look for more ways of generating energy, but to decrease energy demand, in order to reduce the dependency of Cuba of the import of energy sources for electricity generation and for other energy needs, and the reduction in the cost of imported oil. The program allowed people to switch their incandescent bulbs to more efficient compact fluorescents, free of charge, to have access to millions of energy efficient appliances, including almost two million refrigerators, over one million fans, around 182 000 air conditioners, and 260 000 water pumps. At the same time, efficient electrical cooking appliances were introduced. Almost 3.5 million rice cookers and over three million pressure cookers were sold to families in the push to have people switch from kerosene to cooking with electricity.

It is important to note that some of these energy efficient appliance were not of high quality, especially those appliance used for cooking, and the intensive use of them provoked a high level of breaking and the need to purchase a high amount of spare parts, creating a negative reaction in the population. The situation of lack of spare parts for all equipment imported still has not being solved and there is a lack of adequate resources to overcome this situation during the coming years. As result of the introduction of the new energy reform, the demand of electricity from the population does not decreased but increased in a significant manner, forcing the government to increase tariff and the introduction of additional measures in order to reduce the increase in the demand of electricity in all sectors.

At the same time, Cuba also embarked on energy savings measures in the State sector. All water pumps in tall buildings and aqueducts were changed to efficient pumps. The 40 W fluorescent tubes used in many government offices were changed to 32 W bulbs with electronic ballasts, and inefficient refrigerators and air conditioners have been replaced with more efficient models.

Despite these efforts, saving energy was not enough, and due to the existence of very old and still inefficient electrical distribution grid, the distribution and transmission losses is higher than international standards (14.4% of the total electricity produced in 2011). The aim is to reduce the current level of losses to 14% at the end of 2011.

According to Cuban government experts one of the best ways to provide for energy security was to move towards decentralized energy, and thus it began the move towards distributed generation. Employing this concept means less vulnerability to natural disasters, which might affect electricity to a whole section of the country. The strategy also diversifies energy sources, while making it easier to ultimately change to alternative sources of energy in the future, such as those produced more locally and sustainably. In 2006, Cuba installed 1 854 diesel and fuel oil micro-electrical plants across the country, representing over 3 000 MW of decentralized power in 110 municipalities. This virtually eliminated the blackouts that plagued Cuba in 2004 and 2005. In addition to the new plants, they also installed over 4 000 emergency back-up systems in critical areas like hospitals, food production centers, schools, and other sites key to Cuba's economy. This represents 500 MW of emergency back-up power.

Furthermore, Cuba embarked on an impressive plan to fix its existing electrical transmission network. They upgraded over 120 000 electrical posts, over one million utility service entrances, almost 3 000 km of cable, and half a million electrical meters. The overall effect of this program meant that, in 2005, while the country needed an average of 280 grams of oil to generate one kWh of electricity, in 2007 this figure had fallen to 271 grams of oil per kWh; this represents a reduction of 3%. While this might seem like a small saving, it translates to thousands of tons of imported oil annually. In 2006-2007, Cuba saved over 961 000 tons of imported oil through their energy saving measures.

What else can be done to improve the energy situation in the country? Cuba's options for improving energy situation include the following elements:

a) Enhance offshore hydrocarbon exploration;
b) Expand household use of liquefied petroleum gas;
c) Expand the use of solar heaters, photovoltaic systems, small, mini, and micro-hydroelectric power plants, windmills, water pumps, solar dryers and distillers, and controlled climate chambers;
d) Increase electricity cogeneration;
e) Introduce new co-generation technologies;
f) Enhance energy efficiency;
g) Determine the potential of wind power and expand its use.

The Energy Reform in Ecuador

Over recent years, Ecuador has made important changes on legislative and regulatory levels, with the approval of the new Constitution. In the new Constitution adopted recently, the State has committed to "the promotion of efficient energy, the development and use of environmentally clean practices and technologies such as renewable energies, diversified energies having low environmental impact that do not put in risk the food sovereignty, the ecological balance of the ecosystems or the right to water".

In 2007, the Ministry of Electricity and Renewable Energy was created. With the current administrative structure, it is clear that the government prioritized the development of the renewable energy sector as much as possible, particularly for electricity generation. The regulatory framework relating to the use of renewable energy sources for electricity generation includes the following laws:

a) *Regulatory Law for the Electrical Sector:* The Law, dating back to 1996 and with later modifications, contains the regulations related to the structure of the electrical sector and its functioning. In Chapter IX of the Law, there is specific mention of the development and use of non-traditional energy resources. This type of resource is prioritized when the Rural and Marginal Urban Electrification Program assigns funds to the rural electrification projects. In addition, it is the National Electrification Council that determines the applicable regulations for the distribution of electricity produced with non-traditional energies, giving them priority and approval;

b) *General Electrical Sector Regime Law:* This Law establishes the regulations and general procedures for the application of the Electrical Sector Regime Law, in the generation and offering of public services of transmission, distribution, and marketing of electrical energy, necessary to satisfy the national demand through the optimal use of natural resources. Regulation N° 009/06, in force since 2007, establishes the prices of the energy produced with renewable and others non-traditional energy resources.

One of the main goals of the energy reform adopted in Ecuador is to reduce the use of oil for electricity generation in the coming years.

The Energy Reform in Mexico

The established goal of the energy policy in Mexico is to ensure a reliable, quality, and competitively priced supply of the energy services demanded by consumers. To achieve this goal, it is indispensable to promote efficient energy use, as well as the use of technologies that allow the negative environmental impact generated by traditional fossil fuels to be reduced as much as possible. Thus, the main objective of the new energy policy is to reconcile society's energy consumption needs with caring for natural resources and the protection of the environment.

In 1992, the Mexican Congress amended the Electric Power Public Utility Law to allow, for the first time, some private investment in power generation in the following types of generation facilities:

a) Self-generation or self-consumption (generation dedicated to the exclusive use of theqwertyuiop[] generator and its owners);

b) Co-generation (generation using steam or other thermal energy produced by industrial processes);

c) Independent power production (generation by plants greater than 30 MW for the sole purpose of selling the energy and capacity produced to the Federal Electricity Commission (CFE);

d) Small production (generation by plants of less than 30 MW for the sole purpose of selling the energy and capacity produced to CFE);

e) Generation exclusively for import (to satisfy the permit holder's own needs) and for export purposes.

The mentioned Law also provided that permit holders (i.e., the private generators described above) could enter into contracts with CFE for the sale of up to 20 MW of their excess capacity and associated energy or the sale of excess energy (i.e., energy other than that required to meet the permit holder's needs). However, it is important to stress that this reform has not been as successful as had been hoped. The main reason for this shortfall has been uncertainty regarding the tariffs that private parties can charge, as well as the relatively low level of tariffs that resulted from calculating the tariff on the basis of delivered energy only.

On October 2008, the Mexican Congress passed a bill to amend and create several federal laws and statutes related with the energy industry, called the "Energy Reform". One of the objectives of the reform is to foster private participation in the energy sector and bring business opportunities for both domestic and international companies. The Energy Reform also includes the enactment of new laws related to the development of renewable energy sources and clean energies that will certainly foster development of private power generation projects and energy efficiency in Mexico.

The Energy Reform provide for:

a) Reorganization of PEMEX's Board of Directors, giving it broader authority and autonomy from the Executive Branch, and including independent members in the Board (experts in the energy sector);

b) Broader management, budgetary, indebtedness, and investment-decision autonomy from the federal government;

c) Creation of subsidiary entities and affiliate companies as well as participating in joint venture companies without requiring authorization from the Executive Branch;

d) Elimination of some procurement constraints and giving PEMEX more contracting flexibility;

e) Creation of a special Strategy and Investment Committee and a Procurement Committee, which will propose the above-mentioned contracting rules and guidelines.

Table 2. Number of permits for independent power producers approved

Modality	Number of permits	Total capacity (MW)	Percentage of total national capacity (%)
Auto-generation	589	6 102	6%
Co-generation	57	3 255	4.5%
Independent power production	22	13 250	19.5%
Small generation	19	3	-

Source: CRE (2009).

Pursuant to the Energy Reform private parties will be able to enter into any kind of works and services contracts with PEMEX, provided that it shall always maintain control over the exploration and development activities, and provided further that fee payment to contractor or service provider is made in cash (as opposed to payment in kind) and no property, percentage or share over hydrocarbons or PEMEX's profits is granted. The participation of the private sector represents 25% of the total electricity generation capacity installed in the country.

In accordance with the Energy Reform, ordinary procurement of goods and services by PEMEX will remain subject to current federal government procurement laws and regulations, while substantive contracting by PEMEX (i.e., procurement of services and works to conduct the strategic activities, including activities related with exploration, production, and refining) will be subject to ad-hoc rules issued by the PEMEX's Board of Directors and prepared by the Procurement Committee.

The Renewable Energy Development and Financing for Energy Transition Law entered into force in November 2008, and mandated Secretary of Energy to produce a National Strategy for Energy Transition and Sustainable Energy Use and a Special Program for Renewable Energy. The main objective of the Law is to regulate the use of renewable energy resources and clean technology, as well as to establish a national strategy and financing instruments to allow Mexico to scale-up electricity generation based on renewable energy resources. Secretary of Energy and CRE are responsible for defining those mechanisms and establishing legal instruments to allow Mexico to increase renewable power generation in the near and medium-term.

Finally, it is important to stress the following: In response to the threats from climate change and to energy security, the Mexican government has made a commitment to a change in its energy matrix. This process will lead to a better use of fossil fuels and the development and promotion of the use of different renewable energy sources, particularly for electricity generation. Its aim is to diversify the use of primary energy sources for the production of electricity and mitigate the impact on the environment as the result of the reduction in greenhouse gases caused by the burn of fossil fuels, which currently are the main energy source used for electricity generation at world level.

The Energy Reform in Nicaragua

At the beginning of the 1990s, the government started the reform of the electricity sector aiming to ensure efficient demand coverage, in order to promote economic efficiency and to attract resources for infrastructure expansion. In 1992, the Nicaraguan Energy Institute (INE) was allowed, by law, to negotiate contracts and concessions with private investors. The Nicaraguan Electricity Company (ENEL) was created in 1994, as the State company in charge of electricity generation, transmission, distribution, commercialization, and coordination of the operations previously assigned to INE, who kept its planning, policy making, regulatory, and taxation functions.

The reform process was consolidated in 1998, with the adoption of the Law 272 (Electricity Industry Law - LIE) and the Law 271 (INE Reform Law). The reform of the INE led to the creation of the National Energy Commission (CNE), which assumed the policy making and planning responsibilities. Law 272 established the basic principles for the operation of a competitive wholesale market with the participation of private companies. Electricity generation, transmission, and distribution were unbundled and companies were prohibited to have interests in more than one of the three activities. ENEL was restructured in four generation companies (Hidrogesa, Geosa, Gecsa, and Gemosa); two distribution companies (Disnorte and Dissur), both acquired by Union Fenosa and then merged into a single company, and one transmission company (Entresa, now Enatrel).

The privatization process that started in 2000 with a public offering of the four generation companies was complicated due both to legal problems and to lack of interest by investors. As a result, ENEL maintained a more relevant role than initially expected. Hidrogesa remained in public hands as the only player in hydroelectric generation while its profits serve to finance the losses of Gecsa, which owns the thermal power plants that did not attract private interest, and the rural electrification plans in isolated areas.

The energy reform of the 1990s did not achieve their objectives. It had been expected that privatization would bring investment in new generation capacity, but very little was added in the years that followed the implementation of the energy reform. Moreover, the generation capacity added in the last decade has been mainly dependent on liquid fuels, making the country more vulnerable to rising oil prices. In addition, distribution losses have remained at very high levels (28%), more than double international standards. The energy reform also aimed at implementing gradual changes in electricity tariffs that would reflect costs, which proved to be politically unfeasible.

The Energy Reform in Peru

In 1992, the Peruvian government started the deregulation of its economy by the adoption of the Electric Power Concession Law. The Law established a new regulatory framework that promoted competition and efficiency in generation, transmission, and distribution of electric power by requiring the unbundling of these activities. The Law also called for the privatization of all State-owned commercial operating assets. It also permitted to set electricity tariffs, according to marginal costs and free market. Large customers received the freedom to negotiate directly with generation and distribution companies.

From 1997, single investors could own a maximum of 15% of generation, transmission, and distribution or a maximum of 5% across the industry as a whole. The Law also gave the government the right to deny mergers in the electricity sector, if this action is not in the national interest.

It is important to note that with the adoption of the Law, consumers using small amounts of electricity received protection from large tariff increases, with pricing overseen by an autonomous entity, the Electricity Tariffs Commission, which was later renamed as the "Energy Tariffs Commission". The Law also created the Committee for the Economic Operation of the Interconnected System to be in charge of dispatch of the system. The Committee comprises of the owners of the generation plants and transmission systems of each interconnected system, and coordinates the operation of the system at the lowest possible cost. It works to guarantee the safety of the electricity supply, and to ensure the best possible use of the electricity resources of each interconnected system. The Law created another body to oversee compliance with provisions that make up the legal, technical, and commercial regulatory framework governing electricity production.

Generation and distribution have both undergone privatization, which had disposed of more than 60% of the State's holdings in the sector by the end of 1998. Electrolima and Electroperú, the largest electric power companies in Peru, were the first to be unbundled and partially privatized. The regional utilities have been restructured into separate generation, transmission, and distribution units.

The Energy Reform in Uruguay

Towards the end of the 1990s, Uruguay, although it continued to have an integrated State monopoly under the National Administration of Power Plants and Electricity Transmission – also introduced an accounts division by segment of the electricity chain, i.e., generation, transmission, and distribution, implemented a wholesale market, opened the demand of its largest users to competition, and admitted free private initiative for new generation and transmission projects.

Summing up the following can be stated: According to Deutsche Montan Technologie GmbH Essen, OLADE and CIEMAT (2005) report, several countries in the Latin American and the Caribbean region have taken important steps for the liberalization of the energy sector, to create or strengthen public regulatory and control agencies, and to encourage the participation of private companies, especially in electrical energy production, distribution, and marketing.

For different reasons some countries have failed to complete the processes, some others are retaking public control of certain activities, including the energy sector, while others are incorporating second-generation reforms based on market experience in order to ensure the proper functioning of power markets with the purpose of attracting the required investments for the expansion of the energy sector.

Most Latin American and the Caribbean countries have partially segmented the sectors of power industry in order to ensure proper competition in the power generation sector, adequate availability, free access to transmission systems, and comparative competition in the electricity distribution and marketing sector. It is expected that increased interconnections between countries will bring about the consolidation of regional energy markets with optimized dispatching systems.

Outcome of the Energy Reforms

As result of the implementation of the energy reforms in different countries, the energy sector has been divided in the following manner:

a) *Exclusive State ownership*: All electrical system assets were owned by the State;
b) *Mixed ownership*: Private investors are shareholders of companies with additional participation of the State;
c) *Private property*: The electrical system is predominantly under private ownership. In this case there are two options. The first involves vertical segmentation with an obligatory separation between generation, transmission, and distribution activities; the second includes a possibility for vertical integration, i.e., generation, transmission, and distribution activities may remain in one hand.

From the operating options, the following elements characterized the energy sector in the region:

a) *Central control:* Traditionally, the entire chain of power generation and distribution was considered a natural monopoly. So it was logical that a single entity should own and operate the electrical service for an area, either owned by the State or by private companies. For years, the power sub-sector was considered monopolistic and a single company had a concession. The majority of the countries of the region provided for many years electrical service through a single State-owned company;

b) *Single buyer:* This principle has been applied to the region for several years and has allowed private entities to participate in the energy sector through a limited opening. This has especially been the case for generation, and was part of a process in some cases and a complete step in others;

c) *Integrated and autonomous*: This type of coordination involves a different distribution of the roles between the State and the company(s) that operate(s) in the sector. The latter perform their activities according to their own initiative, planning, and execution. The State has to approve the pertinent decisions on investments, rates, etc. It carries out regulatory functions either on its own behalf or through an agency that represents society, because it is a public service. A multitude of companies from the private, public or mixed sector participate in these activities. However, effective competition among them does not exist, because they often have exclusivity under a concession contract for an area of supply or companies divide a sector among themselves by area or type of customer;

d) *Open market*: Natural monopolies are only maintained for main electrical power transportation and distribution activities, where its disputability is considered necessary. In sufficiently large systems that permit and ensure competitive behavior, several participants can compete in the generating and marketing sectors.

RESISTANCE TO PRIVATIZATION OF THE ENERGY SECTOR

The Southern Cone was where the first market opening and liberalization reforms of the electric sector structure over the last decades were introduced without too much resistance, specifically in Chile and Argentina. Both countries divided their electricity industry vertically and horizontally, created wholesale markets, fostered the liberalization of the retail market for major users, and privatized State assets.

The process of privatization of the energy sector adopted later by most of the Latin American and the Caribbean countries, with the exception of a very few of them[12], took the

---

[12] It is important to stress that Cuba do not adopted any reform with the purpose of privatizing its energy sector. Costa Rica is another of the very few countries in the region that has not undertaken energy reforms aimed at the creation of deregulated markets. Generation, transmission, and distribution assets of the utility have been separated under a corporate structure but apart from legislation that permits the private sector to connect up to 30% of the installed capacity of the country or to sell to the utility through Boot schemes, it is hard to interconnect private sector plants. Biomass cogenerating plants face a tough limitation due to the seasonality of generation and due to the fact that no thermal power based generation can be in private hands. Argentina, Bolivia, Ecuador and Venezuela are now applying an energy policy in favor of the State control of the energy sector.

effect of transferring existing State-owned generation facilities to the private sector, and private participation has occurred mainly in the context of wider reforms involving vertical separation of the electricity sector. However, after 2000, the privatization process confronted strong resistance from different sectors of the public opinion in several countries. Apart from the characteristics of the privatization process of the energy sector in Chile, the dynamics of the response to the economic crisis in Argentina, and the approach of the government in Brazil, there has been significant resistance to electricity privatization in other Latin American and the Caribbean countries. For example, in Ecuador former governments attempts to privatize electricity assets have repeatedly encountered organized resistance from trade unions, provincial, and local governments, and indigenous organizations, among others. In 2002, these campaigns forced the abandonment of proposals to sell electricity distributors, after Ecuador's Congress passed a resolution rejecting the privatization, and a Constitutional Court ruling that the sales were unconstitutional. A further attempt at privatization was abandoned in February 2004, when there was not a single tender for any of the companies. Now, the new Ecuadorian government is promoting another approach to develop its energy sectors but under the control of the State.

In Peru, the privatization of generating companies, which began in 1995, has faced powerful opposition, particularly during the second step when the government tried to complete the privatization of the smaller distribution companies. In June 2002, there were riots in Arequipa after two electric power plants (Egasal and Egesur) were sold to Tractebel. The government was forced to suspend the sale, and Tractebel backed out of the deal.

In Colombia, there has also been public resistance to the privatization of the electricity sector, notably in defense of the well-established municipal utilities, and in Venezuela the government rejected the attempt to privatized PdVSA as promoted by the private sector and some foreign energy companies.

In Mexico, successive attempts to privatize the electricity system have been defeated by strong campaigns led by the trade unions, resulting in court rulings and parliamentary decisions, which have prevented the President from implementing privatization plans as initially it would foresee.

THE CURRENT REGIONAL SITUATION OF THE ENERGY SECTOR

Reliable and affordable energy services are essential to the modern world. Secure access to energy services, particularly the stability of their prices, are key concerns for governments and parliaments all over the world. For countries that are predominantly dependent on imported fossil fuels for their electricity generation, there are many associated long-term risks in this regard, including the potential economic disruptions due to oil prices volatility, the vulnerability of fuel shipping and storage systems to terrorism, and negative environmental impacts associated with fossil fuel combustion, wars, and political instability of the main oil's producers, among others. There exists much potential in the Latin American and the Caribbean region for increased energy supply, particularly in the realm of the so-called "unconventional and difficult hydrocarbons" –like Canada's tar sands and Venezuela's ultra-heavy oil, which together (some 500 billion barrels) might be the equivalent of two Saudi Arabia– and the Hemisphere's many potential sources of offshore and ultra-deep water oil and gas, particularly in Brazil and Mexico but also potentially in the USA, and in the Caribbean and Andean zones. However, the obstacles to increase energy supply are immense, while primary energy demand is set to continuing growing, less so in North America (0.6% annually until 2030) but significantly in Latin American and the Caribbean region (2% annually for the same period; this represents more than three times the increase foreseen in the USA). Despite the region's apparent energy potential, the Hemisphere will become ever more dependent on hydrocarbon imports from outside the region and ever more vulnerable to the destabilizing impacts of fossil fuel-induced climate change unless status-quo dynamics are drastically altered during the coming years (Isbell, 2009).

With oil trading in 2012 over US $100 per barrel, natural gas in short supply, and a new wave of droughts threatening hydroelectricity production, several Latin American and the Caribbean countries are once again facing the possibility of energy shortages. In contrast to shortages in the past, which were blamed on short-term factors, many analysts now believe that energy scarcity will be a long-term problem. The two fundamental reasons are the demand driven by sustained economic growth in emerging economies, such as China, India, Brazil, Russia, and South Africa, among others, and the difficulty of obtaining new sources of fossil fuels. The Latin American and the Caribbean countries exemplify both trends.

Energy demand has been growing a record rate in the past five years. In Chile, for example, it expanded 7% in 2007 alone. But with the exception of Brazil, which discovered in 2007 significant offshore deposits and in Venezuela with the highest oil reserve in the world, oil and gas production in the region is either stagnant or declining and no new significant reserves of oil and gas has been found in the past years. Current spending on exploration and new fossil fuel infrastructure is far below what is needed to meet anticipated demand, according to most analysts. Though the region has considerable untapped hydroelectricity potential, dams are expensive, take a long time to build, are increasingly opposed by environmentalists in several countries of the region, and should be built in areas located far from urban centers. Renewable sources like biomass, solar, and wind power are growing but they can supply only a tiny slice of the region's total energy needs. It is expected that this situation will not change in the coming years. It is important to know that, at the beginning of the 21th century, the energy growth in the region was leading by the production of natural gas, with 3.21% annual growth, and of coal with an increase of 12.67%. The production of oil for the contrary declined in 1.85% (Poveda, 2004).

Oil Reserves

According to IEO (2010) and World Energy Council (2008), the Latin American and the Caribbean region have 10% of the world's oil reserves, 5% of the world's natural gas reserves, and 1.6% of the world's coal reserves. The region has sufficient energy reserves for its consumption needs and for export to other regions of the world as well but these reserves are concentrated in a very few countries. In 2010, only Venezuela has been included in the list of 10 top countries with important oil reserves. Brazil occupies the place 14th, Mexico the place 16[th,] and Ecuador the place 18th in the mentioned list (see Figure 24).

Energy Infrastructure

Figure 3 shows the capacity of 1 295 power plants in operation in the Latin American and the Caribbean region in 2004.

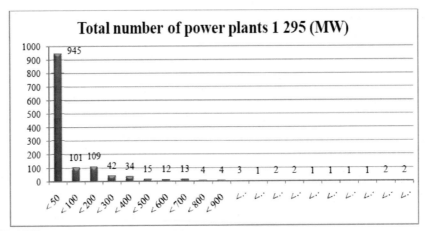

Source: OLADE.

Figure 3. Capacity of the different power plants in operation in the Latin American and the Caribbean region in 2004.

From Figure 3, the following can be stated: Almost 73% of the power plants operating in the region have a capacity below 50 MW, almost 8% below 100 MW, and 8.4% below 200 MW. Very few power plants have a capacity higher than 300 MW (140 power plants or 10.8% of the total).

Many Latin American and the Caribbean countries report high level of transmission and distribution power losses, which is in average about 19% for the whole region. This level represents 9% above the technical level of losses considered acceptable at international level. However, the technical power losses are not equally distributed; some countries have 30% of power losses, while others have power losses below 10%.

The Latin American and the Caribbean region are split into two operating power networks with different frequencies: The southern countries, which operate on 50 Hz, whereas the northern countries operate on 60 Hz. The difference in the frequency in the power networks used in the Latin American and the Caribbean region make more difficult any interconnection of the northern and southern systems.

In the Latin American and the Caribbean region both the quantity and quality of energy infrastructure (including power plants, transmission grids and electricity distribution networks, oil and gas pipelines, refineries, and LNG export and import terminals) is insufficient across most of the region. The IEO (2010) reference scenario foresees "a trebling of electricity generation and a doubling of capacity requiring an enormous amount of investment (over US $1 trillion in the electricity sector alone), if demand is to be met in the whole Latin American and the Caribbean region leading up to 2030. By itself, the infrastructure challenge is significant enough to constrict demand in many parts of the region, to say nothing of placing severe constraints on renewable energy deployment, particularly centralized forms of wind and solar power (wind and solar farms), across the Hemisphere.

The IEA estimates that Latin American and the Caribbean countries will need to invest at least the equivalent of 1.5% of its total GDP to 2030 –some 50% more than average energy investment requirements worldwide– in expanded energy supply and infrastructure, if its foreseable energy demand is to be satisfied (Isbell, 2009).

In early 1990s, the power sector infrastructure prevailing in the Latin American and the Caribbean countries had the following similarities:

a) A single central agency, like a Ministry or a State-own-enterprise, plays the roles of policy maker, planner, regulator, financier, entrepreneur, and operator in the sector;

b) A central agency or a State-own-enterprise generally prepares a master plan, which determines the investment decisions in generation and transmission to be followed by all participants. Regulation was performed by the State or a State-own-enterprise, and was generally limited to rate-setting based on macroeconomic and political considerations;

c) The State guarantees the loans to finance the expansion of main energy infrastructure and, in many cases, had to serve the debt service due to State-own-enterprises precarious financial condition;

d) The State-own-enterprises were not managed as commercial enterprises but, in most cases, as State offices with government interference in day-to-day operations and subject to closed command and control arrangements: Participation of government officials in the Board of Directors, approval of investment programs, annual budgets and foreign currency loans by ministries and planning departments, control of tariff increases by the government, fiscal controls through the General Comptroller Office, and imposition of performance plans by the government;

e) High level of vertical and horizontal integration, dominated by State-owned monopolies and with little participation of private companies.

However, it is important to single out that there is also great diversity between countries in the technical and managerial capacity of the public and private power sectors, the strength of capital markets and, in general, the endowments for supporting the development of the power sector on a commercial basis with the participation of private capital. While countries like Brazil, Mexico, Chile, and Argentina are quite developed in this regard, small countries, like Guyana and Haiti, lack the basic local resources to undertake the necessary energy reform (Dussan, 1996).

On the electricity sector of the Central America region, it is important to single out the following: According to the World Energy Council (2008), Central American countries already have a Framework Agreement on the Central American Electricity Market for the Regulation of Regional Electricity Exchanges. This agreement was signed on 30 December 1996, by Guatemala, El Salvador, Honduras, Nicaragua, Costa Rica, and Panama. The project, now under implementation, promotes the interconnection of national markets through the Sepia Line. The main characteristic of the Regional Electricity Market (MER) is that it is considered to be a regional market coexisting with the national markets. The objective of the MER Framework Agreement according to its Section 1 is "the gradual formation and development of a regional competitive electricity market based on reciprocal non-discriminatory treatment that will contribute to the sustainable development of the region within a framework of respect for, and protection of the environment."

Besides establishing the rights and obligations of the parties, the MER Framework Agreement is designed:

a) To establish the necessary conditions for the growth of the sub-regional electricity market, which should supply the electricity required for the economic and social development of Central American countries in a sustainable way;
b) To encourage a greater and more competitive private participation in the electricity sector;
c) To encourage the interconnection infrastructure necessary for the development of the MER Framework Agreement;
d) To create the conditions necessary for contributing to an acceptable quality, reliability, and safety electricity supply in the sub-region;
e) To enforce objective, transparent, and non-discriminatory rules to regulate the operation of the MER Framework Agreement and the relationships between the agents, as well as creating suitable regional entities to achieve these aims;
f) To pave the way for the benefits derived from the MER Framework Agreement to reach all the inhabitants of the countries of the sub-region.

The MER Framework Agreement is based on the following principles:

a) Competition (freedom in the development of service rendering based on objective, transparent, and non-discriminatory rules);
b) Gradualness (provisions for the progressive evolution of the MER Framework Agreement through the incorporation of new participants, the progressive increase in coordinated operation for the development of interconnection networks, and the strengthening of sub-regional bodies);
c) Reciprocity (right of each State to apply to other States the same rules and regulations that the State applies temporarily according to the gradualness principle).

It is foreseen that the MER Framework Agreement will evolve gradually towards a wider, more open and more competitive situation, in accordance with the development of a sub-regional and national infrastructure.

To ensure the implementation of the MER Framework Agreement, the following sub-regional organizations have been created:

1. *The Regional[13] Electric Interconnection Commission (CRIE):* It is the MER Framework Agreement regulating agency, which must ensure the fulfillment of the Agreement and secure the development and the consolidation of the sub-regional market;
2. *The Regional Operating Agency (EOR):* It is in charge of sub-regional electricity operation and dispatch according to economic, safety, quality, and reliability criteria. Operational functions are performed in co-ordination with the national dispatch bodies. It is responsible for the formulation of the indicative expansion plan of sub-

---

[13] The word "regional" in the name of the diferent organizations established within MER has been used to cover only the Central American sub-region.

regional generation and transmission and backs- by supplying information- the MER Framework Agreement evolution processes. The EOR is economically and functionally independent and has its own technical expertise;

3. *The Grid Proprietor (EPR):* It is the company in charge of the design, development, financing, construction, and upkeep of the first sub-regional transmission system called "SIEPAC Line". According to the MER Framework Agreement, the EPR is governed by private law. For its constitution, it was decided that each country would appoint a government agency to participate in EPR, which could be of public capital or have private participation. No member can have controlling interest in the company. Besides, according to the legal procedures in each country, by the MER Framework Agreement the EPR were given the respective authorizations to build and exploit the first sub-regional interconnection system for an extendable thirty years period.

Table 3. Summary of the institutional structures in the energy sector in Central America

Country	Energy Exchange	Natural Gas	Electricity	Electricity Market Regulator
Costa Rica	Deficit – Hydrocarbons import	No	Generation: private participation Transmission and distribution: Costa Rica Energy Institute (ICE). Trade: exclusive Expansion decisions: by the State.	ARESEP
El Salvador	Deficit – Hydrocarbons import	LNG Project	Generation: private companies and some state-owned companies.. Distribution: mostly private. Expansion decisions: by the market	SIGET
Guatemala	Deficit – Exports crude but imports of refined products	No	Generation: hydropower by the State and thermal by private companies. Transmission: totally state-owned. Expansion decisions: by the state.	CNEE
Honduras	Deficit – Hydrocarbons import	No	National Energy Utility (ENEE) operates in the three segments. Private participation is allowed, except for transmission. Expansion decisions: by the State.	CNE
Nicaragua	Deficit – Hydrocarbons import	No	The State operates in the three segments. Private participation is important in distribution and is forbidden for transmission (fully operated by state-owned ENTRESA). Expansion decisions: by the state.	INE
Panama	Deficit – Hydrocarbons import	Project from Colombia	Generation and distribution are in private hands. State-owned Panamanian Transmission Company (ETESA) controls transmission. Expansion decisions: by the state.	ANASEP

Source: World Economic Council (2008).

Age of the Power Plants Operating in the Region

Regarding the age of power plants located in different Latin American and the Caribbean countries and its impact in their performance, the following can be stated: With the increase age of a power plant it tends to become less reliable. Their performance and efficiency decline, and operating and maintenance costs increase. De-rating of the power plant due to equipment ageing and changes in operating regimes may also occur. These are the main reasons to modernize a power plant, or to stop it operation.

According to expert's opinion, the maximum age of a power plant in operation in the region should be between thirty and forty years. If thirty years of operation of a power plant is used as reference for its replacement or modernization, then probably a high number of power plants now operating in the region should be replaced or modernized in the coming years. The different governments of the region with or without the support of the private sector should allocate the necessary resources to carry out this modernization or replacement process in the coming years. The investment could reach the amount of US $1,600 billion in order to modernize or replace several of the current power plants in operation.

Energy Schools and Policies

One important characteristic of the region's current energy scene, particularly in the case of South-America, is the existence of two energy schools and policies: a) Energy nationalism policy; and b) Energy pragmatism policy. Venezuela, Bolivia, Ecuador, and Argentina have adopted an energy nationalism policy outside of the current liberal economy trends, remaining somehow on the margins of the globalization economy process. Partially as a result of the application of this policy, their energy sectors have become increasingly dominated by the State. For this reason, more prohibitive restrictions on foreign and private sector exploration and production in the form of tighter fiscal and access conditions for international oil and gas companies in Latin American hydrocarbons sites have been adopted. As result of the adoption of this policy, a lack of foreign investment has been affected oil and gas output levels in these countries. The impact can be seen in the evolution of production levels. For example, Venezuela and Argentina are producing now approximately 25% less oil than their respective production peaks some ten years ago.

On the other hand, a number of other countries in the region, including Brazil, Chile, Peru, and Colombia, have continue to pursue more pragmatic energy policies which, without abandoning or denying a legitimate role for the State, remain more open, transparent, rules-based, and market-oriented. Other countries, such as Mexico, remain stuck between these two energy policies, for the moment incapable of overcoming the domestic geography of special-interest resistance to energy-sector reform, even though they continue to engage the liberal and globalizing economy beyond energy (Isbell, 2009).

Energy Efficiency

One of the main elements, if not the most important one, that need to be considered during the preparation of any energy development program in Latin American and the Caribbean countries is energy efficiency. What is energy efficiency? It is important to know that energy efficiency, in its broad concept, attempts to maintain the same service provided but reducing, at the same time, energy consumption. According to Poveda (2007), energy efficiency involves actions on the supply and demand sides, without sacrificing human comfort or economic productivity, and improving supply security.

In the case of the energy sector, worries more with the demand side because it depends on the decision of thousands of users instead of few entrepreneurs, as it is the case in the supply side. Moreover, it brings savings in both energy consumption and economy of the general population. At the same time, it reduces greenhouse gas emissions, reducing the negative impact in the environment due to the use of fossil fuels and other contaminating energy sources in the production of electricity and remarkably improves the finances of energy companies. This is very important because the establishment of private utilities to generate energy has led to a natural interest to improve energy efficiency production with the purpose of reducing costs without affecting the quality of the service. Moreover, energy reforms adopted by several countries of the region eliminated subsidies bringing the right price signal to consumers in order to increase their interest and to motivate them to incorporate energy efficiency, which is a necessary signal but not enough to increase efficiency in electricity generation[14].

According to OLADE's conservative estimates, the Latin American and the Caribbean region could accumulate savings on fuels of US $156 billion until 2018, if strong energy efficiency national programs that are long-term oriented were promoted and implemented in all countries. The investments required to implement energy efficiency programs are very profitable, such as the case of Mexico, where the investment of the State to the responsible institution of energy efficiency in 2005 was US $5.5 million in order to amount savings of US $398 million.

Why energy efficiency programs became so important? According to Poveda (2007), the potential size of energy efficiency programs is evident: Only 37% of all primary energy becomes useful energy. The chain of transformations and processes that energy products go through before providing a required service, causes a 63% loss in its potential capacity. In other words, almost two third of the energy produced is lost in the chain covering production and consumers.

On the other hand, it is important to know the following: The new structure of the energy sector is characterized by the increase in the amount of players, which brings as consequence the dispersion of the responsibility of energy efficiency development, if it is not assumed by the State. Furthermore, the efficiency benefits to vertically integrated companies are not clear for private generators and transmission companies, especially if the improvement in demand side efficiency, which may defer new investments, is a benefit for the society and not for a single generator. Distribution companies that were privatized had to consolidate their position to meet shareholders requirements by confronting urgent problems such as bill collection improvement and reduction of technical and non-technical losses, among others. In this case, demand side energy efficiency has low priority in the private company's plans and this is so if there is any interest on this matter. In other words, the development of energy efficiency in

---

[14] The overall efficiency of the combined heat and power plants process "e" is defined by the equation: $e = (H + E) / F$; where E is the quantity of electricity produced; H is the quantity of heat produced, and F is the quantity of fuel consumed in the transformation process. In the case of conventional power plants (production of electricity only) the overall efficiency is calculated by the equation: $e = E/F$.

the region was affected and survived only in few countries with well-established institutions ready to implement energy efficiency programs.

There is not general conscience among Latin American and the Caribbean governments and stakeholders towards the importance of energy efficiency. Some authorities and other actors within the energy sector believe that expanding the supply is the only solution available to satisfy demand, and, for this reason, they do not consider that actions taken in the demand side are also valid options. Once heightened awareness has been achieved, it is important to adopt a firm political decision encouraging long-term activities that lead to concrete results in the goal of reducing the energy demand.

Moreover, the need to persist in energy efficiency programs demands the presence of an institution responsible for energy efficiency, with autonomy and technical recognition, equipped, and with enough resources to carry out its functions properly. Mexico is one of the countries of the region applying successfully energy efficiency programs with a rate of 2% per year in energy intensity reduction.

Countries of the region are very heterogeneous not only by their size but also in their level of energy development. The participation of subsectors in energy consumption also varies among countries. Industrial consumption is predominant in countries with relatively higher levels of development, while the commercial sector is the most important component in other countries. There is even a third group where residential consumption has predominance. All this makes energy intensity to vary a lot among countries, and the regional index a key indicator of the most important consumptions.

Table 4. Energy intensity growth rates

Sub-region/ year	1996-2002	2000-2005	1995-2005
Mexico	-2.7%	-0.4%	-2%
Central America	0.1%	0.7%	0%
The Caribbean	0.4%	1%	0.7%
Andean zone	-0.6%	0.2%	-0.5%
South cone	0.5%	0.2%	0.6%
Latin American and the Caribbean region	-0.4%	0.3%	-0.2%

Source: OLADE.

Table 5. Savings from energy conservation

Sub-region	Accumulated savings 2003-2018 (Million of US dolars)
Mexico	36,600
Central America	7,200
The Caribbean	9,900
Andean region	24,900
Brazil	53,600
Southern cone	23,500
Latin American and the Caribbean region	155,700

Source: OLADE.

From Table 4, the following can be stated: For the whole region, an increment in energy productivity is observed, in which Mexico stands out followed by the Andean zone. Nevertheless, other sub-regions do not follow the same trend and the consequence is an annual regional decreasing rate of 0.2% between 1995 and 2005. The region energy efficiency efforts have been limited and focused on only a few countries. During the period 2000-2005, energy efficiency in the region grew only 0.3% but during the period 1995-2005, the decline was -0.2%.

From a study carried out by OLADE, the economic potential of energy efficiency in the region is estimate to be between 10% and 20%. A very conservative use of this potential, between 3% and 5% only, will represent a savings of around US $156 billion for the entire region (see Table 5)[15]. This table shows the magnitude of the savings in financial terms, which could be achieved by implementing national energy efficiency plans.

According to Poveda (2004), the most important and common aspects to achieve energy efficiency participation in energy supply are the following:

a) *Awareness building among energy sector actors.* The long years of emphasis on supply-side options have lead energy sector authorities and executives to base energy security solely on expanding supply, despite the fact that demand-side options are equally valid, require less investment and are friendly with the environment;

b) *Political decision.* The pre-condition for actions to achieve significant energy savings is the determination at the highest levels of the government, energy companies, the academia, and professionals associations, to raise energy sector efficiency to the category of a State's policy;

c) *Determination of the national institution in charge of the elaboration and implementation of energy efficiency programs.* Next in importance, after political will, it is to designate or if necessary create a national institution in charge of developing and implementing energy efficiency programs. This institution should convey an image of independence from all other institutions in the energy sector and from energy companies, and its decisions should be based on technical studies that support their validity, in such way that its recommendations will command the respect of all players in the sector;

d) *Establishing the objectives of the plan.* Energy efficiency contributions should be clearly identified, to ensure that they are considered a part of supply. This requires coordination with sector policies and basing them on end–use studies, to first determine their potential and then set goals. The national's energy policy should be very clear in order to include within its framework energy efficiency activities;

e) *Definition of the strategy to achieve the plan's objectives.* Once goals have been set and the respective studies are available, it is essential to propose a strategy to achieve the purposes proposed. The energy efficiency strategy should be understood as a policy's document instead of a technical document because the work required, essentially from the demand-side, implies appropriate actions to make the clients of the sector take several decisions towards the achievement of the goal desired by changing their habits of energy use and adopting more efficient technologies. This

---

[15] The price of the oil barrel was estimate to be US $50.00, which is less than half of the oil price in May 2012.

strategy should contemplate deadlines, costs, expected results, and the roles of the different actors involved. It should also define priorities among proposed activities, such as information and education campaigns, subsidies, or others;

f) *Plan development and implementation.* Once the strategy is defined, the guide will be available to develop the plan, which should lean on the understanding that it is a long-term effort that should include several elements in order to guarantee a successful result. An energy efficiency plan is complete when it considers two groups of activities: a) The implementation of measures; and b) Complementary actions;

g) *Plan follow up and evaluation.* This is a task that should receive special attention during the energy efficiency plans implementation. If successful results are obtained from the efforts invested, the reduction in demand should be shown comparing it with the situation that would have occurred if the programs would not be adopted and implemented.

Finally, let present a concrete example of the importance of adopting energy efficiency programs in the Latin American and the Caribbean region. In 2001, Brazil was hit by severe droughts that crippled the hydroelectric facilities that were supplying more than 80% of its electricity supply. Faced with the prospect of mass blackouts, the government implemented an innovative energy efficiency plan that offered financial rewards to consumers who cut back on electricity consumption and expensive penalties to those who did not. The results exceeded all expectations.

Brazil reduced its electricity consumption by a stunning 20% in a little more than a month, according to a study carried out by the International Energy Agency and others. This was a far larger reduction than what fully industrialized countries have been able to achieve when forced to quickly reduce electricity consumption during an emergency. And, what is important to stress, the reductions were accomplished without causing serious disruptions to the economy. But an even bigger surprise awaited policymakers in 2002, after the drought ended and the government discontinued the incentives and penalties. Contrary to expectations, electricity consumption did not shoot back up to previous levels. In fact, it took almost four years for Brazil's electricity consumption to grow back to its pre-2000 levels. "People discovered that they could use less electricity and still live comfortably, so they chose to continue saving" says Arnaldo Vieira de Carvalho, a renewable energy expert at the IDB. In essence, Brazil proved that voluntary changes in behavior, combined with modest investments in energy-saving equipment, can produce huge savings without compromising human welfare or economic growth.

The above experience of Brazil can yield a much bigger payoff than expected. The McKinsey Global Institute carried out a study entitled "Curbing Energy Demand Growth: The Global Energy Productivity Opportunity." The report offered a simple but stunning conclusion. Its authors calculated that growth in energy demand can be cut in half, without compromising economic growth, simply by increasing energy productivity through comprehensive conservation measures that include widespread adoption of existing technologies. This finding has enormous implications for the Latin American and the Caribbean countries.

In Mexico, for example, electricity demand is expected to expand at an estimated 5.6% per year up to 2013 - significantly faster than predicted economic growth. The IDB estimates that merely to keep up with that demand, Mexico will need to invest US $5.5 billion per year in new energy production capacity. If the McKinsey study's recommendations were adopted in Mexico, the country could save more than US $2 billion per year in new capacity expenditures. Mexican authorities have been convinced of this reality for some time. The government created a National Energy Saving Commission for Energy in 1989, and a year later it established a Trust Fund to Support Energy Efficiency in the Electricity Sector to carry out concrete energy efficiency programs in specific sectors such as lighting and industrial machinery.

Chile is another country that also has well-established energy conservation programs with proven track records. Other countries, including Argentina, Bolivia, Cuba, Ecuador, Nicaragua, Uruguay, and Venezuela, are ramping up plans to promote the use of compact fluorescent light bulbs and other energy-saving technologies. "The alternatives are pretty clear," says the IDB's Vieira de Carvalho. "You can spend a lot trying to increase energy supply in order to avoid blackouts, or you can spend very little to get the same result through greater efficiency." Brazil has already proven that a developing country can use sophisticated conservation measures to avoid an energy crisis. The question now is whether the region will use similar measures to achieve long-term energy security.

In Argentina the energy efficiency of the thermal sector has increased by 10% since 1990, reaching 41% in 2009. That improvement was achieved through a switch in the power generation mix to natural gas and to the rise in gas combined cycle plants since 1995. In 2009, gas combined cycle plants accounted for more than 40% of the country's thermal capacity.

Summing up the following can be stated: While there have been no comprehensive studies of energy efficiency potential in the Latin American and the Caribbean region as a whole, there is sufficient evidence to show that there is significant untapped energy efficiency potential in the region. In addition, based on the energy efficiency and conservation programs that have been already implemented in the region, efficiency is one of the least-cost ways of satisfying growing energy demand.

Energy efficiency gains can be achieved on the supply-side by improving the production of electricity and by reducing transmission and distribution losses. Electricity distribution losses alone in the region in 2005 were equal to the entire electricity consumption of Argentina, Chile, and Colombia combined.

Distribution losses vary significantly in the region, ranging from a low of 6% in Chile to a high of above 40% in the Dominican Republic, with a Latin American and the Caribbean average of around 19%. If distribution losses could be reduced to the levels of the best performers in the region over the coming twenty years, annual electricity savings from distribution improvements alone could reduce demand by about 78 TWh (6% of the incremental foreseen demand of 1 325 TWh) by 2030.

On the demand-side, energy efficiency can be improved by adopting policies and programs that encourage the efficient consumption of electricity by end-users. Among the energy efficiency measures that can be expanded in the region are standards for widely-used industrial and residential equipment, building codes, consumer education, and energy management programs within industry, the buildings sector, and public utilities. Electric motors, pumps, fans, and compressors, which are estimated to account for as much as two-thirds of industrial electricity consumption worldwide, can reduce their electricity consumption by around 40% through the use of variable-speed drives.

The IDB has estimated that electricity consumption in the Latin American and the Caribbean region could be reduced between 105 MW and 143 TWh over the coming decade through the investment in widely available energy efficiency equipment and technologies, and that these savings could be achieved at about one-third the cost of installing new generation capacity. Other estimates of the potential for demand-side efficiency improvements, based on energy efficiency programs implemented in the Latin American and the Caribbean region range between 18% and 30% of estimated additional electricity demand in the region by 2030.

Additional incentives – such as electricity tariff and subsidy reform – could improve the efficiency of electricity use. While industry often has a sufficient direct financial incentive to improve its electricity efficiency – depending in part on the level and structure of electricity tariffs – the market alone often provides inadequate incentives to promote energy efficiency in the residential, buildings, and public sectors. Overcoming information, principal-agent, budgeting and finance, and regulatory constraints through dedicated public energy efficiency programs can help improve efficiency in these sectors (Yepez- García et al., 2010).

FORESEEN INCREASE IN THE WORLD'S ENERGY PRODUCTION AND DEMAND

In accordance with the opinion of different experts in the field of energy all over the world, the use of energy at world's level will continue to increase gradually until 2030. However, it is important to be aware of the following: According to United Nations and the IEO (2009) reports, current estimates indicate that 1.6 billion people are without access to electricity, and 2.4 billion people have no access to modern fuels for electricity generation. In the specific case of the Latin American and the Caribbean region, in 2008 around 7% of the Latin-American people (34.1 million) do not have access to electricity (see Table 13). Expanding energy access to this group of people is essential for alleviating poverty and, in fact, for achieving all of the Millennium Development Goals adopted by the United Nations a few years ago. Improving energy access for the alleviation of poverty also means promoting small and medium scaled businesses, industrial development, and better transportation networks in a general effort to improve socio-economic well-being. All of this will require greater energy use.

The provision of adequate and reliable energy services at an affordable cost, in a secure and environmentally benign manner, and in conformity with social and economic development needs, is an essential element of sustainable development. Many areas of the world have no reliable and secure energy supplies, and hence no affordable and adequate energy services, which limits their economic and social development.

In other areas, environmental degradation from energy production and use inhibits sustainable development. Adequate and affordable energy services have been critical to economic and social development and for the transition from subsistence agricultural economies to modern industrial and service-oriented societies. Energy is central to improved social and economic well-being, and is indispensable for industrial and commercial wealth generation.

Then, the main question that needs to be asked is the following: How much the energy demand will increase during the coming years and how this demand is going to be met? To respond to this question in a satisfactory manner, it is important for policy makers to understand the implications and impacts of different energy programs that could be implemented, the level of energy reserves available, alternative energy policies, strategies and plans that could be applied in shaping the economic and social development within the different countries, and the feasibility of making development sustainable over time, among others elements.

According to studies made by the French Association of Oil Professionals, "it is expected that for 2030, the world's energy demand will be double, and it is probably that could be triple for 2050". Until 2030, the primary energy demands at world's level are expecting to increase annually in 1.7%, which is somehow smaller than the world's average growth of 2.1% registered during the past three decades.

It is also expected that 90% of the increase in the world's energy demand in the coming decades will be satisfied with fossil fuels. This means that around 15 300 million tons of oil equivalent will be consumed at world level in 2030 (Morales Pedraza, 2008). Around 10% of the world's energy demands are expected to be satisfied by the use of nuclear energy and by different types of renewable energy sources.

Energy Production

With respect to the level of energy production in the Latin American and the Caribbean region, it is important to single out the following: Overall, the Latin American and the Caribbean region has considerable fossil fuel and renewable energy reserves to satisfy the foreseable energy demand for the coming years. Approximately 56% of the electricity produced in the region, considering twenty six countries members of OLADE, is provided by hydro power, 40% by fossil fuels, 3% by nuclear power plants[16] and 1% by the use of geothermal, wind, and solar energy sources. The energy produced by auto-generators represented only 10% of the total electricity produced in the region (Poveda, 2004). The use of different renewable energy sources for the electricity generation in the region is still very low and, for this reason, it participation in the energy balance is almost non-existent in most of the countries.

On the other hand, several major producers in the region[17] have faced declines in production, linked with (in the case of Mexico and Colombia) questions over the size of their remaining reserves. Given limited local capacity and attracting private know-how and funds is a key factor in further fossil fuel production. Recent estimates of current and planned investment in energy supply infrastructure in the region confirm, that there is likely to be underinvestment in energy supply infrastructure in the coming years, and the level under consideration is lower than in all other developing regions (including Africa) on coal, oil, natural gas, and in total. Only power investments are likely to be sizeable in the coming years.

---

[16] Other publications indicate that nuclear power generates around 2% of the total electricity produced in the Latin American region.

[17] Brazil, Mexico, and Argentina are the countries with the greatest installed power capacities for producing electricity in the Latin American and the Caribbean region.

It is important to note that the largest exporter of electrical power in the region is Paraguay[18], and the country that imported more energy is Brazil. It is envisaged that new interconnections that are being implemented, or under study, will cause an increase electrical power transactions between Central American and South American countries.

Energy Consumption

Regarding electrical power consumption in the Latin American and the Caribbean region, it is expected that there will be a greater degree of industrialization that will improve the standard of living of the population in the future. But more industrialization means more energy needs and an increase in the electricity consumption. The electricity generation in 2010 in the Latin American and the Caribbean region was 1 082.3 TWh and the consumption reached the amount of 873.51 TWh; this represents 81% of the electricity produced in that year. It is important to stress that in 2006, the level of energy consumption was 1 175.97 TWh; this represents 35% higher than the level of consumption in 2010. The total reduction in the consumption of electricity was of 302.46 TWh during the past four years.

From Figure 4, the following can be stated: Brazil is by far the country with the highest electricity consumption in the whole region (with more than double the consumption level of Mexico), followed by this last country, and by Argentina, Chile, Colombia, Peru, Cuba, Ecuador, and the Dominican Republic.

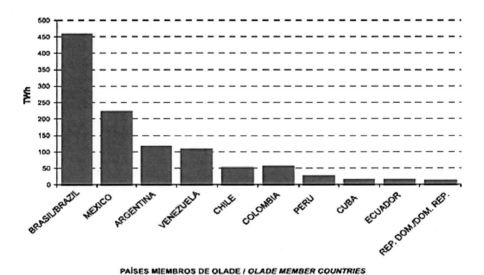

Consumo de Electricidad AL&C / *Electricity Consumption LA&C*

Source: OLADE.

Figure 4. Electricity consumption in some Latin American and the Caribbean countries.

---

[18] Mainly due to the export to Brazil of part of the electricity produced by the Itaipú hydro power plant located in the border of Paraguay and Brazil.

It is important to single out that the level of the electricity consumption in the Latin American and the Caribbean region is only higher than the level of electricity consumption in Africa and in the Middle East but lower than in Asia and the Pacific, Europe, and North America.

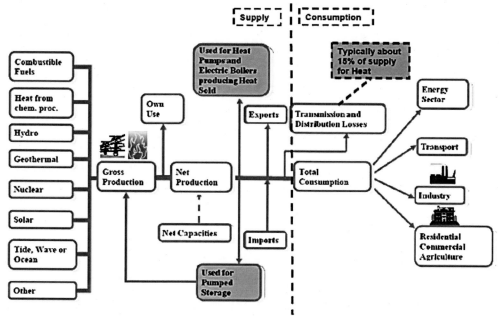

Source: OLADE- SIEE (2005).

Figure 5. Primary energy supply and consumption.

According to the IEO (2009) report, the energy consumption in Central and South America sub-regions is expected to increase from 873.51 TWh in 2010, to 1 104.60 TWh in 2030; this represents an increase of 26% for the whole period. The average annual percentage change of the level of electricity consumption in Central and South American sub-regions during the period 2006-2030 is expected to be 1.9%, which is 0.4% higher than the world's average (1.5%). However, and despite of this increase foreseen in energy consumption in the region for the coming years, the per capita energy consumption in the industrialized countries is five times higher.

According to the IEO (2010) report, electricity generation in Central and South America will increases by 2.1% per year from 1 trillion kWh in 2007 to 1.7 trillion kWh in 2030 and to 1.8 trillion kWh in 2035. However, the recent global economic crisis slowed the region's economies and lowered the electricity demand, especially in the industrial sector. In the long-term, however, the region's electricity markets are expected to return to trend growth as the economic difficulties recede.

The fuel mix for electricity generation in Central and South America is dominated by hydroelectric, which accounted for nearly two-thirds of the region's total net electricity generation in 2007. Of the top seven electricity-generating countries in the region, five generate more than 65% of their total electricity from hydro power. These countries are: Paraguay, Uruguay, Brazil, Peru, and Venezuela.

Several nations in Central and South America have been trying to increase the amounts of natural gas used in their generation fuel mixes by increasing both pipeline and LNG supplies[19]. Chile, for instance, relies on Argentina for its natural gas supplies but beginning in 2004, Argentina began to restrict its exports of natural gas to around 10% of the agreed level after it was unable to meet its own domestic supply. As a result, Chile has been forced to use diesel-fueled electric generating capacity periodically to avoid power outages during the winter months. In response to the lack of a secure source of natural gas from Argentina, Chile began construction of two LNG regasification projects.

In the IEO (2010) reference case, natural-gas-fired generation in Central and South America (excluding Brazil) increases by an average 2.2% per year, and the natural gas share of total electricity generation rises from 22% in 2007 to 29% in 2035; this represents an increase of 7% for the whole period.

In the Central American sub-region, consumption times and patterns differ among countries, and power consumption structures are dissimilar in each. This affects the configuration of load curves that, upon comparison, show evident differences in peak demand times. This situation is highly favorable for interconnected system operation, as is the different seasonal variation coefficient among countries, where future generation capacity could be achieved from diverse power plants connected to a sub-regional line, thus supplementing the energy need in each of the countries.

With regard to energy supply, the Central American sub-region currently supplies the power market with hydroelectric plants, thermoelectric steam plants consuming fuel oil, geothermal plants, diesel engines, gas turbines using diesel as a fuel, co-generation, and a modest contribution from wind, biomass and solar power plants. Actually, an installed reserve capacity in the order of 27% is anticipated and, under average hydrological conditions, hydroelectric plants will cover up to 49% of all sub-regional power consumption. Although hydroelectric infrastructure plays an important role in the sub-region, substantially modifying price structures, its share percentage has dropped considerably, while the oil bill grows continually in these countries.

According to the power and energy balance, and bearing in mind energy reserve installed capacity, the Central American sub-region currently need new power plants for electricity generation to satisfy future demand starting from 2010, although some countries will require new isolated generation power plants prior to that date. In 2010, 2015, and 2020, the entire integrated system will need access to new power facilities with a capacity in the order of 1 300 MW, 4 800 MW, and 9 005 MW, respectively.

More efficient use of energy should be made at regional level and, as a consequence of the increase in energy efficiency, electrical losses in the transmission and distribution system should be reduced. Regional electricity demand is estimated to be about 1.9 million GWh in 2020. Of this figure, 24% will be commercial consumption (including transportation and other services), 50% industrial, and 26% residential.

---

[19] In the Southern Cone, the largest consumer of primary energy is Argentina, followed by Chile, while Uruguay and Paraguay have similar consumption to that of the Central American countries. The percentage of oil and by-products in the energy mix of Uruguay is 51%, in Chile 43%, in Argentina 37% and 14% in Paraguay. Hydro power is significant in Paraguay (100%), in Uruguay (99%), in Brazil (83.9%), in Peru (81%), and in Venezuela (73.4), while natural gas is essential in Argentina (54.3%) and in Uruguay (16%) (World Energy Council, 2008 and IJHD, 2010).

From an energy point of view, four countries (Mexico, Brazil, Argentina, and Venezuela) consume 73% of the energy and 79% of the electricity produced in the whole region. Industry (34%) and transportation (31%) are the sectors that consume more energy in the region. From the consumption point of view, Brazil tops the list for the region with an average of 2.1-2.3 million barrels of oil per day over the past years, followed very closely by Mexico with an average of 2-2.1 million barrels of oil per day. This might seem somewhat surprising given that Brazil has a larger economy and population than Mexico; however, the agriculture, cattle ranching and forestry industries in Brazil, which make up a large proportion of total's economic activity, demand comparatively low hydrocarbon consumption. Other sizeable consumers of hydrocarbons in the region are Chile and Colombia.

INVESTMENT IN THE ENERGY SECTOR

Latin American utilities and municipalities are currently developing 513 power generation projects that will cost a total of US $230 billion, according to the latest Power Tracker report published by Industrial Info Resources. The main purpose of this immense investment in the energy sector is to allow countries of the region to be in a position to satisfy the foreseen demand of energy in the coming decades.

Latin America's vast natural resources and growing GDP are driving the next phase of development in the region, according to the Power Tracker report. In all, more than 183 GW of new power generation units are currently being evaluated in Latin America to meet the growing power requirements of the region, all the way from Mexico through Central and South America. Because of South America's vast river systems, hydroelectric generation will continue to be a major source for new power generation on that continent, but its participation in electricity generation will decrease in percentage. More than 800 hydroelectric power units are currently under development, representing about 85 GW of power, according to the Power Tracker report. In a notable example, Brazil intends to construct the Tapajós hydro power complex as part of the country's 2019 Energy Expansion Decennial Plan. That project alone would require investments of US $53.9 billion in hydro power generation. Trailing hydroelectric power, the second most important energy source for Latin America for electricity generation will be natural gas, where almost 300 units are planned, contributing a total of 27 GW of power. Coal ranks third as a power source, with 75 units planned, totaling almost 20 GW. Other important projects will develop wind, solar, and other sources of energy, including nuclear energy in Argentina and Brazil, and perhaps later in Mexico.

Total investment in the construction of new capacity in the energy sector in the Latin American and the Caribbean region will be almost equally divided between capital-intensive hydro power and low capital cost gas-fired power plant.

New investment in the construction of gas-fired power plants will depend on the cost of natural gas, the development of the natural gas infrastructure system and the tariffs and contracts for the supply of natural gas. Natural gas investors seek long-term contracts to protect their investments. But in an electricity market dominated by hydro power, electricity prices will be highly dependent on the rainfall levels, and, for this reason, the economic attractiveness of gas-fired power plants for foreign investors will depend critically on the type of contracts established (Deutsche Montan Technologie GmbH, OLADE and CIEMAT, 2005).

Investment in Latin American gas-supply infrastructure will grow steadily to meet rising demand and export volumes. Upstream investments will remain the largest component but the development of transmission networks will absorb an increasing share of the investment foreseen in the gas sector. Domestic demand and exports are set to rise significantly in the next three decades. Upstream financing will require large inflows of foreign capital. This might be problematic, depending on the degree of opening of the gas sector and on the political stability of the region, among other elements.

Cross-border pipeline and LNG projects will come on stream, if a clear and stable regulatory framework is set and co-operation among countries develops fruitfully. Cumulative investment needs in the Latin American and the Caribbean gas sector are projected to total US $247 billion, or more than US $8 billion per year, over the period 2001-2030, amounting to 8% of world's gas sector investment. Gas-sector policies will need to be integrated with electricity policies, as gas-to-power projects are the key to ensuring the financial viability of the gas chain. Upstream development will absorb more than half of total capital flows, transmission, and distribution pipelines accounting for another 36%.

In 2000, investment in exploration and development in the gas sector reached US $2.1 billion. It is expected to rise steadily to US $2.8 billion per year in the current decade and US $6.8 billion per year until 2030. More than US $49 billion, or US $1.6 billion a year, will be needed over the next three decades to build and expand cross-border pipelines and national transmission lines. The average annual capital expenditure is expected to increase over time. Spending will average about US $1 billion per year during the current decade, compared with US $700 million during the past ten years; this represents an increase of 43%. Investment will reach an average of US $2.3 billion per year in the third decade, due to more technically challenging projects, with high per unit cost, and the faster expansion of the transmission network. The development of the domestic distribution network and underground gas storage will call for an additional US $41 billion, or US $1.4 billion per year.

Some Latin American countries will invest heavily in LNG export facilities in the coming years. Most of the LNG will go to the North American market and to importing countries in the region. Investment in liquefaction plants is expected to total US $15 billion over the period 2001-2030 (Deutsche Montan Technologie GmbH, OLADE and CIEMAT, 2005).

From Table 6, the following can be stated: The major investment in the period 2001-2030 will be to increase the generating capacities of the current power plants in operation in the region, the use of renewable energy sources for the electricity generation, refurbishment of existing power plants, and to reduce distribution and transmission losses (56% of the total). Investment in the oil sector will be the second priority with 25% of the total and in the gas sector 18%. The lowest level of investment will be in the coal sector with only 0.7% of the total.

Investment in Latin American and the Caribbean oil sector is expected to be dominated by projects in several countries, particularly Brazil and Venezuela. From Table 6, the following conclusion can be reached: In the oil sector, the total investment that will be required by the Latin American and the Caribbean region in order to satisfy the foreseen increase in the energy demand will amount to $336 billion over the period 2001- 2030. Because of strong growth in production, annual capital spending in the region will increase sharply, from an average of US $9.1 billion from 2001-2010 to 11.2 billion during the period 2011-2020, to over US $13 billion in the decade 2021- 2030.

Table 6. Total investments required in the Latin American and the Caribbean electrical sector in different period

Investment (billion dollars)		2001-2010	2011-2020	2021-2030	2001-2030
	Total Regional Investment	339	440	558	1,337
OIL	Total	91	112	133	336
	Exploration and development	70	81	90	241
	Non-conventional oil	15	17	27	59
	Refining	6	14	17	37
Gas	Total	54	78	115	247
	Exploration and development	28	45	68	141
	LNG liquefaction	7	3	4	15
	LNG regasification	-	-	-	-
	Transmission	10	16	23	49
	Distribution	9	12	19	39
	Underground storage	0	1	1	2
Coal	Total	3	3	4	10
	Total mining	3	3	3	9
	new mining capacity	2	2	2	6
	Sustaining mining capacity	1	1	1	3
	Ports	0,4	0,3	0,5	1,2
Electricity	Total	191	247	306	744
	Generating capacity	86	111	120	317
	of which renewables	63	78	69	211
	Refurbishment	5	6	8	19
	Transmission	32	41	55	128
	Distribution	69	89	124	281

Source: Deutsche Montan Technologie GmbH, OLADE and CIEMAT (2005).

Cumulative investment of around US $10 billion in coal mining and port infrastructure will be required in the Latin American and the Caribbean region until 2030, with the purpose of satisfying the foreseeable increase in the electricity demand. Coal production in the region is expected to grow at 2.6% per annum, from almost 54 million tons in 2000 to 115 million tons in 2030; this represents an increase of 112%. Primary energy demand for coal in Latin American and the Caribbean countries is projected to grow at 2.3% per annum, from almost 33 million tons in 2000 to around 70 million tons in 2030; this represents an increase of 112%. Exports will increase from 44 million tons in 2000 to more than 92 million tons in 2030; this represents an increase of 102%. The new productive capacity that will need to be added is around 103 million tons, of which 61 million tons represents new capacity to meet demand growth (59% of new capacity to be built), and 42 million tons is needed to replace depleted mines (41% of the total capacity to be built). The corresponding investment needs will be US $6 billion (60% of mining investment) for new capacity to meet demand growth, and for new capacity to replace depleted capacity. Around US $3 billion will be required for sustaining capital investment to maintain and increase the mine productivity and around US $1 billion for coal ports (see Table 6). This relatively large investment is due to the more than 100% increase in exports and to the currently sparse existing infrastructure, in particular in Venezuela, which will require significant new investment, if projections of export growth are to be met.

The total investment implemented during the period 2001-2010 was US $191 billion. The foreseen total investment in the electricity sector during the period 2011-2020 and 2021-2030 is US $247 and US $306 billion, respectively; this represents an increase of 29% and 60%, respectively respect to the period 2001-2010.

Total private-sector investment in the regional electricity sector implemented between 1990 and 2002 amounted to US $97 billion, although this has been in decline in recent years. The reasons for the observed decline in private investment include badly designed economic reforms, economic crisis, and bad business judgments. Investments in the electricity sector in the region are dominated by the growth of power demand in Brazil. It is expected that Brazil's electricity demand will increase by 2.5 times from 2000 to 2030, growing at an average annual rate of 3.2%. To meet this big increase, the country will need to invest more than US $330 billion in the power sector during that period, more than half in transmission and distribution networks.

There are several factors that have a major impact on the risks perceived by the private investor when considering any investment in the energy sector in the Latin American and the Caribbean region and, therefore, determine its cost of capital and its required return on investment, the feasibility of financing new investments, and the participation of qualified firms interested in providing a public service on a long-term basis. Some of these factors are:

a) Stability of the country's macroeconomic environment;
b) A legal structure that clearly defines the rules and procedures for private sector participation;
c) An independent legal system that ensures the stability and enforcement of contracts;
d) The form of regulation and a clear definition of the wholesale and retail tariff setting mechanisms:
e) The level, predictability, and stability of public service revenues during the term of the contract;
f) The terms and conditions of the concession, franchise or other type of contracts.

From the regulatory point of view there is a tradeoff between creating a stable low-risk regulatory environment for private investors and creating an environment that fosters competition and provides incentives for economic efficiency. Particularly, implementation of competition in the energy market, with an active spot market and regulation by licenses, may increase the risks perceived by private investors and its cost of capital. On the other hand, competition for the energy market with regulation based on contracts and well defined price setting mechanisms would mitigate these risks. To attract private capital to small-or medium-size countries in the region with relatively high country risks, it would be essential to adopt a method of regulation that minimize the regulatory risks for the private investors (Dussan, 1996).

ELECTRICITY GENERATION AND CONSUMPTION

In 2009, the installed electrical generation capacity of the Latin American and the Caribbean region was, according to British Petroleum (2010) of 1 082.3 TWh, a decrease of 4% respect to 2008. The consumption was, according to EIA (2010) of 873.51 TWh; this represents 77.4% of the total electricity generated in the region. According to Business Monitor International sources for 2010, Latin American and the Caribbean power generation assumption was 1 198 TWh, an increase of 11% over 2008 and the forecast for 2014 is 1 359 TWh, representing an increase of 13.5% between 2010 and 2014. The BMI report forecasted for 2010, that Latin American thermal power generation would reach 445 TWh[20], accounting for 37.1% of the total electricity supplied in the region. The BMI forecast for 2014 is 480 TWh, implying 8% growth between 2010 and 2014. BMI forecast a growth in regional generation to 1 320 TWh by 2013, representing a rise of 16.9% for the next five years or 3.4% per year.

Latin American and the Caribbean thermal power generation in 2008 was 453 TWh, accounting for 40% of the total electricity supplied in the region. The forecast for 2013 is 523 TWh, implying 15.5% growths. It is foresee that the energy demand in Latin American and the Caribbean region will increase 75% by 2030, requesting an investments of US $1,600 billion in the next decade alone to support this increase. The region will require a 50% increase in its energy installed capacity or more than 90 GW to satisfy the foreseable energy demand.

World's net electricity generation is expected to increase by an average of 2.1% per year from 2006 to 2030, according to the IEO (2010) reference case. In the case of the Latin American and the Caribbean region, the IEO (2010) foresee an increase in electricity generation from 1 082.3 TWh in 2010 to 1 700 TWh in 2030; this means an increase of 57% in the next 20 years, and to 1 800 TWh in 2035; this represents a further increase of 6% in the next five years.

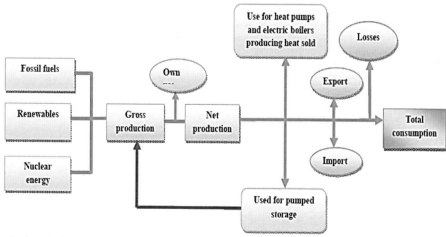

Source: Author design.

Figure 6. Simplified flow chart for electricity generation.

---

[20] A decrease of 2% respect to 2008.

Table 7. Electricity production por regions (in percentage) during the period 1971-2004

Electricity Production	1971-1980	1981-1990	1991-2000	2001-2004
World	4.8%	5.6%	2.5%	4.2%
Latin America and Caribbean	8.7%	5.4%	4.3%	4.0%
East Asia & Pacific	8.3%	8.2%	8.0%	12.7%
Middle East and North Africa	12.2%	8.1%	6.5%	7.1%
South Asia	7.2%	9.3%	6.3%	5.0%
Sub-Saharan Africa	7.8%	4.0%	2.5%	4.4%
Norrth America	4.0%	2.9%	1.7%	2.6%

Source: Yepez-Garcia (2010).

Table 8. Electricity installed capacity in the region during the period 1999-2008

ELECTRICITY – INSTALLED CAPACITY LA&C (MW)										
Países/ Countries	1999	2000	2001	2002	2003	2004	2005	2006	2007	2008
ARGENTINA	24,899	25,957	27,559	27,643	30,599	28,185	28,185	28,185	28,063	28,063
BARBADOS	186	166	166	210	210	210	210	210	210	210
BOLIVIA	1,252	1,325	1,227	1,387	1,314	1,420	1,379	1,403	1,499	1,454
BRASIL / BRAZIL	68,181	73,600	76,139	82,458	86,505	90,733	93,634	96,916	100,974	100,974
CHILE	9,299	9,729	10,269	10,503	10,738	10,738	12,193	13,538	15,886	13,126
COLOMBIA	13,190	12,715	13,463	13,852	13,200	13,407	13,350	13,398	13,410	13,468
COSTA RICA	1,529	1,704	1,715	1,803	1,938	1,961	1,962	2,096	2,092	2,359
CUBA	4,284	4,287	4,411	3,959	3,959	3,764	4,275	5,176	5,430	5,795
ECUADOR	3,634	3,499	3,136	3,269	3,302	3,331	3,567	3,998	4,489	4,187
EL SALVADOR	1,004	1,118	1,192	1,136	1,106	1,096	1,236	1,230	1,372	1,422
GRENADA	27	43	42	32	32	32	32	32	32	32
GUATEMALA	1,359	1,694	1,697	1,513	2,009	2,016	2,091	2,113	2,140	2,287
GUYANA	301	301	301	308	308	308	308	308	308	308
HAITI	241	240	244	244	244	244	244	244	244	244
HONDURAS	920	920	923	1,044	1,045	1,279	1,527	1,548	1,598	1,593
JAMAICA	663	897	811	782	811	811	838	854	854	854
MEXICO	41,178	41,724	42,484	45,761	49,538	46,553	46,534	48,897	49,851	51,248
NICARAGUA	708	645	641	672	693	756	775	768	841	896
PANAMA	1,182	1,248	1,260	1,423	1,555	1,583	1,684	1,467	1,467	1,654
PARAGUAY	7,395	7,396	7,416	7,416	7,416	7,416	7,416	8,116	8,136	8,136
PERU	5,742	6,066	5,906	5,936	5,970	6,016	6,239	6,658	7,028	7,158
REP.DOM. / DOM. REP.	3,081	3,081	5,082	5,112	5,530	5,396	5,518	5,548	5,518	5,518
SURINAME	389	389	389	389	389	389	389	389	389	389
TRINIDAD & TOBAGO	1,253	1,417	1,417	1,416	1,416	1,416	1,416	1,354	1,425	1,425
URUGUAY	2,182	2,182	2,172	2,172	2,171	2,093	2,029	2,228	2,227	2,047
VENEZUELA	21,186	21,233	21,318	20,577	20,577	22,124	22,135	22,215	22,540	23,124
ALAC / LA&C	215,264	223,574	231,379	241,216	252,574	253,275	259,164	268,889	276,022	277,971

Source: OLADE.

From Table 8, the following can be stated: Countries with the highest installed capacity in 2008 in the region are: Brazil, with 100 974 MW, followed by Mexico (51 248 MW), Argentina (28 063 MW), and Venezuela (23 124 MW). Between 10 000 and 20 000 MW of installed capacity are Colombia (13 468 MW) and Chile (13 126 MW). Below 10 000 MW of installed capacity are 20 countries. The country with the lowest installed capacity is Grenada with 32 MW.

From Tables 9, 10, 11 and 12, the following can be stated: The country with the highest electricity generation in 2008 is Brazil with 456 782 MW, followed by Mexico (235 871 MW), Argentina (115 213 MW) and Venezuela (116 086 MW). The country with the lowest generation is Grenada with only 171 MW. The country with the highest demand of electricity in 2008 is Brazil with 498 842 MW, followed by Mexico (235 246 MW), Argentina (122 859

MW); and Venezuela (110 086 MW). The country with the lowest demand is Grenada with only 171 MW. Brazil is the country with the highest level of electricity imported in 2008, with a total of 42 743 MW, followed by Argentina (10 275 MW), Chile (1 628 MW); and Uruguay (963 MW). The country with the lowest import of electricity in 2008 is Guatemala with 5 MW. Fourteen countries do not imported electricity in 2008. Paraguay is the country with the highest level of electricity exported in 2008 with 46 292 MW. The country with the lowest level of electricity exported is El Salvador with 7 MW. Fourteen countries do not exported electricity in 2008.

From Figure 7, the following can be stated: The Dominican Republic is the country with the highest electricity losses within the whole region, with more than 40% of the total electricity produced in the period considered. The country with the lowest electricity losses is Chile with less than 8%. Countries with electricity losses lower than the international level are, in addition to Chile, Costa Rica, El Salvador, Bolivia, Antigua and Barbuda, and St Lucia. Panama, Grenada, and Peru have electricity losses very closed to international standards.

Table 9. Electricity generation in the region during the period 1999-2008

ELECTRICITY - GENERATION LABC (GWh)

Paises / Countries	1999	2000	2001	2002	2003	2004	2005	2006	2007	2008
ARGENTINA	80,756	88,990	90,150	84,599	92,064	104,293	105,885	113,437	115,213	115,213
BARBADOS	802	788	828	860	871	895	930	948	948	948
BOLIVIA	3,899	3,952	3,973	4,188	4,269	4,434	5,230	5,291	5,800	6,240
BRASIL / BRAZIL	334,628	348,818	328,423	345,581	364,846	387,451	402,897	419,337	444,583	456,782
CHILE	38,390	40,078	42,532	43,671	45,055	47,136	52,484	55,320	58,510	58,510
COLOMBIA	44,148	43,952	43,463	45,241	47,682	50,291	50,665	54,855	54,550	56,833
COSTA RICA	5,277	6,934	6,729	7,484	7,565	8,197	8,240	8,697	9,047	9,484
CUBA	14,492	15,032	15,301	15,700	15,909	15,652	15,343	16,469	17,621	17,662
ECUADOR	10,305	10,612	11,050	11,888	11,546	12,585	13,404	14,814	17,339	18,609
EL SALVADOR	3,761	3,820	3,878	4,466	4,764	5,069	4,829	5,597	5,639	5,639
GRENADA	117	134	146	153	162	157	166	171	171	171
GUATEMALA	5,106	6,048	5,856	6,191	7,063	7,456	7,822	7,916	8,755	8,717
GUYANA	867	897	919	914	820	835	862	868	868	868
HAITI	698	547	547	470	512	547	556	570	779	779
HONDURAS	3,432	3,680	3,917	4,099	4,530	4,853	5,545	5,983	6,313	6,537
JAMAICA	6,395	6,606	6,656	6,934	7,146	7,217	7,422	7,473	7,473	7,473
MEXICO	180,917	192,761	197,236	201,252	203,863	208,634	218,971	225,079	232,553	235,871
NICARAGUA	2,147	2,288	2,473	2,554	2,590	2,823	3,051	3,210	3,209	3,361
PANAMA	4,637	4,674	5,152	5,380	5,671	5,860	5,827	6,077	6,468	6,427
PARAGUAY	51,960	53,464	45,311	48,203	51,762	51,928	51,156	53,782	53,722	55,454
PERU	19,047	19,923	20,786	21,982	22,926	24,267	25,510	27,370	29,943	32,443
REP.DOM. / DOM. REP.	7,675	8,539	10,307	12,894	13,489	13,759	12,899	14,150	14,839	15,414
SURINAME	1,440	1,448	1,467	1,483	1,496	1,509	1,572	1,618	1,618	1,618
TRINIDAD & TOBAGO	5,246	5,459	5,643	5,643	6,437	6,430	6,700	6,901	7,662	7,662
URUGUAY	7,194	7,588	9,250	9,605	8,578	5,899	7,683	5,619	9,424	8,768
VENEZUELA	80,585	85,211	89,973	87,406	89,817	94,034	101,544	112,438	110,086	110,086
ALBC / LABC	914,001	962,243	951,066	978,843	1,021,431	1,072,210	1,117,192	1,173,909	1,223,134	1,247,569

3.1.4 ELECTRICIDAD - GENERACIÓN POR SUB REGIONES (GWh)

ELECTRICITY - GENERATION BY SUB-REGIONS (GWh)

Sub - regiones / Sub-regions	1999	2000	2001	2002	2003	2004	2005	2006	2007	2008
Mexico	180,917	192,761	197,236	201,252	203,863	208,634	218,971	225,079	232,553	235,871
América Central / Central America	24,440	27,443	28,004	30,175	32,182	34,258	35,314	37,480	39,431	40,166
Caribe / Caribbean	37,731	39,449	41,815	45,052	46,841	47,001	46,450	49,168	51,979	52,595
Región Andina / Andean Region	157,984	163,650	169,245	170,704	176,241	185,611	196,352	214,768	217,718	224,211
Brasil / Brazil	334,628	348,818	328,423	345,581	364,846	387,451	402,897	419,337	444,583	456,782
Cono Sur / Southern Cone	178,300	190,121	187,243	186,078	197,459	209,256	217,208	228,158	236,870	237,944
ALBC / LABC	914,001	962,243	951,066	978,843	1,021,431	1,072,210	1,117,192	1,173,909	1,223,134	1,247,569

Source: OLADE.

Table 10. Electricity demand in the region during the period 1999-2008

ELECTRICITY - DOMESTIC DEMAND (GWh)

Paises / Countries	1999	2000	2001	2002	2003	2004	2005	2006	2007	2008
ARGENTINA	86,111	90,217	91,906	90,519	97,101	107,761	109,763	114,662	122,859	122,859
BARBADOS	802	788	828	860	871	895	930	948	948	948
BOLIVIA	3,908	3,962	3,982	4,197	4,279	4,434	5,230	5,291	5,800	6,240
BRASIL / BRAZIL	374,579	393,144	366,261	382,144	401,981	424,836	441,939	460,500	483,415	498,642
CHILE	38,504	41,268	43,918	45,484	46,722	48,880	54,636	57,605	60,138	60,138
COLOMBIA	44,155	43,993	43,293	44,630	46,569	48,658	48,923	53,064	53,713	55,437
COSTA RICA	5,150	6,424	6,478	7,081	7,488	7,959	8,251	8,786	9,211	9,414
CUBA	14,492	15,032	15,301	15,700	15,909	15,652	15,343	16,469	17,621	17,662
ECUADOR	10,328	10,612	11,072	11,944	12,598	14,191	15,111	16,383	18,162	19,071
EL SALVADOR	4,011	4,516	4,187	4,849	5,089	5,416	5,113	5,599	5,671	5,671
GRENADA	117	134	146	153	162	157	166	171	171	171
GUATEMALA	4,932	5,344	5,616	5,806	6,665	7,033	7,510	7,836	8,631	8,646
GUYANA	867	897	919	914	820	835	862	868	868	868
HAITI	698	547	547	470	512	547	556	570	779	779
HONDURAS	3,568	3,957	4,225	4,514	4,861	5,245	5,602	5,990	6,325	6,526
JAMAICA	6,395	6,606	6,656	6,934	7,146	7,217	7,422	7,473	7,473	7,473
MEXICO	181,441	193,635	197,292	201,439	202,980	207,675	217,767	224,303	231,379	235,246
NICARAGUA	2,207	2,402	2,490	2,562	2,581	2,824	3,068	3,254	3,272	3,389
PANAMA	4,578	4,792	5,076	5,367	5,491	5,731	5,776	6,028	6,352	6,500
PARAGUAY	5,934	6,134	6,202	6,433	6,589	6,926	7,375	8,077	8,589	9,162
PERU	19,048	19,923	20,786	21,982	22,926	24,267	25,502	27,370	29,943	32,443
REP.DOM. / DOM. REP.	7,675	8,539	10,307	12,894	13,489	13,759	12,899	14,150	14,839	15,414
SURINAME	1,440	1,448	1,467	1,483	1,496	1,509	1,572	1,618	1,618	1,618
TRINIDAD & TOBAGO	5,246	5,459	5,643	5,643	6,437	6,430	6,700	6,901	7,662	7,662
URUGUAY	7,717	7,974	7,997	7,877	7,873	8,228	8,427	8,437	9,218	9,702
VENEZUELA	80,585	85,211	89,973	87,406	89,817	94,034	101,544	111,896	110,086	110,086
ALAC / LAAC	**914,486**	**962,957**	**952,568**	**979,287**	**1,018,452**	**1,071,898**	**1,117,985**	**1,174,250**	**1,224,742**	**1,251,968**

3.1.6 ELECTRICIDAD - DEMANDA POR SUBREGIONES (GWh)
ELECTRICITY - DEMAND BY SUB-REGIONS (GWh)

Subregiones / Sub-regions	1999	2000	2001	2002	2003	2004	2005	2006	2007	2008
Mexico	181,441	193,635	197,292	201,439	202,980	207,675	217,767	224,303	231,379	235,246
América Central / Central America	24,445	27,434	28,072	30,180	32,175	34,208	35,319	37,494	39,462	40,146
Caribe / Caribbean	37,731	39,449	41,815	45,052	46,841	47,001	46,450	49,168	51,979	52,595
Región Andina / Andean Region	158,024	163,701	169,106	170,199	176,190	185,584	196,310	214,003	217,703	223,277
Brasil / Brazil	374,579	393,144	366,261	382,144	401,981	424,836	441,939	460,500	483,415	498,842
Cono Sur / Southern Cone	138,266	145,593	150,022	150,313	158,285	171,795	180,200	188,781	200,804	201,861
ALAC / LAAC	**914,486**	**962,957**	**952,568**	**979,287**	**1,018,452**	**1,071,898**	**1,117,985**	**1,174,250**	**1,224,742**	**1,251,968**

Source: OLADE.

Table 11. Electricity imported by the region during the period 1999-2008

ELECTRICITY-IMPORT LAAC (GWh)

Paises / Countries	1999	2000	2001	2002	2003	2004	2005	2006	2007	2008
ARGENTINA	6,435	7,250	7,417	8,776	7,579	7,613	8,016	7,418	10,275	10,275
BARBADOS	0	0	0	0	0	0	0	0	0	0
BOLIVIA	15	16	9	9	9	0	0	0	0	0
BRASIL / BRAZIL	39,958	44,333	37,844	36,570	37,141	37,392	39,202	41,447	40,866	42,743
CHILE	114	1,190	1,386	1,813	1,667	1,744	2,152	2,285	1,628	1,628
COLOMBIA	33	77	40	8	69	48	16	21	39	77
COSTA RICA	1	22	128	36	41	202	81	149	203	96
CUBA	0	0	0	0	0	0	0	0	0	0
ECUADOR	23	0	22	56	1,120	1,642	1,723	1,570	861	500
EL SALVADOR	458	808	353	413	428	456	322	11	38	38
GRENADA	0	0	0	0	0	0	0	0	0	0
GUATEMALA	211	123	95	55	31	41	23	8	8	5
GUYANA	0	0	0	0	0	0	0	0	0	0
HAITI	0	0	0	0	0	0	0	0	0	0
HONDURAS	141	281	308	415	331	407	58	19	12	0
JAMAICA	0	0	0	0	0	0	0	0	0	0
MEXICO	655	1,069	327	531	71	47	87	523	277	351
NICARAGUA	82	116	17	15	12	23	25	53	64	28
PANAMA	38	135	43	35	2	78	55	34	9	105
PARAGUAY	0	0	0	0	0	0	2	1	0	0
PERU	0	0	0	0	0	0	0	0	0	0
REP.DOM. / DOM. REP.	0	0	0	0	0	0	0	0	0	0
SURINAME	0	0	0	0	0	0	0	0	0	0
TRINIDAD & TOBAGO	0	0	0	0	0	0	0	0	0	0
URUGUAY	708	1,328	173	559	434	2,348	1,585	2,835	788	963
VENEZUELA	0	0	0	0	0	0	0	0	0	0
ALAC / LAAC	**48,872**	**56,747**	**48,114**	**49,292**	**48,935**	**52,040**	**53,351**	**56,374**	**55,068**	**56,809**

3.1.8 ELECTRICIDAD-IMPORTACIÓN POR SUBREGIONES (GWh)
ELECTRICITY-IMPORT BY SUB-REGIONS (GWh)

Sub - regiones / Sub-regions	1999	2000	2001	2002	2003	2004	2005	2006	2007	2008
Mexico	655	1,069	327	531	71	47	87	523	277	351
América Central / Central America	931	1,484	944	969	845	1,207	565	275	334	272
Caribe / Caribbean	0	0	0	0	0	0	0	0	0	0
Región Andina / Andean Region	72	93	72	73	1,198	1,690	1,739	1,591	900	577
Brasil / Brazil	39,958	44,333	37,844	36,570	37,141	37,392	39,202	41,447	40,866	42,743
Cono Sur / Southern Cone	7,257	9,767	8,926	11,148	9,680	11,704	11,757	12,538	12,691	12,865
ALAC / LAAC	**48,872**	**56,747**	**48,114**	**49,292**	**48,935**	**52,040**	**53,351**	**56,374**	**55,068**	**56,809**

Source: OLADE.

Table 12. Electricity exported by the region during the period 1999-2008

ELECTRICITY-EXPORT LAAC (GWh)

Países/ Countries	1999	2000	2001	2002	2003	2004	2005	2006	2007	2008
ARGENTINA	1,080	6,023	5,662	2,856	2,543	4,144	4,143	6,193	2,628	2,628
BARBADOS	0	0	0	0	0	0	0	0	0	0
BOLIVIA	6	6	0	0	0	0	0	0	0	0
BRASIL / BRAZIL	7	7	6	7	6	7	160	283	2,034	683
CHILE	0	0	0	0	0	0	0	0	0	0
COLOMBIA	27	37	210	618	1,182	1,682	1,758	1,813	877	1,473
COSTA RICA	128	531	379	440	118	440	70	50	40	166
CUBA	0	0	0	0	0	0	0	0	0	0
ECUADOR	0	0	0	0	67	35	16	1	39	38
EL SALVADOR	208	112	44	30	103	109	38	9	7	7
GRENADA	0	0	0	0	0	0	0	0	0	0
GUATEMALA	465	827	336	440	428	464	335	88	132	76
GUYANA	0	0	0	0	0	0	0	0	0	0
HAITI	0	0	0	0	0	0	0	0	0	0
HONDURAS	6	4	0	0	0	15	2	11	0	12
JAMAICA	0	0	0	0	0	0	0	0	0	0
MEXICO	131	195	271	344	954	1,006	1,291	1,299	1,451	976
NICARAGUA	22	1	0	7	21	22	8	9	0	0
PANAMA	97	18	118	49	182	207	106	83	125	32
PARAGUAY	46,026	47,331	39,109	43,770	45,173	45,003	43,784	45,706	45,133	46,292
PERU	0	0	0	0	0	0	8	0	0	0
REP.DOM. / DOM. REP.	0	0	0	0	0	0	0	0	0	0
SURINAME	0	0	0	0	0	0	0	0	0	0
TRINIDAD & TOBAGO	0	0	0	0	0	0	0	0	0	0
URUGUAY	185	942	1,377	2,287	1,138	19	841	16	995	28
VENEZUELA	0	0	0	0	0	0	0	542	0	0
ALAC /LAAC	48,387	56,034	47,511	48,847	51,914	53,152	52,557	56,113	53,460	52,410

3,1,10 ELECTRICIDAD-EXPORTACIÓN POR SUBREGIONES (GWh)

ELECTRICITY-EXPORT BY SUB-REGIONS (GWh)

Subregiones / Sub-regions	1999	2000	2001	2002	2003	2004	2005	2006	2007	2008
Mexico	131	195	271	344	954	1,006	1,291	1,299	1,451	976
América Central / Central America	925	1,493	877	965	851	1,257	560	261	303	292
Caribe / Caribbean	0	0	0	0	0	0	0	0	0	0
Región Andina / Andean Region	33	43	210	618	1,249	1,717	1,782	2,356	915	1,511
Brasil / Brazil	7	7	6	7	6	7	160	283	2,034	683
Cono Sur / Southern Cone	47,291	54,295	46,147	46,913	48,854	49,165	48,765	51,914	48,757	48,948
ALAC /LAAC	48,387	56,034	47,511	48,847	51,914	53,152	52,557	56,113	53,460	52,410

Source: OLADE.

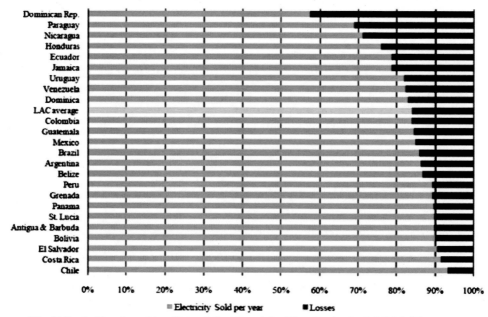

Source: World Bank, Benchmarking Data of the Electricity Dist. Sec in the LAC 95-05.

Figure 7. Annual electricity sales and distributional electricity losses by country in 2005.

Based on the IEO (2009) report, "electricity is projected to supply an increasing share of the world's total energy demand and is the fastest-growing form of end-use energy worldwide in the mid-term. Since 1990, growth in net electricity generation has outpaced the growth in total energy consumption (2.9% per year and 1.9% per year, respectively), and the growth in demand for electricity continues to outpace growth in total energy use throughout the projection. The impact of the recession on electricity consumption is likely to be felt most strongly in the industrial sector, as manufacturing slows as a result of lower demand for manufactured products. Demand in the residential sector is less sensitive to changing economic conditions than the industrial sector, because people generally continue to consume electricity for space heating and cooling, cooking, refrigeration, and hot water heating even in a recession."

In the Latin American and the Caribbean region, the majority of the installed electricity capacity belongs to the public sector (92% of the total) and the rest were auto-generators.

According to historical data, the power sector in Latin America and the Caribbean has experienced steady growth since the 1970s. The regional electricity production grew at an average rate of 5.9% per year between 1970 and 2005, compared to the worldwide average over the period of 4.3%; this represents an increase of 1.6% over the world average. In 2008, electricity generation grew 11.7% respect to 2005. Six countries of the region account for 87% of total electricity production in the Latin American and the Caribbean region in that year. Brazil is the largest electricity producer (36.6% of the total), followed by Mexico (18.9%), Argentina (9.2%), Venezuela (8.8%), Chile (4.7%), Colombia (4.6%), and Paraguay (4.4%). Paraguay is a significant producer through its share of production from the gigantic Itaipú hydro power plant is sold to Brazil.

It is important to stress, regarding the mix of primary fuels, the following: The mix of primary fuels used to generate electricity has changed a great deal over the past four decades on a worldwide basis. Coal continues to be the fuel most widely used for electricity generation, although generation from nuclear power increased rapidly from the 1970s through the 1980s, and natural-gas-fired generation grew rapidly in the 1980s and 1990s. The use of oil for electricity generation has been declining since the mid-1970s, when the oil embargo by Arab producers in 1973-1974 and the Iranian Revolution in 1979 caused oil's prices to increase to levels much higher than those for other fuels. Although world's oil prices contracted strongly at the end of 2008 and into 2009, the high prices recorded in 2012 combined with concerns about the environmental consequences of greenhouse gas emissions, the Iran nuclear power program, and the level of oil's reserves, renewed interest in the development of alternatives to fossil fuels—specifically, nuclear power[21] and renewable energy sources.

Natural gas has become increasingly important for electricity production globally, and particularly in Latin American and the Caribbean region, over the past twenty years, gaining ground at the expense of oil and hydroelectric sources. Hydroelectricity experienced a decline worldwide, falling from 21% to 16%. By comparison, the share of electricity from hydro power plants in Latin American and the Caribbean region remains around 56%. According to the IEO (2009) report, it is expected that "in the coming years, the use of nuclear power and

---

[21] The nuclear accident in the Fukushima Daiichi nuclear power plant in Japan on March 2011 has forced Japan and other several governments to review they current plans for energy development and to stop or postpone the implementation of approved plans for the development of the nuclear power sector, particularly in Europe, and in some Latin American and Asia and the Pacific countries.

renewable energy sources, supported by government incentives and by high fossil fuel prices, will continue to play an important role in electricity generation in almost all regions, particularly in North America, Europe and Asia." Natural gas is the second and coal the third fastest growing sources of energy for electricity generation foresee in the IEO (2009) report. However, the outlook for coal could be altered substantially by the adoption of future legislation that aims to reduce or limit the growth of greenhouse gas emissions. At the same time, the nuclear accident in the Fukushima Daiichi nuclear power plant in Japan could change the current position of some governments regarding the use of nuclear power for electricity generation in the future.

In the case of the Latin American and the Caribbean region with oil trading at more than US $100 per barrel in 2012, natural gas in short supply, and a new wave of droughts threatening hydroelectricity production, several countries are once again facing the possibility of energy shortages. Argentina, Brazil, Chile, Ecuador, and Venezuela are under particular pressure to ensure that overstretched electricity and gas supplies could meet an increase electricity demand during the coming months and years. In contrast to shortages in the past, which were blamed on short-term factors, many analysts now believe that energy scarcity will be a long-term problem. The two fundamental reasons are the demand driven by sustained economic growth in emerging economies, and the difficulty of obtaining new sources of fossil fuels. The Latin American and the Caribbean countries exemplify both trends.

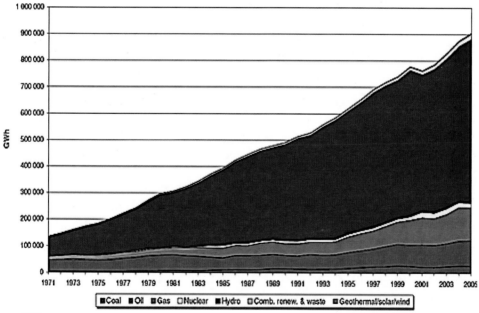

Source: IDB.

Figure 8. Evolution of electricity generation by source during the period 1971-2005.

From Figure 8, the following can be stated: During the period 1971-2005, the main growth in electricity generation in the region was due to the hydro power sector, followed by natural gas, oil, and coal, and these proportions is not expected to change during the coming years.

Andean Zone

In the Andean zone, electricity consumption increased 30% between 1994 and 2004 and reached 168 TWh. In 2007, around 25% of the installed capacity in South America was in the Andean countries and the demand has been rising by 3.3% per year. In this group of countries hydro, coal, gas, oil, wind, and solar energy are used in different proportion for the electricity generation.

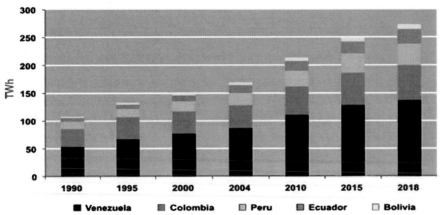

Source: OLADE and World Energy Council (2008).

Figure 9. Evolution of electricity demand and forecast for the period 2010-2018.

From Figure 9, the following can be stated: Venezuela[22] is the country with the highest increase in the demand of electricity and with the highest foreseeable increase in the electricity demand until 2018, followed by Colombia, Peru, Ecuador and Bolivia. This trend is expected to continue without change after 2018.

At the beginning of the 1990s, the electricity system of the Andean countries was in a critical situation, caused by the lack of resources to guarantee the necessary investments to increase the supply and assure the upkeep of the existing infrastructure. Due to this situation, several Andean countries began reorganization of their electricity systems. In general, they tried to separate the State's roles, in order to allow the private sector to act as entrepreneur and foster investments, while the government was restricted to the role of policy maker and regulator.

As a result of implemented changes, the Andean zone, except Venezuela, adopted some ways to trade energy with the obligatory participation by market players. Generally, that meant the creation of wholesale electricity markets.

The common motivation was to create competition in the electricity system in order to improve an infrastructure that is not in a position to meet the growing demand for electricity, to attract foreign investments, and to allow expansion of the installed energy capacity.

Decision 536, approved in December 2002, gave the community a legal framework for promoting the development of the electricity theme among the member countries. As a result of the Decision 536, the Andean Committee of Electric Service Policy-Setting and Regulatory Agencies set to work with the following technical groups:

a) Working Group of Electric Service Regulatory Agencies, formed in June 2003, to formulate proposals for advancing the harmonization of regulatory frameworks needed for full sub-regional interconnection of electric power systems and intra-community exchange of electricity;

b) Working Group of Electric Service Policy-Setting Agencies, created in January 2004, to draw up proposals, coordinate efforts with Andean energy and electric power institutions and reach agreements for fulfilling aspects of information access and coordinated project planning, with a view to the region's integration.

The electric systems of Colombia and Ecuador were interconnected in March 2003 pursuant to the Decision 536, and produced important benefits for both countries. With the interconnection and full operation of the electric systems of Colombia and Ecuador, the electric interconnection of Peru and Ecuador, and the decision of Bolivia to adhere to Decision 536, the Andean electricity market have reached its first level of integration.

Southern Cone

According to OLADE, the major source for the production of electricity in the period in the Southern Cone is hydro power, which is expected to increase its participation in the energy balance in the sub-region from a little more than 100 TWh in 2003 to almost 150 TWh in 2018.

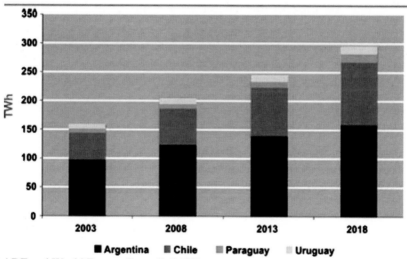

Source: OLADE and World Energy Council (2008).

Figure 10. Foreseable electricity demand for the period 2003-2018.

From Figure 10, the following can be stated: Argentina will continue to be the country in the sub-region with the highest increase in the electricity demand until 2018, followed very closely by Chile. Far from these two countries are Uruguay and Paraguay, with a very little increase in the demand of electricity for the coming years.

Summing up, the following can be stated:

1. By 2030, with a modest rate of economic growth, the region's demand for electricity is expected to reach nearly 2 500 TWh, up from around 1 251 TWh in 2008. Electricity demand in Brazil would more than double to around 1 090 TWh. A total of 239 GW of new electricity generation capacity would be needed to match demand, with Brazil adding about 97 GW, the Southern Cone 45 GW, Mexico 44 GW, the Andean zone 30 GW, Central America 15 GW, and the Caribbean 7 GW;

2. Hydro power and natural gas would provide the majority of additional power capacity. Although the share of hydro will continue to decline, the combined share of hydro and natural gas will be higher. There would continue to be a decline in the use of oil and a slight increase in nuclear power (concentrated in Argentina, Brazil, and perhaps later in Mexico) and in non-hydro renewables;

3. Despite the decline in hydro power's share, many countries and sub-regions are planning to substantially increase the absolute capacity of hydro power plants operating in the region over the coming decades, including Brazil, the Andean zone, the Southern Cone, and Central America. The aggregate increase in hydroelectric capacity by 2030 would be around 85 GW;

4. The high degree of fuel and generation technology diversity in the Southern Cone would become even more dynamic over the period, with the region adding sizeable generating capacity for hydro, natural gas, coal, and nuclear power (in Argentina and Brazil in the near future, and a few years later possible in Mexico);

5. In Central America, hydroelectricity would be the largest source of new capacity (45%), while fuel oil, coal, and natural gas would together account for about 45% of additional capacity;

6. In the Caribbean, the generation mix would continue to be largely fossil fuel-dependent, with gas accounting for 43% of the additional capacity and coal 23%.

7. The investment in new generation capacity is estimated to be about US $430 billion between 2008 and 2030. Investments by country and sub-region would be: Brazil US $182 billion, the Southern Cone US $78 billion, the Andean zone US $58 billion, Central America US $25 billion, and the Caribbean US $9 billion;

8. CO_2 emissions from electricity generation in the Latin American and the Caribbean region would more than double between 2008 and 2030 as a result of the decline in hydroelectricity and an increase in the use of fossil fuels for electricity generation and other uses in some countries.

COST OF THE ELECTRICITY

The cost of the electricity consists mainly of the three following elements: Capital cost, fuel cost, and operation and maintenance costs. In the current trend towards deregulation of the power generation industry, the cost of the generated electricity is a key element when selecting the type of power plant to be constructed. Other factors that need to be considered are the following:

a) Licensing procedure;
b) Financiability and loan structures;
c) Fuel to be used;
d) Environmental concerns;
e) Construction time and depreciation period;
f) Existence of appropriate professional and labor forces with sufficient experience in the energy sector.

Every power plant is designed to keep the production cost as low as possible, and to provide the service with the best quality and security. Legislation and environmental protection give boundary conditions to this goal.

Capital costs per unit of electricity for a given power plant depend on the price and the amortization rate for that plant, on interest or on the desired yield on capital investments (annuity factor), and on the load factor of the plant. Capital costs are also influenced by the interest during construction.

Fuel costs per unit of electricity are proportional to the specific price of the fuel and inversely proportional to the average electrical efficiency of the installation[22], except for nuclear power plants, due to the low level of the fuel cost in comparison with the cost of the construction of the plant. Operation and maintenance costs consist of fixed costs of operation, maintenance and administration, and the variable costs of operation, maintenance, and repair. The cost of the electricity is the sum of the capital, fuel, and operation and maintenance costs. Present value is generally the basis used for economic comparisons. The various costs for a power plant are incurred at different times but for financial calculations are corrected to a single reference time, which is generally the date on which commercial operation starts. These converted amounts are referred to as present value (Deutsche Montan Technologie GmbH, OLADE and CIEMAT, 2005).

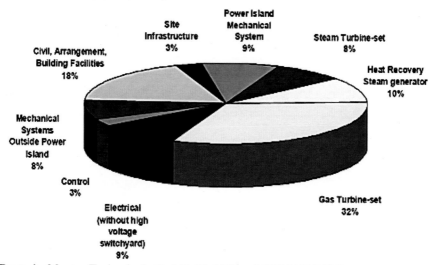

Source: Deutsche Montan Technologie GmbH, OLADE and CIEMAT (2005).

Figure 11. The cost percentage of the different elements for a typical 400 MW turnkey combined cycle power plant.

---

[22] This average electrical efficiency must not be mixed up with electrical efficiency at rated load.

Figure 11, shows the breakdown of the total cost in a combined-cycle power plant between the main equipment.

It is important to understand that the cost of electricity can be classified also in two groups: Fixed costs and variable costs. Fixed costs are: Interest and depreciation on capital and operation, maintenance, and administration. Variable costs depend of the fuel used and the variable costs of operation, maintenance, and repair. The following figure illustrated the comparison for different turnkey power plants in terms of specific price and output.

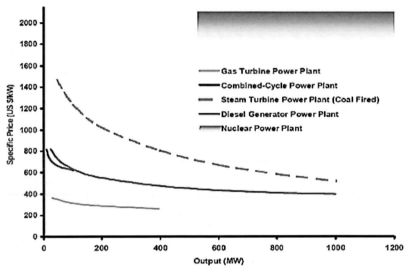

Source: Deutsche Montan Technologie GmbH, OLADE and CIEMAT (2005).

Figure 12. Comparison of different turnkey power plants in terms of specific price and output.

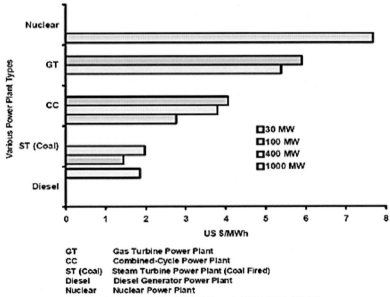

Source: Deutsche Montan Technologie GmbH, OLADE and CIEMAT (2005).

Figure 13. Variable operating and maintenance costs for various power plants of different sizes.

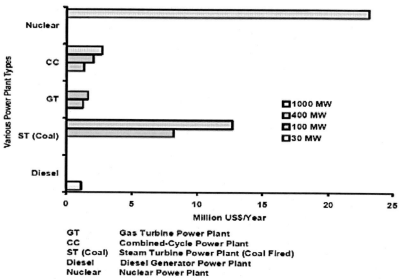

Source: Deutsche Montan Technologie GmbH, OLADE and CIEMAT (2005).

Figure 14. Fixed operating and maintenance costs for various power plants of different sizes.

The following conclusions can be drawn from Figures 12, 13, and 14:

a) The main competition is among combined-cycle gas turbine and coal-fired steam turbine power plants. This situation is unlikely to change in the near future;

b) For small-to medium-power outputs (up to approximately 30 MW), a diesel generator power plant can be a genuine alternative. The high efficiency of modern diesel engines is slightly less than combined-cycle with the same rating. To achieve a higher output with diesel generators, however, multiple units must be combined. Therefore, the diesel-based plant loses its attractiveness for higher power ratings, because investment costs are higher than those for combined-cycle power plants without compensating for that fact by providing greater fuel flexibility;

c) Conventional steam power plants are suitable for use as coal burning plants operating in base-load (or occasional intermediate-load duty), if cheap coal is available or gas is expensive (e.g., LNG) for a combined cycle power plant. Whenever gas or oil is fired in a power plant, the combined-cycle power plant is more economical than the steam power plant due to its higher efficiency and lower specific price;

d) Modern combined-cycle power plants are simpler, less expensive, and operationally more flexible than steam power plants;

e) The choice between a steam power plant and combined-cycle power plant for intermediate-to-base-load applications is a question of fuel availability and price. If natural gas is available and cheap, a combined-cycle design will be selected. If coal is the fuel, a steam power plant will be chosen. However, recent trends in fuel price development show a higher increase with natural gas and oil prices than with the coal price. It is expected that this trend will continue in the future due to the high demand for natural gas and the approach of mid-depletion points in some exploitation regions. This gives coal-fired power plants a good perspective for the medium-term future in the power sector;

f) For short utilization periods (peaking units), the gas turbine power plant is most economical. Gas turbines can serve as intermediate - or base-load units in countries where fuel is abundant at low cost. The lack of water consumption has made this machine popular in dry regions. The short installation time allows a customer to plan a new installation on short notice.

If all fuels are readily available at world market prices, gas fired combined-cycle power plants are the most economical solution for intermediate- and base-load applications. This results in a limited environmental impact (small heat rejection or low water consumption).

In the 1990s, the cost structure of electricity service in most countries in the region had the following characteristics:

a) At the generation level, it shows strong seasonal variations due to the influence of the hydrology in hydro-based generation systems; moderate hourly variations in energy-constrained systems, and moderate spatial variation in interconnected systems related to transmission losses and transmission constraints. Short-run marginal generation costs are highly volatile in hydro-based systems with relatively small reservoir capacity like in Colombia, Brazil, Peru, Panama, Costa Rica, and El Salvador:

b) At the transmission level, costs are capacity related with strong spatial variations in radial networks like Chile and Peru;

c) At the distribution level, costs are capacity related with strong spatial variations depending on the voltage level and the load density (costs for low voltage loads and rural areas may be twice as large as costs for high voltage customers);

d) Transmission and distribution losses are high and have a major impact on cost of service at low voltages;

e) In tropical countries demand has moderate seasonal variations but strong hourly variations, mainly due to the high portion of residential load with low load factors.

Incremental transaction costs between generators, generators and distribution companies, and suppliers and transmission companies, are not significant due to the fact that most national interconnected power systems in the region have modern control centers in operation, and main substations have metering equipment to gather information on wholesale power transactions. However, transaction costs between suppliers and small and medium-size consumers are high, due to the low level of consumption, and the significant costs of metering and telecommunication equipment. Externalities are moderate and mainly related, in the supply side, to the environmental impact of hydroelectric and thermoelectric generation projects and, in the demand-side, to the environmental impact of the use of firewood in rural areas (Dussan, 1996). Some of these characteristics are still valid today.

Finally, it is important to know the following: At current levels of fuel and capital costs, operation and maintenance costs affect the economy of a power plant in a limited manner only. They strongly depend on site specific and local conditions and account for approximately a tenth of the cost of electricity in a combined-cycle power plant. Variable costs for a combined-cycle power plant are lower than for gas-turbine power plant, because these costs are driven by the spare parts of the gas turbine, which can be distributed over a larger output in the combined-cycle power plant.

Summing up, the following can be stated: In the Andean and Central American countries, the most recent connections have adopted tariff principles more in line with market criteria and the following rules:

a) Non-discrimination of national and foreign prices;
b) Free access to networks;
c) Physical use of interconnections by coordinated economic dispatch;
d) Free agreements between markets without extra restraints;
e) Prices and tariffs that reflect economic costs, preventing abuse of a dominant position;
f) Short-term international transactions admissible;
g) Profits from co-management not assigned to international connection;
h) Subsidies, duties or restraints are not admissible.

The major difference in Southern Cone exchanges is that inter-market transactions are made according to the prevailing prices in each country, and the benefit arises through co-management profits (World Energy Council, 2008).

It is interesting that the goal of reducing dependence on high price imported oil products and the goal of reducing environmental impacts and increasing the integration of the region turned out to be complementary. The most direct benefit of an interconnection comes when one country has a source of low cost power and its neighbor does not. The three lowest cost resources for operation at capacity factors above about 30% are the following: Geothermal, wind (including the cost of backup generation), and small hydro. This assumes that high quality sites can be identified and acquired. Geothermal is the source of generation and drives the benefits for many of the interconnections. Thus geothermal on a local and sub-regional basis and wind on a local basis, provide a path toward a less oil-dependent, lower cost, lower environmental impact, and more sustainable future.

ELECTRICITY ACCESS

According to Yepez-Garcia et al (2010), the Latin American and the Caribbean region have relatively high electricity access rates compared to other parts of the world. In comparison with Africa's average electricity access rate of 40% and the world average of 78%, Latin American and the Caribbean electricity access rate reached 93% in 2008. Although electricity access rates for the region as a whole are high, there are large inequalities both within and between countries. For instance, while nearly 98% of Brazil's population has access to electricity, the access rate in Haiti is only 39%. Within countries with high overall access rates, the disparity between the urban and rural access rates is startling in some cases. For example, in Peru, which has an overall national electrification rate of 77%, the figure for urban areas is 96% while the electricity access rates in rural areas is only 28%. Large disparities can also be seen in the rural and urban electrification rates in Haiti, Honduras, and Nicaragua.

Table 13. Latin America and the Caribbean electricity access rates (2008)

Country	Total (%)	Urban (%)	Rural (%)	Without Electricity (Million)
Argentina	97	100	70	1.1
Bolivia	78	98	38	2.2
Brazil	98	100	88	4.3
Chile	99	99	95	0.3
Colombia	94	100	76	3.0
Costa Rica	99	100	98	0.0
Dominican Republic	96	98	90	0.4
Ecuador	92	100	78	1.1
El Salvador	86	97	70	0.9
Guatemala	81	94	68	2.7
Haiti	39	69	12	6.0
Honduras	70	98	45	2.1
Jamaica	92	100	83	0.2
Mexico	97	100	95	3.2
Nicaragua	72	95	42	1.6
Panama	88	94	72	0.4
Paraguay	95	99	88	0.3
Peru	77	96	28	6.5
Trinidad and Tobago	99	100	99	0.0
Uruguay	99	100	82	0.0
Venezuela	99	100	85	0.3
Latin America	93	99	70	34.1
World	78	93	63	1 456.0

Sources: World Bank.

ELECTRICITY CHALLENGES

According to Yepez Garcia et al (2010), among the electricity challenges that Latin American and the Caribbean countries have to face are:

a) *Economic growth and access:* The need to provide for a multiple of current electricity supply over the coming twenty years to support increases in income and to provide electricity access to un-electrified households and communities;

b) *Energy security:* The increasing risk of electricity supply disruptions and price shocks as a result of the growing dependence on imported fossil fuels, and the constraints faced in tapping national and regional renewable (like hydroelectricity and wind) and low-carbon (like natural gas) energy resources;

c) *Economic efficiency:* The need to limit the cost of providing new electricity by promoting competitive contracts and financing by the private and public sectors, improve the efficiency of supply, and avoid new construction when and where demand-side efficiency is the least-cost option;

d) *Environmental sustainability:* The desire to incorporate environmental goals, both national and regional, into power sector planning, policymaking, and investment;

e) *Conducive regulatory framework:* The need to put in place policies and regulations to allow the power sector to meet increasing demand, address growing environmental concerns, and attract private capital to reduce the financial burden on government budgets.

REGIONAL INTEGRATION

The integration of energy markets in the Latin American and the Caribbean region has been discussed for more than three decades. An expression of it was the creation of several regional organizations such as ARPEL (Association of Petroleum Enterprises of Latin America), CIER (Regional Electrical Integration Commission), and OLADE (Latin American Energy Organization), among others, during the decades of the 1960s and 1970s. These initiatives took place within the framework of important participation by the States in companies tied to the energy sector.

During the 1990s, initiatives for energy integration gathered momentum at the continental level. The proposals came about within the framework of the Americas' Summit, which sprung from the Initiative for the Americas, proposed by the US government in 1989. At the core of what was then called the "Hemispheric Energy Initiative", containing a group of reforms outlined by the Washington Consensus. In the energy sector, it was proposed that obstacles to the operation of foreign firms in every branch of the energy industry be eliminated, from exploration and production of gas and oil, to distribution and product sales in the final market. The aim was clear: Opening the energy sector and free access to energy reserves of the region to US companies.

This initiative was not fully implemented due to reigning constitutional limits in some countries and the failure of the America free trade initiative promoted by the US government, which was rejected by a number of Latin American and the Caribbean governments in a Summit carried out in Buenos Aires. Nevertheless, foreign investment laws implemented in most of the countries of the region, through programs with multilateral institutions such as the International Monetary Fund (IMF) and the World Bank, and reflected in the bilateral free trade agreements that some countries have signed or are in the process of negotiating with the USA, have attempted to assure that investments, particularly in the energy sector, operate with the least possible number of restrictions, so as to foster capital investment in this activity, and the access to the energy reserves located in the region by US companies.

To a greater or lesser extent, since the beginning of the 1990s, the countries of the region liberalized their regimes in the treatment of investments, as well as their service sectors. In some cases, such as Chile, the reforms were enacted earlier. In the energy sector, these reforms meant the elimination of obstacles to national and international private firms being able to operate at all levels of the energy industry, from exploration and production of gas and oil, to distribution and sales of petroleum products. Even though most of the countries in the region modified their normative frameworks in the energy sector, the degrees of liberalization were different. In many cases, the modifications were limited by precepts established in their respective constitutions; in others it was determined that this was a strategic sector and should be protected from foreign indiscriminate exploitation. However, the desired results were not achieved.

Liberalizing energy policies were reviewed, especially in South America, due to the failure of the economic reforms applied by several countries following the Washington Consensus. In some cases, strong economic and social crisis appeared as consequences of the application of economic reforms promote by this economic policy. A certain tendency is discernible in some Latin American and Caribbean countries to restore a more active role for the State in energy activities and to make State planning for energy markets an indispensable guiding instrument in channeling and coordinating the investments made by private and public agents. Similarly, the preservation of non-renewable energy resources and the autonomy of the State to regulate tapping them, have now been reclaimed as part of energy policies (Ruiz Caro, 2008).

Nearly all Latin American countries have a power surplus relative to maximum demand, surpluses that could be used in the integration process as electricity interconnections expand. Integration of national energy systems in the Latin American and the Caribbean region would lead to economies of scale, reducing energy costs, and increasing the reliability of energy supply. Developing natural gas supply systems in an integrated manner with electricity systems in the region would minimize the use of liquid fuels and thus increase exportable oil surpluses.

It is important to know that Latin America has a very rich history of trading and cooperation in the energy sector. During the 1970s and 1980s, large multinational hydroelectric dams were built in the region, often in common border of several countries, which received the energy produced by these dams in a proportion with their investment. These included a number of mega dams, particularly the Itaipú Dam which, in 2006, still met 20% of Brazil's and 100% of Paraguay's total energy demands. Nonetheless, a number of these dams have often performed poorly in economic terms, and have had vast environmental and social side-effects. This has led to some popular resistance to new dam's projects in several countries of the region, particularly large ones, and has made potential investors hesitant to get involved in the development of the energy sector.

It is also important to know that during the 1990s and 2000s, regional energy integration and trading received additional attention of several Latin American and the Caribbean countries, particularly the interconnection of the transmission of electric grids, as well as the construction of pipelines for the supply of fossil fuels to different countries.

Why energy integration is so important for the Latin American and the Caribbean countries? Energy crises, past and present, have significantly damaged economic growth in several Latin American and the Caribbean countries. These crises could have been relieved if there had been adequate capacity in the regional energy system. For example, the Brazilian energy crisis in 2001 could have been mitigated, if there had been enough transmission capacity to bring the energy surplus from Argentina into Brazil. Likewise, the current critical state of the energy system in Argentina could be significantly improved, if Argentinean consumers could have access to the energy surplus available in Brazil (World Energy Council, 2008). Another example is Venezuela. The energy crisis in this last country in 2010 was caused by a severe drought affecting the country during several months due to an important reduction of the supply of electricity from its biggest hydroelectric power plant. This situation could have been minimized, if neighboring countries with energy surplus could supply it to Venezuela during that period.

Brazil, by far the largest country and energy consumer in the region, signed various agreements with Venezuela, Uruguay, and Argentina in order to import/export electricity or for the supply of fossil fuels to satisfy the foreseen increase in energy demand in these countries. Other examples of regional cooperation include, among others, Argentina and Brazil gas connections with Bolivia[23], the supply of natural gas from Argentina to Chile, the supply of oil from Venezuela to Cuba and to other Caribbean and Central American countries within the Petro-Caribe Agreement, the integration of the power networks of the Central American countries through the implementation of SIEPAC[24] (System of Power Interconnection in the Central American Countries) project under the Framework Agreement of the Central American Electrical Market, and the creation of the Regional Electricity Market. For many years, the SIEPAC project has been heralded as a key element of a leap forward in regional cooperation among the Central American countries in the energy sector. The SIEPAC project is based on the integration design model so that the construction of the network comes after the creation of a commercial and regulatory structure that permits the countries to gradually progress towards harmonious internal regulations, enjoying the benefits from this integration process.

Integration Promoted by the Central American Countries

Since 1996, the Central American countries have been considering the project of introducing natural gas into the sub-region[25]. Supply options are restricted to the supply from Mexico, Colombia, and Venezuela or possibly using LNG regasification plants. In this framework, studies of different projects have been made, such as building a regional gas pipeline from Mexico-Central American Isthmus or the supply of natural gas from Colombia and Venezuela to Costa Rica and Panama. The gasification project of the Isthmus consists of building a gas pipeline from Mexico to Panama, over almost 2 300 km. Parallel to this project in 2005 Colombia and Panama agreed to a gas-exporting venture between them.

Without any doubt, the Central American sub-region has a firm commitment to integration. Nevertheless, it is important to note that the absence of critical mass of demand, lack of financial resources, technical weakness, poor management, and political instability and confrontation have all delayed the implementation of these projects. The situation of the implementation of the project to introduce natural gas into the Isthmus reflects this situation. It is important to know that the reduction in the consumption of liquid fuels for electricity generation will have a positive impact in the climate due to a reduction in CO_2 emission.

The length of time that interconnected power lines have operated among Central American countries make them the oldest in the region, and their experience gained makes it an example to be followed. Power interconnection began in 1976, when the Honduras-Nicaragua line entered into operations. This interconnection was expanded to Panama in

---

[23] The gas pipeline between Brazil and Bolivia has a length of 3 200 km and connect the city of Santa Cruz de la Sierra in Bolivia with the city of Porto Alegre in Brazil. The capacity of the gas pipeline is 30 million m^3 per day.

[24] SIEPAC is a regional power system that will provide for electric interconnection from Panama to Guatemala and at the outset will allow for 300 MW of electricity to move in both directions, increasing the energy generating capacity of the sub-region to satisfy the foreseen energy demand in the coming years.

[25] The sub-region has no natural gas reserves. Guatemala is the only country producing associated gas in small quantities.

1986, and currently operates at 230 kV with a 138 kV intermediate link in Costa Rica. The Honduras – Nicaragua line arose from a need for Honduras to sell its excess energy produced by the enormous El Cajón hydroelectric power plant to other countries in the area. As years went by, Honduras's demand not only filled but exceeded that plant's capacity, and the country had to ration its energy use, which was relieved by imports from Costa Rica and Panama. Despite the limitations of current transmission capacity, existing interconnection operations have demonstrated to all countries in the sub-region the advisability of maintaining and improving the system.

The sub-region established, in the framework of the sub-regional integration process, the Central America Electrification Council (CEAC), the Regional Electric Interconnection Commission (CRIE), the Regional Operation Entity (EOR), and the Network Owner Enterprise (EPR). The six Central American countries are already interconnected by 230 kV power lines (see Figure 15). They are building a parallel 230 kV power line to reinforce their interconnection (Deutsche Montan Technologie GmbH, OLADE and CIEMAT, 2005).

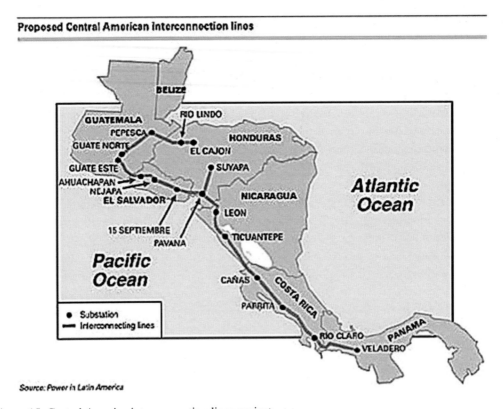

Source: Power in Latin America

Figure 15. Central America interconnection lines project.

According to the Framework Treaty for the Central American Power Market, signed in December 1996 by the presidents of the six countries of the sub-region, and already ratified by their respective legislatures, the SIEPAC project proposes its implementation in two phases to be executed in ten years. The first phase aims at strengthening the existing power systems by building a 1 802 km interconnection line from Guatemala, through each of the countries to Panama, as well as extending the necessary sub-stations along the way. Joint system capacity will be 300 MW in any direction, and the investment for this initial phase is estimate to be around US $300 million. The second phase consists of building a second 230 kV circuit, provided the execution of new generation projects and the existence of sufficiently high demand to use the new lines to be installed. This phase of the SIEPAC project will depend on developing generation projects of a certain size, which obviously can only be justified under a sub-regional power supply system supported by large capacity generating plants at strategic points on the network, instead of a proliferation of small isolated power plants at a national level.

The implementation of the SIEPAC project will allow for more efficient interconnected network operation, respond to environmental restrictions, and make it possible to channel economic resources from private financing agencies for implementation of the project in all participant countries (Deutsche Montan Technologie GmbH, OLADE and CIEMAT, 2005).

The advantage of power interconnection in the Central American sub-region is the opportunity for promoting a competitive power market, taking into account the dimension of the countries involved, the relative small demand of electricity, and the relative small size of the electrical grid of each of the Central American countries, among others. This would ensure lower sales costs to service users, take advantage of the differing climates in each country, and the fact that demand peaks do not coincide, as well as making it possible to reduce power reserves and develop more generation plants with a sub-regional projection.

It is important to stress that the future of the integrated power system in the sub-region should be analyzed, with a view to the ability to respond appropriately to energy demands in time and space over the coming decades.

It is also important and timely to expand the vision to joint generation, which contemplates including other diversified energy sources on the matrix, as well as using new technologies and the advantage of scale economies to ensure continuity in the supply of clean and affordable energy for all users.

According to information provided by the Central American countries through the CEAC, the power sector is expected to grow over the next two decades at a rate of approximately 5.5% per year. At one end of the spectrum, Guatemala is projecting an average growth of 6.2%, while, at the other end, Nicaragua has established its power demand development at a yearly rate of 4% (Deutsche Montan Technologie GmbH, OLADE and CIEMAT, 2005).

Petro-America Initiative

Petro-America Initiative has been launched by the Venezuelan government on the basis of the following principle: Regional integration is a matter for States and governments, without the exclusion of private enterprise sectors. The agreements contained in the Petro-America Initiative propose that "State energy enterprises in Latin America and the Caribbean be integrated, leading to agreements and joint investments in exploration, exploitation, and commercialization of oil and natural gas." It also "seeks joint economic activities and a reduction in the negative effects of energy costs - originating in the increase in the global demand for oil, as well as in speculative and geopolitical factors - for the countries in the region." The process is meant to be implemented in stages and, according to what is indicated in the proposal, will begin to be realized through bilateral or sub-regional actions and agreements. The proposal also includes "preferential financing mechanisms in the supply of oil for the nations of the Caribbean and Central American sub-regions."

In the Petro-America Initiative there are three sub-regional energy integration projects: Petro-Sur (Argentina, Brazil, Venezuela, and Uruguay); Petro-Caribe (fourteen countries of the Caribbean area); and Petro-Andina (Bolivia, Ecuador, Colombia, Peru, and Venezuela). Of the three integration projects mentioned above Petro-Caribe is the best structured (World Energy Council, 2008).

Integration Promoted by the Andean Countries

The main scenarios for future energy integration in Latin America follow one of the three regional configurations (see Figure 16): Central America/Andean countries; Andean countries/Southern Cone/south Brazil; and Andean countries/north Brazil. In the long-term, the Amazon will be interconnected with these three sub-systems. These regional energy integration scenarios are aimed at transforming competitiveness, environmental protection, institutions, and the quality of life in the South America sub-region, as well as for the development of the energy industry, fostering sub-regional harmony, increasing the security of energy supply, and reducing the cost of investments in developing countries in a peaceful and equitable way. Fulfilling these objectives requires the design of energy integration policy with a focus on the cost efficiency, which takes into consideration political and regulatory risks, as well as the possibility of an amicable disputes resolution for all the countries involved (World Energy Council, 2008).

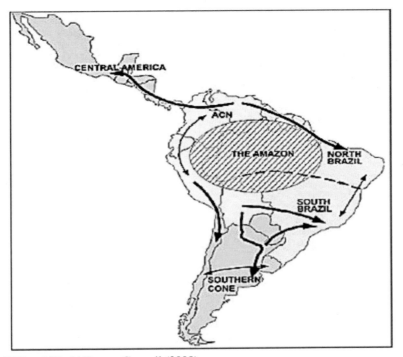

Source: OLADE and World Energy Council (2008).

Figure 16. Main scenarios for future energy integration in the Latin American region.

It is important to stress, in the case of the Andean zone, the following: The zone is characterized by two factors: Its wealth of energy resources, and its severe political, social, and ethnic crises. The abundance of energy resources means that most of the Andean countries are net energy exporters with substantial oil, natural gas, coal, and hydroelectric power reserves. The energy self-sufficiency of these countries means that integration is almost non–existent in the energy sector. Major bilateral agreements between Colombia and Venezuela and between Ecuador and Venezuela have been signed in the 2000s. However, the political crisis between Venezuela and Colombia due to the military agreement signed in 2009 between this last country and the USA for the use of seven Colombian military bases, among other factors, affected all bilateral cooperation between them. This bilateral cooperation was suspended until the arrival of the new government in Colombia in 2011. The new government in Colombia adopted several mesuares to change this situation and all economic and political relationships between Colombia and Venezuela has been restored since the second part of 2011.

The fact that several countries in the region suffered hydro power shortages due to the high reliance on this type of energy sources to meet the domestic demand, led them to encourage a more comprehensive energy integration that would improve the reliability of energy supply in the future. A fundamental step in this direction was taken in 2002, with the approval of Andean Community Nations Decision 536 "General Framework for the Sub-regional Interconnection of Electricity Systems and Electricity Intra-community Exchange," a juridical communitarian framework that was established to facilitate the development of the energy sector among member countries[26]. Besides, conditions were created to offer incentives to the development of an infrastructure based on the common use of the transmission networks. The purpose was a transmission network built using the "built-operate-transfer" model, to operate a coordinated economic dispatch since both would belong to a single sub-regional transmission system[27].

The fundamental rules for international transactions among member countries adopted since the entry into force of the Andean Community Nations Decision 536 are the following:

a) No price discrimination between national and foreign markets and no subsidies, tariffs or any other kind of restrictions to the intra-communitarian trade of energy should be established;

b) Free access to international interconnected lines is guaranteed;

---

[26] The agreements that enable the harmonization of the regulatory frameworks in the Andean zone have as main background the Meeting of Cartagena de Indias, Colombia, in September 2001, in which the Agreement for the Sub-regional Interconnection of the Electricity System and Intra-community Exchange was signed. The agreements adopted were incorporated into Andean Community Nations Decision 536.

[27] As it requires supra-national coordination of the decision and construction planning process of the transmission nets, as well as of the international unions, the Andean Committee of Standard Bureaus was created, backed by Andean Community Nations Decision 536 and Regulatory Agencies of Electricity Services. The performance of this bureau is centered on two working groups: The Working Group of Electricity Service Regulatory Bureaus, created in June 2003, which is the responsible body for the formulation of proposals that allow making progress in the standard marks of the harmonization process necessary for the implementation of the sub-regional interconnection of the electric systems and the electricity intra-communitarian interchange. The Working Group of Planner Organisms of Electricity Services, created in January 2004, which is the responsible body in charge of drawing up proposals that assure the coordinated action of the energy and electricity entities of the member countries, permit access to information, and guarantee coordinated planning of projects for regional integration (World Energy Council, 2008).

c) Free contracting is allowed among the agents of the electricity market of the participant countries, provided the contracts are signed in agreement with the legislation and the frameworks in force in each country. No restrictions can be imposed, aside from those already stipulated in the contracts for national markets;

d) Short-term international electricity transactions are compulsory. They are not subject to surpluses and limited only by the capacity of the international links;

e) Revenue that may arise from congestion charges of an international link shall not be credited to their owners;

f) Electricity prices at both ends of the intra-communitarian interconnections arising from physical flows determined by coordinated economic dispatches serve as a basis for setting the value of short-term international electricity transactions.

Since then, there has been progress in the development of regulatory frameworks of the Andean countries, especially concerning standard and commercial aspects, which enabled them to take the first steps towards a major interconnection of the national electric systems in order to improve efficiency and cut costs[28].

Table 14. Main integration projects in the Andean countries

Project	Comments
Electricity	
• Colombia - Ecuador Interconnection	Extension of the current line from 250 MW to 500 MW.
• Ecuador – Peru Interconnection	Regulatory and tariff combination is fundamental to implement the increase from 100 MW to 250 MW.
Natural Gas	
• Ecuador-Peru gas pipeline	Stage 1: Reform the production platform in Corvina, build a gas pipeline of 3.5 Mm³/d as far as the mainland and a thermal power plant in Nueva Esperanza (Peru) with 160 MW. Stage 2: Connection with gas pipeline of 2 MMm³/d for a thermal power plant of 300 MW in Arenillas (Ecuador). Stage 3: Connection by gas pipeline of 4.5 MMm³/d to Guayaquil (Ecuador)
• Colombia – Ecuador gas pipeline	Gas pipeline of 8.9 MMm³/day and 790 km long between Cali and Guayaquil.
• Colombia -Venezuela – Panama gas pipeline	Gas pipeline of 4 Mm³/d will connect Ballenas province in Colombia to western Venezuela. Later it may be extended and connected to the eastern Venezuela to export gas to Panama
• Peru – Chile gas pipeline	A gas pipeline will first carry 1 MMm³/d from Humay in Peru to Tocopillas in Chile. Later it shall be extended to carry up to 14.1 MMm³/d in its third phase.
LNG	
• Camisea II (Peru)	A gas pipeline of 17 MMm³/d will connect the gas bearing complex of Camisea with the coast, where a natural gas liquefaction plant will be built for exports. It also includes a combination carrier for liquid exports.

Source: OLADE and World Energy Council (2008).

---

[28] Recently, within the scope of Andean countries, a resolution was passed to link the market directly to their prices. Modern interconnections between Colombia, Ecuador, and Peru are the reflection of these new links based on market prices.

It should be mentioned that expansion of international interconnections in the Andean zone, besides providing quality benefits mainly related to higher reliability of supply, also produces several quantitative benefits that translate into greater economic efficiency. This arises from decreased use of non-renewable fuels and then replacement by better use of the existing generating capacity and, mainly, from a better use of the water stored in the reservoirs of three countries: Ecuador, Peru, and Colombia. These interconnections also allow the use of idle infrastructure and make better use of other assets e.g., thermal generation, which at present is not used in Colombia, could be essential for the "Central de Paute" in Ecuador that causes high volatility in the domestic prices (World Energy Council, 2008).

Integration Promoted by the Southern Cone Countries

Energy integration matters in the Southern Cone are quite different from those in the Central America, the Caribbean, and in the Andean sub-regions.

All Central America and the Caribbean countries are almost dependent from other countries to satisfy its energy needs. On the contrary, all Andean countries are able to satisfy its energy needs from inside.

Brazil and Chile alone account for half of Latin America's overall demand for energy imports but each faces a very different situation. Chile produces only 4% of the oil it needs, while Brazil produces 75% of them. However, this percentage could increase in the future as result of the finding of new off-shore oil reserves. About 70% of Brazil's imports come from outside the region, primarily from Nigeria, Algeria, and countries in Asia, while Chile satisfies 70% of its oil needs from within the region.

Although reserves are falling, Argentina is still able to meet its own oil and gas needs. However, while Argentina remains, for the time being a net natural gas exporter, growing domestic demand, the absence of new significant discoveries, and the lack of new investment in exploration and production could turn Argentina into a natural gas importer in the future.

Uruguay and Paraguay produce no oil or natural gas and, in the specific case of Paraguay, despite of its sizable hydroelectric generating capacity, remains energy independent and export 95% of the electricity produced by the Itaipú hydro power plant to Brazil.

As a part of the Initiative for the Integration of South American Regional Infrastructure (IIRSA), there is an important hydro electrical project under construction, the Madeira River project, an initiative to integrate Brazil, Bolivia, and Peru. The project consists of two hydroelectric dams Santo Antonio (installed generating capacity of 3 150 MW) and Jirau (installed generating capacity of 3 300 MW), which are going to supply electricity to all participants.

Grid Interconnections

In the 1960s, most countries in the region developed a national interconnected grid that joined isolated power systems, served in many cases by private utilities, and assigned to new State-owned enterprises holding a monopoly position, the responsibility of developing the generation, transmission, and distribution systems; the purpose is to increase service penetration and to meet a high demand growth.

This model of organization worked relatively well from the 1960s to early 1980s, a period characterized by high rates of growth of demand and service penetration, large economies of scale in generation projects, strong economic development, and major support from the national budget for investments in the energy sector. In the 1960s and 1970s, most countries in the Latin American and the Caribbean region developed their electric power infrastructure by integrating, in a national interconnected grid, several isolated power markets. In most countries, the generation capacity was duplicated every seven years. During this period, the electricity generation activity was characterized by substantial economies of scale, long lead times to develop a project, large sunk costs, and site dependency. The development of the industry mirrored these technical and economic characteristics: Creation of State-owned utilities holding a monopoly position in the energy sector, and centralized planning and operation of generation and transmission resources.

The power systems and markets developed in the region during this period share common characteristic. According with Dussan (1996), these are the following:

a)   Predominantly hydro-based generation;
b)   Modest electricity market size in several countries;
c)   High and volatile growth of electricity demand;
d)   Low electricity penetration in some countries;
e)   Large proportion of electricity consumption in the residential and industrial sectors.

However, within this pattern, there is a great diversity:

a)   There were four large electric power systems (installed generation capacity larger than 10 000 MW), seven medium-size systems (between 2 000 and 10 000 MW), and more than 14 small-size systems (less than 2 000 MW);
b)   There are large reserves of oil, coal, and gas but more than 90% of these are concentrated in seven countries (Argentina, Bolivia, Brazil, Colombia, Ecuador, Mexico, and Venezuela). Most of the Central American and the Caribbean countries depend on imports to meet their energy demand, making them very vulnerable to external factors;
c)   There is a large hydroelectric potential (62%), representing about four times the actual generation installed capacity. However, about 65% of the potential is concentrated in four countries, and development of a large part of this potential is besieged by environmental concerns, public opposition, technical difficulties, and high costs;
d)   Installed capacity in power generation is mostly hydro (61%) but five countries have already a hydro component larger than 75%. The entire Caribbean sub-region has very little hydro potential. The high use of renewable energy sources for electricity generation is concentrated in the Central American sub-region.

Table 15. Central American electricity interconnections

To/from	Capacity (MW)
Guatemala-El Salvador	100
El Salvador- Guatemala	95
El Salvador-Honduras	100
Honduras-El Salvador	100
Honduras-Nicaragua	80
Nicaragua-Honduras	80
Nicaragua-Costa Rica	60
Costa Rica-Nicaragua	60
Costa Rica-Panama	70
Panama-Costa Rica	110

Source: CRIE (2008).

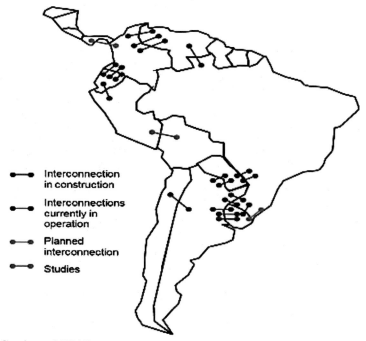

Source: Yepez-Garcia et al (2010).

Figure 17. South America interconnections.

In principle, regional interconnection and electricity trade between countries is an attractive approach for expanding the supply of electricity. The reasons are the following:

a) Trade can enhance the reliability and security of the local network by linking it with a larger grid and a greater number of generation sources, thus increasing the diversity of the generation system;

b) Trade may reduce generation costs due to economies of scale associated with power generation from larger facilities. Optimizing capital requirements for the electricity sector can free up capital resources for other investments and improve the domestic fiscal situation;

c) Interconnection (and the ability to acquire power through trade) allows individual countries to have lower reserve requirements, which reduces the need (and cost) of investing in reserve power capacity;

d) Trade may allow more competition in open markets as it increases the availability of electricity from different sources at varying costs. In addition, interconnections between markets may allow for some convergence of electricity prices, since the connected areas can function as a single market. Interconnection may lead to an important reduction in variable costs as countries do not need to import expensive fuels.

In the case of seasonal renewable energy resources such as hydro power, interconnection allows the linking of basins with different hydrology. This increases the firm energy that can be supplied by the same set of dams. This balancing of variable renewable energy resources also applies to wind and even biomass energy. Despite the potential benefits of inter-connections, electricity trade, and cross-border electricity projects (defined as those that rely on multi-country markets), there have been significant political and regulatory barriers in Latin America and the Caribbean that have hindered trade. When planning and beginning a project across borders, there are likely to be different technology standards, regulatory regimes, pricing policies, environmental concerns, and legal frameworks. More significantly, there can be different views about investment costs and how they are shared. Nevertheless, such issues can be resolved if there is a clear economic and commercial motivation behind the project that benefits all countries. Other issues that can affect project development are market changes, the emergence of new sources of fuel or electricity, and demand shocks, such as a financial crisis, that may dramatically alter the conditions for trade. Ultimately, the greatest uncertainties tend to be connected with political decision-making, and these may be particularly difficult to predict or address. Industrial consumption of electricity in the region is, according to different sources, about 50% of total consumption. However, while seven countries with large electro-intensive industries show a participation higher than 50%, in more than six countries, with modest industrial development, this is less than 30%.

Integration Promoted by the Caribbean Countries

It is important to know that all interconnections among the Caribbean countries are through submarine cables, except the Dominican Republic–Haiti link. According to the Nexant report (2010), the interconnections are:

1. Nevis – St. Kitts: 50 MW submarine cable capacity; 5 km submarine cable length; US $328 per kW;
2. Dominica – Martinique: 100 MW; 70 km submarine cable length; US $588 per kW;
3. Dominica – Guadeloupe: 100 MW; 70 km submarine cable length; US $588 per kW;
4. Nevis – Puerto Rico: 400 MW; 400 km submarine cable length; US $1,791 per kW;

5. Nevis – US Virgin Islands: 80 MW; 320 km submarine cable length, US $3,541 per kW;
6. Saba – St. Maarten: 100 MW; 60 km submarine cable length; US $528 per kW;
7. Dominican Republic – Haiti: 250 MW; 563 km; US $1,899 per kW.

Basic data and cost estimates for four potential interconnections that might form part of a "Northern Ring", a conceptual set of interconnections in the northern Caribbean potentially linking Florida, Cuba, Haiti, Dominican Republic, Puerto Rico, and Nevis or some subset of those areas, are included below.

a) Puerto Rico – Dominican Republic: 400 MW; 150 km submarine cable length; US $705 per kW;
b) Haiti – Cuba: 400 MW; 200 km submarine cable length; US $705 per kW;
c) Haiti – Jamaica: 400 MW submarine cable length; US $998 per kW;
d) Florida – Haiti: 400 MW; 1 100 km submarine cable length; US $348 per kW.

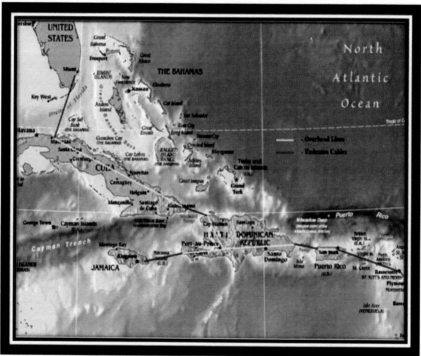

Source: Nexant report (2010).

Figure 18. Electricity interconnections in the Caribbean.

The Current Situation of the Regional Integration Processes

According to World Energy Council (2008), the main integration process stands as follows: IIRSA is a highly political project involving twelve countries of South America[29]

---

[29] IIRSA member countries are: Argentina, Bolivia, Brazil, Chile, Colombia, Ecuador, Guyana, Paraguay, Peru, Surinam, Uruguay and Venezuela.

that was adopted at the first summit of South American Heads of State in Brasília, Brazil, held in 2000. Its main objective is to improve competitiveness of the regional economy to achieve a global level of performance and promote sustainable socioeconomic development by integrating logistics infrastructure in the energy, telecommunication, and transport sectors. The governments, private sector and international financial institutions will be jointly financing the approved projects. Infrastructure projects for integration must be complemented by regulatory and administrative systems that facilitate interconnections and operation of the whole system. In this way, IIRSA promotes the convergence of regulations and institutional mechanisms, removing the regulatory, legal, operative and institutional barriers that restrict the efficient use of the existing infrastructure, as well as the drawbacks to investments in a new infrastructure. At later stages the creation of supranational institutions would be encouraged in order to increase even more sector efficiency and regional competitiveness.

Table 16. Integration and development zones proposed by IIRSA

Zone	Countries
Andean zone	Bolivia, Colombia, Ecuador, Peru, Venezuela
Amazon one	Brazil, Colombia, Ecuador, Peru
Guiana Shield zone	Brazil, Guyana, Suriname, Venezuela
Capricorn zone	Argentina, Brazil, Chile, Paraguay
Central Inter-ocean zone	Bolivia, Brazil, Chile, Paraguay, Peru
Mercosur-Chile zone	Argentina, Brazil, Chile, Paraguay, Uruguay
South zone	Argentina, Chile
Paraguay-Paraná waterway zone	Argentina, Bolivia, Brazil, Paraguay, Uruguay
Peru-Bolivia-Brazil zone	Bolivia, Brazil, Peru
Southern Andes zone	Argentina, Bolivia, Chile

Source: IIRSA (OLADE and World Energy Council (2008)).

However, it is important to stress that small or mid-size projects in progress or under study in the Southern Cone are more feasible for local than regional development. They seem to be aimed at developing the national energy markets. These projects, although more modest than the Grande Libertadores Gas Pipeline between Venezuela and Argentina, must be interpreted as components of future integration projects. Accordingly, long-term planning is essential, together with good political and economic dialogue between the countries of the region.

The situation of the main integration process involving Mercosur, the Southern Cone and south Brazil are summarizes in Table 17.

Table 17. Main integration projects covering Mercosur, Southern Cone and south Brazil

Project	Comments
Electricity	
Hydropower projects	
• River Madeira	River Madeira hydropower complex, with facilities in Brazil and Bolivia to reach 7480 MW.
• Corpus Christi	River Paraná hydropower scheme (Argentina-Paraguay) with 2900 MW.
• Garabi	River Uruguay hydropower scheme (Argentina-Brazil) with 1800 MW.
• Yacyretá	Increase of elevation to 83 metres: 1100 MW.
Electricity interconnection lines	See description
Natural Gas	
• Southern gas pipeline network	Consists of different natural gas transport infrastructures between Argentina, Bolivia, Brazil, Chile, Paraguay, Peru and Uruguay. A regulatory framework is planned for infrastructure.
• Humay-Tocopillas gas pipeline	Peru-Chile
• Northeast Argentine gas pipeline	Bolivia-Argentina
• Uruguayana-Porto Alegre gas pipeline	Argentina-Uruguay-Peru
• Grand Southern gas pipeline	This mega-project will connect the Venezuelan reserves with the demand centres in Brazil and Argentina, over a distance of 9300 km.
• Bolivia-Paraguay gas pipeline	
LNG	
• Bahía Quinteros plant	Chile began building a LNG regasification plant to start operating in 2008.
• Regasification plants in Brazil	Petrobras is designing the installation of two LNG plants to assure supply.

Source: OLADE and World Energy Council (2008).

Table 18. Natural gas interconnections

Country	Name of the natural gas main	Cities	Diameter (inches)	Length (km)	Capacity (Thousands of m³ per day)
Brazil	Aldea Brasilera-Uruguayana	Aldea Brasilera-Uruguayana	24	440	10
Uruguay	Cruz del Sur	Punta Lara- Santa Ana	24	14+55 (subfluvial)	6
Uruguay	Paysandu	Colon- Paysandu	10	15	1
Chile	Atacama	Cornejo-Mejillones	20	531	9
Chile	Methanex (Bandurrias)	Cabeza de León-Punta Arenas	10	48	4
Chile	Methanex (El Cóndor)	El Cóndor-Punta Arenas	12	9	2
Chile	Gas Andes	La Mora-Sgo de Chile	24	313/152	10
Chile	Norandino	Pichanal -Tocopilla	20	380/400	8.5
Chile	Pacífico	Loma de la Lata-Concepción	24-20	296/160	3.5
Chile	Methanex (Punta Dungenes)	Pta Dungenes-Cabo Negro	8	123	2
Chile	Batería de Recepción 7-T del Fuego	Batería - El Cóndor –Posesión	6	470 m	1.5
Bolivia	Pta Campo Duran-Frontera Arg-Bol	Pocitos - Campo Duran	24	23 (1)	7
Bolivia	Pta Campo Duran-Frontera Arg-Bol	Madrejones-Campo Duran	8	33	1.2
Chile	EGS	Pta. Magallanes -El Cóndor-Posesión (a Methanex)	18	6.5	1 (a)

Source: Argentinean energy authorities.

Source: REPSOL.

Figure 19. Gas pipeline network system in the Latin American and the Caribbean region and its prospects of development.

The Southern Gas Pipeline

The President of Venezuela has been actively promoting a southern gas pipeline in the past years to other South American countries[30]. The propose pipeline would run from Venezuela, through Brazil, Uruguay, and Argentina (see Figure 20). With a planned length of over 9 000 km, the pipeline would be an unparalleled feat of infrastructure engineering. For example, Europe's longest pipeline, which runs from the Caspian Sea to the Mediterranean, is less than 1 700 km and took a decade to be built and consumed an important level of resources. Without doubt, the propose southern gas pipeline would be the most important energy integration project ever built, not only in the Latin American continent but in the entire world, if the project can be implemented in the future.

On the basis of the resources that should be available to carry out this megaproject in the coming years, the following question need to be answered. Countries of the region interested in the implementation of this important integration energy project are in a position to allocate the necessary resources to support it under the current economic and financial crisis? Associated to the implementation of such megaproject there is always a number of serious obstacles that need to be overcome, including environmental, technical, and economic obstacles, in order to ensure the successful conclusion of the project.

---

[30] These countries are the following: Argentina, Bolivia, Brazil, Chile, Paraguay, Peru, and Uruguay.

Source: Petrobras.

Figure 20. Natural gas pipeline from Venezuela to Argentina.

Environmentalists surely will reject any policy that opens up the pristine Amazon jungle to development by the energy industry, on the basis of their experience with other energy projects implemented in the area in the past.

In addition to the above, and according to Arriagada (2006), after 3 000 km of pipeline, LNG with regasification plants at the destinations is a preferable and less costly option. Transportation costs at 9 000 km require the supplier to sell at US $2 per million BTUs or less to ensure competitiveness with Bolivian natural gas and liquefied natural gas. In addition, Southern Cone energy needs do not warrant an investment of this magnitude. The current natural gas shortfall in the region's largest net importers (Brazil and Chile) does not exceed 55 million of coal bed methane per day. Spending an estimated US $23 billion to serve a market with this level of needs makes no economic sense (Arriagada, 2006).

The most serious threats to the implementation of the above megaproject, in addition to its technological complexity, the high cost involved, and the high number of professionals, technical personnel, and qualify workers that need to be involved, are the following:

a) Brazil's recent announcement that it intends to reach gas self-sufficiency, on the basis of the new off-shore oil fields found in 2007 around 300 km from its coast;

b) Argentina has decided to expand its current nuclear power program with im order to drastically cut down natural gas needs during the coming years;

c) Bolivia has enough natural gas to satisfy the needs of Argentina, Brazil, and Chile, so pumping Venezuelan natural gas into the region could represent an economic threat to the Bolivian economy. Pumping gas from Puerto Ordaz makes no sense, if Bolivia can feed São Paulo from Santa Cruz de la Sierra through a 2 200 km pipeline, 7 000 km shorter than the southern natural gas pipeline proposed.

d) Venezuela alone cannot finance such an enormous project and, for the time being, there are no other potential investors that are ready to participate in financing this megaproject. The Venezuelan oil industry is already under financial pressure due by numerous and costly international projects is supporting in a group of countries inside and outside the region and the assistance that PdVSA is providing to numerous domestic social projects now under implementation in the country.

In addition to the above difficulties for the development of the southern gas pipeline proposal, there are other natural gas pipeline interconnection proposals more limited in size under consideration in the Southern Cone. Both Argentina and Bolivia have abundant non-associated natural gas reserves that they are eager to export to neighboring countries. More than US $7 billion have been invested in transmission pipelines over the past ten years, including the US $2.1 billion Bolivia-to-Brazil pipeline and the first stage of the US $250 million Argentina-to-Brazil pipeline. Several new pipelines are planned or under construction, providing the basis for a sub-regional natural gas transportation network. Large natural gas reserves in the north offer potential for LNG projects.

The San José Accord

For over a quarter century, Central American and the Caribbean countries have sought international assistance in relieving their oil shortages, which grow more severe every time world prices spike. For this reason, Venezuela and Mexico signed in August 1980 the so-called "San José Accord", whereby each supplies 80 000 barrels per day of oil or refined products to Belize, Costa Rica, El Salvador, Guatemala, Guyana, Honduras, Nicaragua, Panama, Haiti, the Dominican Republic, Barbados, and Jamaica. They charge market prices but offer soft loans that cover from 20% to 25% of costs. The agreement has been renewed on an annual basis.

The Caracas Accord

In October 2000, Venezuelan criticism of the San José Accord led to the so-called "Caracas Accord" between Venezuela and all San José Accord members, except Jamaica. The Accord also involves supplying 80 000 barrels per day of oil. The largest share - 20 000 barrels per day - goes to the Dominican Republic, and the smallest to Belize, with 600 barrels per day. The importers receive the oil at market prices but are offered financing terms of 2% annual interest for up to 17 years.

Petro-Caribe Agreement

In June 2005, Venezuela created the so-called "Petro-Caribe", an agreement bringing together the nine Caribbean nations that are not involved in either of the previous accords, in addition to existing members Belize, Jamaica, and the Dominican Republic. Petro-Caribe is seen as a replacement and an enhancement of the Caracas Accord. The Petro-Caribe model is based on the concept of State involvement in the energy sector whereby surpluses achieved would be used to help meet expenses (through subsidies) in health care, education, housing for the poor, and other's needs. While oil is sold to member countries at unsubsidized market prices, buyers are provided with long-term financing linked to increases in world prices. In other words, the higher the price, the greater the percentage that is eligible for special terms. Supplies are for domestic consumption only and cannot be resold. This accord has at least two factors that distinguish it. First, it creates a permanent organization with a seat in Caracas, including a Ministerial Council and an Executive Secretariat that Venezuela controls. Second, it links Petro-Caribe to the Bolivarian Alternative for Latin America (ALBA) through a fund called "ALBA–Caribe". This program was set up with an initial US $50 million grant from Venezuela in order to finance social and economic development programs in its members States. Without any doubt, these accords certainly provide an important relief for Central American and Caribbean countries due their high dependence from imported oil to ensure its social and economic development, and the high price that these countries has to pay, if they are forced to buy oil in the open market. On the other hand, humanitarian efforts promoted by Venezuela to help these countries should not be ignored or underestimated because it represents an important financial contribution to their economic and social development.

The Puebla–Panama Plan

In June 2001, the presidents of Mexico, Belize, Guatemala, Honduras, Nicaragua, El Salvador, Costa Rica, and Panama announced the so-called "Puebla–Panama Plan", an initiative to increase integration among seven countries of Central America and nine States in southern Mexico. Initially, the idea did not inspire much enthusiasm in Mexico, which concentrated solely on improving international road networks but this position changed. The current focus of the Puebla–Panama Plan is energy and oil. In mid–2005, it called for international lenders to build a US $340 million power grid for Central America. Plans include collaborating with Mexico and Colombia to develop oil and gas resources in both countries.

In November 2005, the presidents of Central America countries and Mexico agreed to build a US $7 billion refinery in Central America. The proposed facility will process between 350 000 and 400 000 barrels per day and 40% of the financing will come from Mexico, 20% from Central America, and 40% from private investors. If successful, the initiative will give Central America improved access to crude oil markets. Without any doubt the energy integration of the region could be a decisive mechanism for a better geopolitical position of the region in the international arena. To achieve that goal, it is fundamental to construct an adequate infrastructure and to have an institutional scheme to regulate the way in which said infrastructure will operate. To be precise, the design of the technical as well as institutional mechanisms for the development of a common energy market is still a challenge to fulfilling the region's prevailing political will (Ruiz Caro, 2008).

Finally, it is important to stress the following: In addition to the best use of local generating power plants in each country, with each year that passes more countries are becoming interconnected with others, allowing them to make the best use of their energy reserves and complementarities of energy supply, as well as the non-simultaneities of the energy demand, increasing the efficiency in the use of all available energy reserves. This interconnection creates the necessary conditions for a substantial increase in regional integration in the future.

Table 19. Power network interconnections in Latin America and the Caribbean in 2004

Country: Location	Country: Location	V (kV)	Power (MW)	Notes
Colombia: Ipiales	Ecuador: Tulcán	115/138	40	Operating (60 Hz)
Argentina: Paso de los Libres	Brasil: Uruguayana	132/230	50	Operating (50/60 Hz)
Brasil: Foz de Iguazú	Paraguay: Acaray	138	60	Operating (50/60 Hz)
Brasil: Rivera	Uruguay: Libramento	230/150	70	Operating (50/60 Hz)
Argentina: Clorinda	Paraguay: Guaramberé	132/220	80	Operating (50 Hz)
Colombia: Tibú	Venezuela: La Fría	115	80	Operating (60 Hz)
Colombia: Pasto	Ecuador: Quito	230	260	Operating (60 Hz)
Argentina: Yacyreta	Paraguay: Yacyreta	500/220	800/130	Operating (50 Hz)
Colombia: Cuestecita	Venezuela: Cuatricentenario	230	150	Operating (60 Hz)
Colombia: San Mateo	Venezuela: Corozo	230	150	Operating (60 Hz)
Brasil: Boa Vista	Venezuela: Santa Elena	230/400	200	Operating (60 Hz)
Chile: Norte Grande Chile (SING)	Argentina: Cobos	345	643	Operating (50 Hz)
Argentina. Rincón	Brasil: Garabí	500/525	2,000	Operating (50/60 Hz)
Argentina: Salto Grande	Uruguay: Salto Grande	500	1,750	Operating (50 Hz)
Brasil: Itaipú	Paraguay: Itaipú	750CC/220	10,787	Operating (50/60 Hz)
Colombia	Panamá	230		Under study
Ecuador: Machala	Perú: Zorritos	230/220	60 (200)	Under construction (60 Hz)
Bolivia: La Paz	Perú: Puno	230/220	150	In study
Argentina: El Dorado	Paraguay: Mcal A. López	132	33.6	Operating (50 Hz)
Argentina: Colonia Elia	Uruguay: San Javier	500	1000	Operating (50 Hz)
Argentina: Conceptión	Uruguay: Paysandú	132/150	100/50	
Argentina: C.H. Alicura	Chile: Valdivia	220	250	Projected
Central American Intercn.	The six Countries	230	250	Operating (60 Hz)

Source: OLADE.

The Future of Regional Integration

The difficulties facing the sub-regional blocs for their energy integration seem to multiply with wider integration schemes now under implementation in the Latin American and the Caribbean context. When there is a concrete integration project, from an economic viewpoint it is heavily dependent on the political context, under which the project is going to be implemented. The current political difference among Latin American and the Caribbean governments and the strong influence of the USA in several of them are two of the main obstacles for the success implementation of these projects. The lack of financial resources is another important obstacle than cannot be underestimated.

It is important to stress that energy integration is only one of the aspects involved in the process of economic and political integration of countries that share a geographical area. Energy integration was conceived in the IIRSA project "as a necessary condition for development but whose sustainability is linked to major transformations in four key dimensions: Competitiveness, environmental quality, institutional quality, and social quality. In this way, energy integration may have various objectives, some of which are as follows:

a) Increase in the security of the energy supply;
b) Reduction in cost of investments in the supply system;
c) Peaceful and equal economic and social development of the countries in the region.

To achieve such objectives, it is necessary to approach the design of the integration projects with an overall focus that considers the questions of efficiency relating to the economic costs of the projects, i.e., the degree of political and regulatory exposure, and the possibilities for equal, harmonious and sustainable economic and social development of the countries involved in the integration process.

On short-to-medium-term new installations of fossil-fuel-fired power generation will be mainly based on natural gas and corresponding power generation technologies. The favorite technology may be the highly efficient combined-cycle gas turbines. The request of the Southern Cone countries to refurbish their fuel oil driven power plants to natural-gas-fired power plants is in line with this view. Oil will be preferentially used to satisfy the demand of the transportation sector and for exports to the USA in the future.

ENVIRONMENTAL CONSIDERATIONS

Environmental considerations during the development of the energy sector have been particularly intense in the last years in the Latin American and the Caribbean region and environmental studies have been prioritized by several countries of the region. However, the energy and environmental policies have not received, in all countries, the importance that they deserve, and their levels of development have been very dissimilar among countries.

The implementation of the energy reforms was an opportunity to integrate environmental regulations, and to concentrate responsibilities in one or two institutions by country. The issue of public participation in developing, implementing, and supervising environmental standards is perhaps where most regulatory activity is seen in the countries of the region, especially with regard to energy development and attention to ethnic minorities. The progress has been made in terms of participation in the process of environmental impact assessment, and regarding rulings legitimating the filing of administrative or judicial actions in defense of the environment and its components. However, it is still necessary to integrate this set of elements into a coordinated procedure, whose terms will be tailored to each particular circumstance. In this regard, it is important to point out that while the first generation of environmental impact study legislation in the region made no reference to establishing objective guidelines or criteria to orient the assessment of environmental impact studies, there are already examples – albeit embryonic in some cases – of enormous progress towards ensuring the effectiveness of the tool and the transparency of the process (Deutsche Montan Technologie GmbH, OLADE and CIEMAT, 2005).

It is important to recognize that progress in mechanisms for environmental policy administration and implementation goes hand in hand with a renewed emphasis on economic and social growth, which translates as a marked tendency to adjust the legal requirements of environmental protection for development activities, tendency that should be in the mind of government and the public opinion in order to avoid an excessive adjustment of environmental protection regulations.

Without any doubt, the protection of the environment and the access to energy in the form of electricity is one of the main manner to improve the quality of life of the population of a given country or region. Improving the population's quality of life through equitable access to energy is also a topic that is at the head of policy programs throughout the region, and has direct impact on the relationship between environmental protection and development. This concern tends to give way to legislative promotion of alternative energy development, particularly regarding energy access by rural sectors, and those located in remote areas relative to existing supply networks. Also noteworthy is the new impetus given by the concept of energy efficiency as one of the best roads to a cleaner, more sustainable energy future. This trend is currently seen reflected in different programs, policy papers, and a few isolated rulings that promote efficiency and demand management (Deutsche Montan Technologie GmbH, OLADE and CIEMAT, 2005).

MAIN CHALLENGES

Summing up can be affirmed that the main challenges for the energy sector in the Latin American and the Caribbean region during the coming years are, among others, the following:

1. Adopt an energy policy and strategy adequate to the different energy sources available in the region;
2. Achieve sustainability of energy supply and rational use of all available energy resources in the coming decades;
3. Use of the most energy efficiency technologies available in the region;
4. Provide energy access for the whole population at a reasonable price, particularly in rural areas;
5. Reduce urban pollution problems and the extreme vulnerability to climate change by the reduction of the use of fossil fuels for electricity generation;
6. Establishment of an adequate regulatory and institutional frameworks;
7. Identify pre-investment resources to support project preparation and development;
8. Allocate sufficient financial resources to develop the energy sector with the purpose of satisfying the foreseeable increase in energy demand;
9. Reduce the dependency of oil for electricity generation;
10. Increase the use of renewable energy sources for the electricity generation, particularly wind, solar, and geothermal energy sources;
11. The continued use of nuclear power for electricity generation in those countries of the region with the conditions to use this type of energy using the most strict safety guidelines;
12. Ensure energy supply[31].

Based on the experience of many Latin American and the Caribbean countries, State must carry out a proactive role in the energy sector. This role must come together with the private sector in a joint effort to achieve the goals of a sustainable and equitable energy policy. Specific goals should, therefore, be included regarding access to energy for sectors currently without access, particularly in rural areas. Regulatory framework should be established to protect poor consumers in order to guarantee access to clean, efficient, and modern energy sources at affordable prices.

---

[31] A long-term perspective of the energy situation in Latin America should take into account the United States' insatiable thirst for petroleum (which ethanol cannot allay), and the new demand for oil from China and India.

In the specific case of policies for rural areas, it will be necessary to:

a) Identify mechanisms to guarantee the continuity and expansion of electricity supply to households;
b) Move towards programs that ensure the provision of sufficient energy to improve the productivity of economic activities of rural communities in order by this means to achieve poverty reduction;
c) Promote replacement of firewood as an energy source wherever possible and, where this is not possible, use must be made sustainable by means of efficient equipment;
d) Set thresholds for access to electricity so that sufficient power is provided for productive use.

In the case of urban areas, there will be a need to:

a) Set basic consumer standards;
b) Introduce reduced rates;
c) Give considerations to cross subsidies;
d) Adopt energy efficiency policies.

Since programs of this kind can have a considerable impact on total energy consumption, long-term overall and sectorial planning is needed in order for energy consumption to be sustainable.

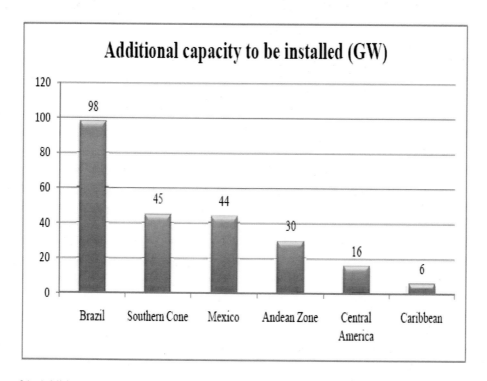

Figure 21. Additional capacity to be installed in the region.

LOOKING FORWARD

In the Latin American and the Caribbean region as a whole, it is estimated that an additional 239 GW of installed capacity will be required to satisfy the foreseeable increase in electricity demand. It is estimated that Brazil will add approximately 41% of this additional capacity. The Southern Cone is expected to be the second largest contributor with about 45 GW, followed closely by Mexico and the Andean zone, with about 44 GW and 30 GW respectively. Central America and the Caribbean will contribute with an additional 16 GW and 6 GW, respectively.

The similarities and differences in the development of the energy sector in the different sub-regions are briefly described in the following paragraphs:

a) *The Andean zone:* The Andean zone electricity demand is expected to grow 75% in the coming years. The generation mix is expected to be composed mainly of hydro power. However, it is important to note that the current energy infrastructure is not being utilized to its maximum capacity in some Latin American and the Caribbean countries. Beginning in 2016, the share of fossil fuel-based generation is expected to increase, reaching 40% by 2030. The sub-region is not expected to diversify its generation mix by expanding into nuclear, geothermal, or wind technologies in the coming years. The implications for the Andean zone of this situation are that it will become increasingly dependent on fossil fuels (mainly natural gas) after 2016 and, as a result, more affected by volatile fossil fuel prices. It is important to know that the additional energy capacity requirements from 2008 to 2030 in the Andean zone will be met largely by two different types of energy sources: Natural gas (50% of the additional generating capacity) and hydro power (40%);

b) *Southern Cone:* Demand in the Southern Cone will grow nearly 80%. The existing high degree of diversification in the region in terms of generation technologies and fuels will become even more dynamic over the period 2008-2030. The fuel source that increases the most is coal, which rises from 7% to 12%. Nuclear power accounts for 6% of additional capacity as a result of new capacity planned in Argentina and Brazil and a few years later in Mexico. Renewable sources, including wind and geothermal power, are expected to increase modestly, with their share rising from close to zero to 3%. This increase is partially driven by an anticipated increase in the Argentinean wind market. The share of coal is expected to nearly double the current level largely as a result of the cost minimization assumptions, which do not include global environmental costs. It is important to note that the increases in nuclear, coal, and non-hydro renewables will take place at the expense of hydro power and natural gas, whose shares are estimated to decline. Nonetheless, the Southern Cone's additional capacity is projected to be dominated by two different energy sources: Natural gas (33%) and hydro power (28%);

c) *Central America:* For Central America, the share of natural gas it is expected to increase significantly between 2008 and 2030 from zero to 13%. Central America is also the only sub-region where the share of hydro power marginally increases between 2008 and 2030 (from 45% to 46% of total generation). Similarly, the sub-region is expected to increase its reliance on coal, from around 2% in 2008 to over

11% by 2030. By contrast, the share of fuel oil and diesel for electricity generation is expected to decline significantly, due largely to the preference to move away from the use of fossil fuels for this purpose and due to expected changes in relative generation costs. The bulk of generating capacity to be added in Central America between 2008 and 2030 is projected to be largely represented by hydro power (45%), with coal, fuel oil, and natural gas also playing important roles (11%, 20%, and 14% of additional capacity, respectively). Renewable energy sources, such as wind and geothermal energy, begin to play an increasingly important role in Central America and together it is expected to represent about 7% of the new generating capacity installed by 2030;

d)   *The Caribbean:* In the Caribbean sub-region, the generation matrix is expected to remain largely fossil fuel-dependent. Over the entire period, the share of fossil fuel based technologies is expected to increase slightly from 93% to 95%. One important development is an increase in natural-gas based generation in the Dominican Republic. By contrast, the proportion of hydro power in the sub-region is expected to decrease, due to the lack of large river in the whole sub-region. For this reason, the sub-region will continues to rely largely on conventional electricity generation sources in the coming years, with fuel oil and diesel contributing 32% of the added capacity between 2008 and 2030, and coal contributing 17%. The bulk of future capacity (45%) is based on gas technologies, driven mainly by the Dominican Republic.

Chapter II

THE CURRENT AND FUTURE ROLE OF OIL IN THE REGION ELECTRICITY GENERATION

GENERAL OVERVIEW

According to the IEA sources, petroleum is a complex mixture of liquid hydrocarbons, chemical compounds containing hydrogen and carbon, occurring naturally in underground reservoirs in sedimentary rock[32]. Crude oil is a naturally occurring substance found trapped in certain rocks below the Earth's crust formed more than 300 million years ago. It is a dark, sticky liquid which, scientifically speaking, is classed as a hydrocarbon. This means, it is a compound containing only hydrogen and carbon. Crude oil is the most important oil from which petroleum products are manufactured but several other feedstock oils are also used to make oil products[33]. There is a wide range of petroleum products manufactured from crude oil. Many are for specific purposes, for example motor gasoline or lubricants; others are for general heat-raising needs, such as gas oil or fuel oil.

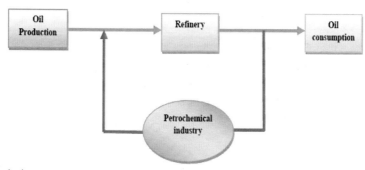

Source: Author design.

Figure 22. Simplified flow chart for oil.

---

[32] Coming from the Latin petra, meaning rock, and oleum, meaning oil, the word "petroleum" is often interchanged with the word "oil". Broadly defined, it includes both primary (unrefined) and secondary (refined) products.

[33] Crude oil can be produced from different locations, onshore or offshore fields, or from different types of wells, in association with natural gas or not. Any gas extracted from associated oil wells may be flared, vented, reinserted or form part of natural gas production.

Oil is the largest traded commodity worldwide, either through crude oil or through refined products. Although oil supply continues to grow in absolute terms, its share in global total energy supply has been decreasing from over 45% in 1973 to around 36% in 2006; this represents a decrease of 9%[34]. It is expected that, in 2030, the oil share in global total energy supply decrease further to 32%; this represents a decrease of 4%.

The first oil well was open in Pennsylvania, USA, in 1859. Since that year, the oil consumption increased systematically in all countries[35]. The world's average level of oil consumption per habitant and per year is now around 1.6 ton. However, the level of consumption varies significantly between countries and regions. For example, in the USA and Canada, average oil consumption per habitant per year is around 8 ton; this represents five times world average. In Third World countries, that average level could be around 500 kg only; this represents 0.0625 times world average (Morales Pedraza, 2008).

After so many years of discriminatory oil consumption in the world, now this type of fossil fuel faces a serious problem that can limit, in a future not very distant, the possibilities of economic growth of many countries due to the following reasons:

a) A decrease of the oil's world proven reserves;
b) The current high level of oil consumption;
c) The ongoing high world's oil price;
d) The negative impact on the environment.

The IEO (2009) reference case projects an increase in the world consumption of marketed energy from all fuel sources over the 2006 to 2030 projection period. Fossil fuels (liquid fuels and other oil, natural gas, and coal) are expected to continue supplying much of the energy used worldwide.

Liquids fuels supply the largest share of world energy consumption over the projection period; however, their share falls from 36% in 2006 to 32% in 2030, as projected high world's oil prices lead many energy users, especially in the industrial and electric power sectors, to switch away from liquid fuels, when feasible. It is important to be aware that this process will take place in a context where the production and supply of hydrocarbons will be characterized by a new paradigm of high prices and a large degree of volatility, geopolitical tensions, an intensifying environmental debate at the international level, competition for access to new regions with probed reserves, demands for greater participation in hydrocarbon financial gains, especially in several Latin American countries, and an increment in the number of mergers, acquisitions and profits without precedent.

---

[34] While petroleum products main uses are for their energetic properties, there are a number of non-energy uses of petroleum, most notably in the petrochemical industry. Petrochemicals are chemicals derived from petroleum, and used as the basic chemical building blocks for a variety of commercial products. Dating back to the early 1920s, the petrochemical industry today is very diverse, supplying the raw materials for the manufacturing of plastics, synthetic fibers and rubbers, fertilizers, pesticides, detergents, and solvents. Industries as diverse as textile, food, pharmaceutical, automobile, and paint manufacturing use petrochemicals. Petrochemical feedstock are created from a number of petroleum products, mainly naphtha, LPG, and ethane. The petrochemical industry, however, is not only a large consumer of petroleum products, it is also a producer of petroleum products, as it extracts the necessary components for production of petrochemicals and then returns the by-products to the refineries or to the market.

[35] Oil is used to produce different kind of products. Around 80 000 different products are manufactured from oil, and this figure increases every year.

Natural gas is plentiful in countries like Argentina, Bolivia, Brazil, Trinidad and Tobago, Peru, and Venezuela but still needs to be developed in some of these countries. In the last decade, these countries have increased their energy consumption owing to their economic and social development and to the growth in their population. This increase has generated an augment in their greenhouse gas emissions in several of these States motivating them to find other energy sources to satisfy their foreseen increase of energy needs in the future. From an energy point of view, four countries (Mexico, Brazil, Argentina, and Venezuela) consume 73% of the energy and 78% of the electricity produced in the region in 2008. By sectors, the industry and transportation are the sectors that consume more energy in the region. Energy resources used in electricity generation in the region come from renewable energy resources (70%), mainly hydro power, followed by thermal generation (14% oil, 11% natural gas, 3% coal, and 2% nuclear).

Mexico and Central and South American nations delivered nearly 14% of world oil production in 2005, and possess in 2010 approximately 10% of world's oil reserves, with 6.5% in Venezuela[36] and 1.1% in Mexico alone. However, in 2008, the region produced only 8.8% of the world's oil production[37], representing a reduction of 5.2% in only three years but maintaining its position regarding world's oil reserves (around 10%). In the specific case of Central America, Guatemala has the highest energy consumption in the sub-region. All countries in the sub-region heavily depend on petroleum and by-product imports: Panama (66%), Costa Rica (52%), Honduras (50%), Nicaragua (44%), Guatemala (42%), and El Salvador (21%).

Energy Strategies

In the Latin American and the Caribbean region three different energy strategies for the development of the energy sector can be identified. One strategy is towards rising State control of all energy resources available in the country, which is followed mainly by Argentina, Bolivia, Cuba, Ecuador, and Venezuela. A second strategy is toward creative fiscal regimes that welcome foreign investment and require State-owned companies to compete with private and international companies, with independent regulators that promote fair and efficient regulation. Countries following this model are Brazil, Colombia, Trinidad and Tobago, and Peru. The third group of countries is giving high priority to the private sector for the generation and distribution of electricity such as Chile, in which its energy sector is in the hand of the private industry.

OIL PRODUCTION, CONSUMPTION AND RESERVES

In 2010, the world's proved oil reserves were estimated on 1,354 billion of barrels. Latin American countries with the largest crude oil reserves are show in Table 20. The Latin American and the Caribbean oil reserve represent 10% of the world's oil reserves in 2010.

---

[36] Venezuela (296.5 billion barrels of oil) has now the largest confirmed world's oil reserves, followed by Saudi Arabia (264.5 billion).
[37] In 2011, the average world's oil production reached 88.45 million barrels per day.

From Table 20 can be stated the following: Venezuela, Mexico, and Brazil, are the Latin American countries with major oil reserves within the region. In the Southern Cone, the largest oil reserves are located in Argentina.

The Andean zone accounts for almost 27% of South American oil consumption, which has been on the increase, especially in Venezuela in recent years. All Andean countries have oil reserves. Bolivia produces what it consumes. Colombia has smaller production than consumption, with proven oil reserves sufficient for several years at the current rate of consumption. Ecuador, as an oil exporter, should encourage exploration in order to prevent importation of oil in the future.

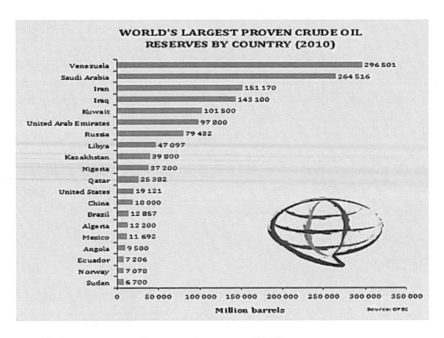

Figure 23. World's largest proven oil reserves by country (2010).

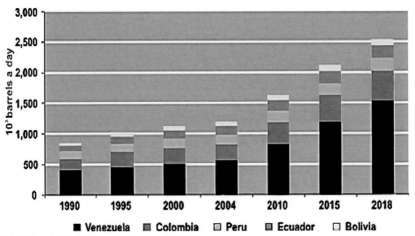

Source: OLADE and World Energy Council (2008).

Figure 24. Oil demand in the Andean zone. Forecast for the period 2010-2018.

In Peru, consumption exceeds mid-term production and, if the country fails to find new oil reserves, then it may have to start importing oil in the near future. Venezuela, with large oil reserves, will continue to be an oil exporter country in the coming years.

From Figure 24, the following can be stated: Venezuela is the country with the highest oil demand forecast in the Andean zone until 2018, followed by Colombia, Ecuador, Peru, and Bolivia. The oil demand is expected to increase from around 750 000 barrels per day in 1990, to around 2.5 million barrels per day in 2018; this represents an increase of 333%.

It is important to single out that the situation with regard the production and import of oil to satisfy the energy needs of the Southern Cone differs significantly country to country. No oil is produced in Uruguay and Paraguay while oil production in Chile is very small. Chile produces only 4% of the oil its needs and import around 70% of its oil needs from within the region. Chile imports oil from Argentina, Brazil, Nigeria, and Peru. Forecasts included in Figure 26 show that with an increase in oil demand in Chile, Uruguay, and Paraguay, these countries will have to import oil from other regions, since the Argentinean oil and gas reserves will be used mainly to satisfy their internal energy needs. Brazil produces 75% of its oil needs but 70% of its oil import come from outside the region (primarily Nigeria, Algeria, and countries in Asia).

Table 20. List of oil producers in the Latin American and the Caribbean region

Position	Countries	Amount barrels per day	Date
8	Mexico	2 910 000	2012
10	Venezuela	2 480 000	2012
12	Brazil	2 055 000	2010
26	Colombia	786 000	2010
27	Argentina	642 000	2010
32	Ecuador	486 000	2009
45	Trinidad and Tobago	151 600	2009
46	Peru	148 000	2009
64	Cuba	48 340	2009
66	Bolivia	47 050	2010
75	Virgin Islands	16 870	2009
78	Suriname	15 190	2009
79	Guatemala	13 530	2009
84	Chile	10 850	2009
98	Belize	3 990	2009
102	Aruba	2 235	2009
103	Puerto Rico	1 783	2009
104	Uruguay	997	2010
107	Barbados	765	2009
112	Paraguay	31	2009
115	Panama	2	2009

Source: EIA, Oil Market Report, and other public sources.

Table 21. Crude oil imports (top 15 countries) (Thousand barrels per day)

Country	2011	2010
Canada	2 114	1 928
Saudi Arabia	1 122	1 068
Mexico	1 108	1 130
Venezuela	917	918
Nigeria	886	981
Colombia	348	306
Iraq	403	483
Angola	308	408
Russia	228	250
Algeria	253	313
Brazil	211	276
Kuwait	142	201
Ecuador	166	190
Congo (Brazzaville)	54	90
Norway	54	39

Source: Author compilation from different public sources.

Table 22. Top 15 oil exporter countries

Rank	Country	Oil - exports (barrels per day) January 2011
1	Saudi Arabia	8 900 000
2	Russia	5 080 000
3	Norway	3 018 000
4	United Arab Emirates	2 540 000
5	Iran	2 520 000
6	Canada	2 274 000
7	Mexico	2 268 000
8	Venezuela	2 203 000
9	Kuwait	2 200 000
10	Nigeria	2 141 000
11	United Kingdom	1 956 000
12	Algeria	1 724 000
13	Iraq	1 670 000
14	Netherlands	1 546 000
15	Libya	1 326 000

Source: Author compilation from different public sources.

Oil is expected to remain, in the coming years, the world dominant energy source, according to the IEO (2009) reference case projection, particularly in the transportation and industrial sectors. World use of liquids and other petroleum products it is expected to grows from 85 million barrels per day in 2006 to 91 million barrels per day in 2015, and between 107 and 121 million barrels per day in 2030. With the level of oil consumption of 2006, and the available oil resources today, approximately 1,354 billion barrels[38], current oil reserves are enough to satisfy the oil demand until 2060. It must be noted, however, that reserves estimation is as much an art, as a skill. Estimates are not accurate and could change considerably. For example, new technologies could increase the recovery rate of existing wells, high oil prices could make more resources recoverable, and non-conventional oil resources could amount to 7,000 billion barrels.

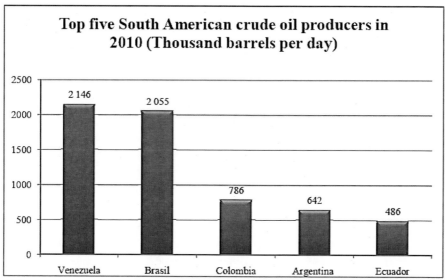

Source: EIA.

Figure 25. Top South American oil producers in 2010.

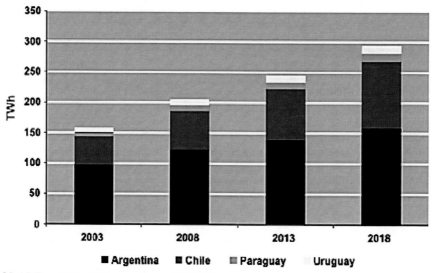

Source: OLADE and World Energy Council (2008).

Figure 26. Oil demand in Southern Cone. Forecast until 2018.

---

[38] The OPEC controls nearly 78% of all worldwide proven oil reserves.

For some oil-rich countries, it is assumed that current political barriers to increase oil production will not continue after 2015. For instance, both Mexico and Venezuela currently have legislation that restricts foreign ownership of hydrocarbon resources. The nationalization of their energy resources has limited foreign investment and hindered their ability to increase or even maintain historical production levels. In the IEO (2008) reference case, both Mexico and Venezuela are assumed to ease restrictions at some point after 2015, allowing some additional foreign investment or involvement in their oil sectors with the objective of increasing liquids production, including from deep-water prospects in Mexico, and extra-heavy oil in the Orinoco Belt in Venezuela. In the particular case of Venezuela, for example, foreign investment have been already approved in 2010 for exploration and exploitation of extra-heavy oil in the Orinoco Belt, involving Chinese, Iranian, and Russian oil companies, among others.

Latin American production of crude oil[39] averaged 7.15 million barrels per day in 2003, and it is expected to increase to almost 12 million barrels per day by 2030; this represents an increase of 4.75 million barrels per day or 68%. Production is dominated at present by Mexico, Venezuela, Brazil, Ecuador, Colombia, and Argentina. Venezuela and Mexico are the most important oil exporter's countries in the Latin American and the Caribbean region (see Table 22). While Brazil, Colombia, Ecuador, and Argentina are important destinations for foreign investment, helpfully, produce enough oil to meet their own domestic needs, particularly in the case of Brazil. It is important, however, to stress that these countries while contributing to the global oil export market they are not considered strategic oil suppliers at this time. Within the region, only Mexico, Brazil, and Venezuela produced in 2010 more than two million barrels per day (see Table 20).

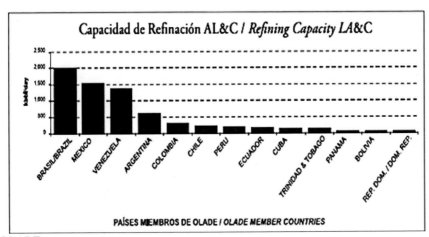

Source: OLADE.

Figure 27. Refining capacity of the Latin American and the Caribbean region.

The Latin American and the Caribbean region is also a major refining center, with nearly 9.2% of the world's refining capacity.

---

[39] The average world's oil production in 2011 reached 88.5 million barrels per day. The average world's oil consumption in that year reached 89.1 million barrels per day, exceeding the production in 0.6 million barrels per day. The deficit between the production and consumption is due to an increase in the demand in China, India, and some other countries in the Asia and the Pacific region.

It is important to stick out that most of the regional refineries are designed to serve the specialized needs of the USA's market. The most important exporters, Venezuela and Mexico, consistently rank in the top four sources of US oil supply along with Canada and Saudi Arabia. The major refining capacity is located in Brazil (thirteen major refineries), followed by Venezuela (eleven refineries), Argentina (eight refineries) and Mexico (six refineries). Five countries in the region have no refining capacity at all. These countries are the following: Barbados, Grenada, Guyana, Haiti, and Honduras.

OIL AS INSTRUMENT OF GOVERNMENT POLICY

Oil can be used as an instrument of government policy. In the 1970s, Arab countries used oil as a political weapon, in order to force Western governments to change their Middle East policy in favor of Israel in its military and political confrontation with Arab countries, particularly with the Palestinians people. This event augment the oil price several times with devastating effects in the economy of many developing countries, and forcing also developed countries to search for new sources of energy, such as coal and nuclear energy, as well as an increase in the efficiency in the use of oil[40]. Again, during the period 1979-1981, following the Iranian revolution and the beginning of the Iran-Iraq war, the oil price were driven up to further heights having a negative impact in the economy of many countries, particularly developing countries.

In the Latin American and the Caribbean region, Venezuela is actively pursuing a change in regional power balances by using oil resources as an instrument of foreign policy. This policy is called by some experts and politician as "Petro-politics". The use of this type of policy encompasses two situations. First, control over oil resources can create asymmetrical relationships among countries with a strong influence in government external policy position. In this case, oil could create relationships of hegemony and subordination among States, as importing nations become dependent on oil producers. Such dependence can be further reinforced, if supplies are sold at preferential prices or terms. Dependence is less likely to occur when the commodity is traded in open and transparent markets but in this case high price could have a strong negative effect in the economy of the importing nation. Light crude oil, for example, is in high demand and its price is set by the market. Heavy crude oil, on the other hand, requires a complex and rare refining process, so it is traded in restricted markets at fixed prices. Second, oil wealth is used to influence relations with other States. Producer nations employ their resources to pressure governments or opposition groups with the aim of obtaining political advantages in the imported country.

Central America and the Caribbean are the areas of the region where oil and gas can be most influential as political instruments. The reason is clear: Large oil producers, such as Venezuela and Mexico, are situated alongside more than 20 importing nations that possess no oil or gas whatsoever (Arriagada, 2006).

---

[40] It is important to note that high oil price makes more economical the exploration and exploitation of previous un-economical oil reservoirs. Additional oil reserves were found within the territories of the OPEC countries and in Brazil in recent years.

It is important to stress that the dependence on oil and gas imports is higher in Central American and the Caribbean sub-regions than anywhere else in the Hemisphere, meaning the prospects for oil diplomacy are higher as well.

Many world and regional powers are trying to increase their influence in Central American and the Caribbean sub-regions for many reasons. The USA certainly plays an important role in this area but so do Mexico and Venezuela through the implementation of the ALBA Treaty[41]. In addition, Brazil has been giving to Central American and the Caribbean countries increased attention and the president of Brazil has declared the intention of the government to become the main Cuban partner in the future, through the implementation of several projects with important economic and social impact in the country. The region is important for several reasons, including population, markets, and proximity to the USA's market.

According to Arriagada (2006), in the case of the Andean zone the dependence on oil and gas imports is almost nonexistence. The abundance of energy resources means the so called "oil diplomacy" has less impact in the Andean countries than in any other country or group of countries in the region. Why? The reason is very simple. The possibility of using oil and gas as political leverage is greater when relations among States are asymmetrical. This type of unbalanced relationship, which opens the door to dependence, does not exist within the Andean countries because most of them are net energy exporters with substantial oil, gas, coal, and hydroelectric power reserves.

The persistent instability in the Andean countries, however, creates perfect conditions for major and intermediate powers to try to achieve energy regional control. They try to influence other countries by sowing instability and financing sympathetic political parties or candidates. However, these activities are not properly described as "oil diplomacy"; it is the exercise of the power of wealth, irrespective of the origin of that money. Some of the Andean countries are especially vulnerable to this interference, primarily because they face severe governance problems, particularly economic and social problems as a result of deep-seated flaws within their political systems.

Summing up, the following can be stated: The energy situation varies throughout the Latin American and the Caribbean region. In Central America and the Caribbean, the chances of using oil and gas as policy instruments are greater because the region has a few large energy producers sitting next to twenty countries that are almost all economically minor and lack any petroleum resources. In the Andean zone, the situation is the opposite. Most nations are energy producers capable of meeting their own demand and even maintaining a positive balance of trade in this area. Matters in the Southern Cone, however, are quite different. In the Southern Cone, two countries have no oil resources, one country is a net importer of energy and the other has sufficiency oil resources to almost satisfy its oil needs now and in the near future.

OIL PRICE EVOLUTION

The vertiginous use of oil at world level was motivated by its low price during so many years. The fluctuations of the world's oil price during the last century are shown in Table 23.

---

[41] ALBA in English means: Bolivarian Alternative for the Americas.

Table 23. Fluctuations of world's oil prices during 1900-2012

Year	1900-1970	1979-1981	1985	1990-1999	2007	2008	2009	2010	March 2012
Price (US)	< $2	> $35	~$10	Max $25	+$98	+$130	>$140	+$70	+$100

Source: Morales Pedraza (2008).

From Table 23, the following can be stated: Oil price went up from US $2 per barrel in 1900 to up to a maximum of US $150 per barrel in July 2008; an increase of US $138 per barrel. During the first seventy years the oil price stayed below US $2 per barrel; between 1979 and 1981, the oil price per barrel was above US $35; in 1985, oil price collapsed reaching around US $10 per barrel; in the 1990s, oil price went up to a maximum of US $25. During the first semester of 2008, the oil price reached US $140 per barrel. In July 2008, the oil price reached its peak of US $150 per barrel. Prices then plummeted to as low as US $35 per barrel in December 2008 and rose again in January 2009 to almost US $50 per barrel. In November of 2010, the oil price jumped again to around US $90 per barrel and reached US $100 or more per barrel by the end of March 2012. According to Annual Energy Outlook (2012), it is expected that oil prices could increase up to US $ 200 by 2035.

The oil price level of US $50 per barrel was still nearly double the long-term average oil price in real terms, and is 30% of the July 2008 peak price level but still below the US $60 per barrel threshold that many large oil producers, like Venezuela, use as their national budget reference price. With world's oil prices projected to return to relatively high levels, US $130 per barrel (in real 2007 dollars) in 2030, oil is the only energy source for power generation that does not grow on a worldwide basis.

Most nations are expected to respond to high oil prices by reducing the use of oil for electricity generation, opting instead for more economical sources of electricity, including coal, gas, and renewable energy sources. Although the recent decline in world's oil prices has forestalled the retreat from oil-fired generation in the near-term, nations turn to alternative fuels for their power sources as oil prices rebound. From 2006 to 2015, oil-fired power plant generation is estimate to growth by 0.7% per year; thereafter, world's oil price is expected to increase to above US $100 per barrel in 2012. The electricity generation from oil is expected to falls by an average of 0.5% per year after 2015. All Latin American and the Caribbean economies are being intensely affected by the current financial and economic crisis. Energy prices have been increased again during 2011 and the first part of 2012, after fallen during 2010. The current recession has dried up investment funds for new energy ventures, and pushed energy security and climate change as policy priorities for several countries. Furthermore, as lower prices during 2010 provoked intense budgetary pressures in producer economies, and, for this reason, the international political subsidization of energy imports in poorer countries become more and more difficult to sustain, with implications both positive and negative, particularly in those countries with an increase economic vulnerability of the poor and deepening energy poverty (Isbell, 2009).

INVESTMENT IN THE OIL SECTOR

In Latin American and the Caribbean region there are two clearly define polices and trends with regards the control of the energy sector, particularly oil. One trend is towards rising State control of energy resources. This trend is clearly visible in Venezuela, Argentina, Brazil, Bolivia, and Ecuador. In the case of Venezuela, the government and parliament approved a hydrocarbons law that mandated a 51% share by the national oil company and a higher royalty rate. In Ecuador, the government seeks to increase windfall revenues from 30% to 50%, and to renegotiate production-sharing contracts, while still embroiled in disputes over company claims for refunds of value added tax payments denied by the government. Argentina reversed a successful fiscal regime by imposing export taxes and other restrictions. Bolivia nationalized its energy industry increasing the royalty to be played by the private companies working in the energy sector.

The increase in the oil domestic production in several countries of the region has had a great impact on the reduction in oil imports in the past years. One of the major concern is the possibility that this trend could limit the growth of global supplies of oil by undermining the value of existing investments, discouraging future investment or barring foreign investment altogether, in addition to a poor government investment policy in the oil sector due to lack of sufficient financial resources available for this specific purpose. The economic consequence of this trend could be that the Latin American and the Caribbean region could contribute less to the diversification of oil supply, thereby increasing the importance of OPEC and other oil suppliers and, over time, undermining economic and social development in the region.

A second trend is toward creative fiscal regimes that welcome foreign investment requiring State-owned companies to compete with international companies, with independent regulators that promote fair and efficient regulation. Countries observing this model are increasing production or stalling the decline of existing reserves. Brazil, Colombia, Trinidad and Tobago, and Peru are key examples of countries where this trend is clearly visible (Lamm, 2009). In the specific case of Brazil, it can be single out for a remarkable change in its terms for welcoming foreign investment, which made Brazil one of the most desirable destinations for oil exploration in the Latin American and the Caribbean region in the past years[42]. Brazil aggressive oil production strategy increased domestic oil production over one million barrels per day over the past eleven years. In 1995, Brazil produced around 700 000 of barrels per day; in 2005, Brazil produced around 1 710 000 barrels per day, an increase of 242%; in 2009, the production was 2 572 000 barrels per day, an increase of 367% since 1995.

It is important to stress that in the past years, foreign investment in the oil sector is shifting away from South America to North America, particularly to Canada oil sands, effectively freezing development of the Hemisphere's largest oil reserves during one of the greatest oil booms in history. However, it is important to stick out the following: In the past two years, Chinese investments have financed energy projects and formed joint ventures in Venezuela, Brazil, and Ecuador with the aim of strengthening the energy sector in the region.

---

[42] According to Deutsche Montan Technologie GmbH, OLADE, and CIEMAT (2005), Brazil electricity demand will increase by 2.5 times from 2000 to 2030, growing at an average annual rate of 3.2%. To meet this big increase, the country will need to invest more than US $300 billion in the power sector, more than half in transmission and distribution networks.

In addition, China has leased a petroleum storage facility on St. Eustatius in the Netherland Antilles, the Dutch-speaking Caribbean islands. There have also been reports in the Caribbean and US press that China national oil corporation has been having talks with the Texas-based refining giant, Valero, about purchasing its refinery on Aruba, another Dutch island in the Caribbean.

OIL EXPLORATION

Current spending on exploration and new fossil fuel infrastructure in almost all countries in the Latin American and the Caribbean region are far below what is needed to meet anticipated energy demand for the coming years, according to most analysts. At the same time, in several countries there is a growing conflict between indigenous rights, environmental preservation, and oil mining, and this situation is reducing the possibilities to explore new areas for oil exploitation in these countries.

The most effective solution to the seeming conflict between indigenous rights, environmental preservation, and oil mining is to encourage responsible mining techniques, requiring oil companies to consult local populations to minimize the effects of mining in the region, and raising awareness with the public regarding the harmful effects of irresponsible mining. The technology required to mine responsibly already exists; it need only be utilized in the proper manner.

Governments can incentivize this form of mining through tax breaks and reduction in import and custom fees. Educated consumers must continue to put pressure on oil companies to behave in a socially responsible way by consulting with native populations and minimizing and environmentally adverse effect of oil mining.

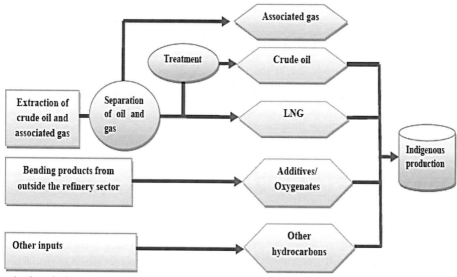

Source: Author design.

Figure 28. Simplified flow chart for indigenous oil production.

Ethical oil production is possible with a two-pronged approach by the government to educate oil consumers, and incentivizing environmentally sound oil drilling. Unethical oil mining damages the environment and threatens loss of an entire cultures, languages, and millennia of collective wisdom and history that can never be recovered or replaced (Lamm, 2009).

In Figure 28, a simplified flow chart for indigenous oil production can be easily seen. In the following paragraphs a brief description of the current situation of the oil sector in a selected group of countries and the possible future role to be played by this type of energy sources in these countries are presented.

ARGENTINA

Argentina is largely self-sufficient in crude oil but imports oil products. Relatively low levels of exploration activity, combined with natural declines from maturing oil fields, explain the gradual erosion of oil production from its peak reached in 1998.

Energy Reform

The Argentinean government began deregulating the oil industry in 1989, and today has one of the most deregulated oil and gas industry in the Latin American and the Caribbean region. Most public enterprises have been sold, and public procurement projects continue to be available as the country modernizes, rebuilds its social and transportation infrastructure, water and sewerage systems, and cooperates with formerly State-owned corporations in the fields of electricity, oil, gas, and telecommunications. Argentinean oil companies have been expanding into other Latin American markets to take advantage of opportunities there. During the 1990s, Argentina followed an energy policy based on three priorities:

1. Aggressive privatization, perhaps the most drastic seen in the region;
2. Strong deregulation that practically excludes the State from control of energy resources;
3. In concession contracts to private companies, rates were set in pesos[43], convertible to dollars at par with the peso.

The initial impact of these policies was that the sector grew at rates of 4.5% (oil) and 5.5% (gas). However, these successes hid serious weaknesses, since they were based on the over-exploitation of known reserves without any regulatory framework establishing obligations to invest in exploration, production, and transport. This seriously damaged the country's future supplies. With the crisis of 2002, convertibility came to an end and wellhead gas prices were partially frozen, creating a relatively major conflict between the oil companies and the government, which was accused of unilaterally breaking the rules of play.

Energy reform introduced a flurry of activity in the hydrocarbons sector. Domestic prices began to track international prices and restrictions on international trade in oil, gas, and

---

[43] Pesos is the country's national currency.

hydrocarbon products were lifted. The government realized almost US $10 billion from the break-up and privatization of the State-oil company YPF. Three refineries and miscellaneous assets belonging to YPF were sold, and what remained was divested through international public offerings. GdE was privatized as ten independent companies (two transmission and eight distribution systems), with restrictions on vertical integration. As a result of this energy reform, the private sector (excluding privatized YPF) controlled more than half the reserves and production of both natural gas and oil. More than 25 international oil and gas companies entered Argentina, increasing competition in oil and gas production and the refining and distribution of oil products. Labor productivity doubled as result of the privatization of the oil and gas industry. However, the impact of the whole privatization process in the economy was a disaster for Argentina, putting the country in the break of collapse.

The fiscal terms for Argentinean oil exploration include a tax on profits of 35%, and a 12% royalty on the value of oil production but this can vary by province according to contracts with operators. Oil is subject to export taxes that limit the profits that oil companies are able to generate from selling Argentinean production abroad. The Oil Plus Program aims to promote exploration and production by entitling firms to sell output from new and unconventional fields above prevailing prices.

Oil Production, Consumption, and Reserves

According to OGJ, Argentina had 2.59 billion barrels of proved oil reserves as of January 1, 2011, which represent around 0.2% of the world's total reserves. Strictly speaking, the country has been a net exporter of oil to date. From 1993 to 2003, Argentine crude oil exports accounted for 11.5% of the country's total exports. However, oil production in Argentina is not growing to meet domestic demand, meaning that oil's contribution to the trade balance will continue to decline in the coming years. The major oil reserves are located in the Gulf San Jorge Basin (predominantly Chubut and Santa Cruz provinces) with over 60% of the country oil reserves followed by Neuquén Basin with 25%.

According to Lynch (2003), Argentina has identified 19 sedimentary basins containing oil; however, only five of these have seen any production. These are the Neuquen (Argentina most productive Basin), Gulf San Jorge, Cyana, Austral, and Northeast Basins. The Neuquen Basin has an estimated recoverable reserve of three billion barrels of oil, and holds nearly 50% of the country's total remaining hydrocarbon reserves (both oil and gas). The Basin has an extensive oil and gas pipeline network, with oil lines connected to export ports on the Atlantic and Pacific coasts, in addition to refineries localized in Buenos Aires province. The offshore continental shelf, which is relatively shallow, appears to be a promising site for future oil discoveries, given its large size (larger than the North Sea). There are important offshore oil reserves in area nears the Malvinas Islands (Falkland Islands for the UK) but they cannot be exploited by Argentina because of the dispute on sovereignty over the islands with the UK. Argentina and the UK signed an agreement in September 1995 to share economic benefits from oil exploration in a 7 000 square mile cooperation zone to the southwest of the islands, and Argentina agreed not to obstruct a licensing round by the Malvinas Islands in areas outside the cooperation zone. Under the agreement, a joint commission will oversee exploration and revenue sharing in the cooperation area. However, the timing and pace of development remains uncertain. In March 2010, the UK's government authorized the search for oil in the Malvinas Islands area, provoking a strong reaction from the Argentinean government. The UK's government action is putting again the unsolved dispute on the sovereignty of the islands back in the international agenda.

In May 2011, Repsol-YPF[44] discovered a new oil deposit in Loma de la Plata in the Neuquen province with an estimate of 150 million of barrels oil equivalent. This new deposit increased YPF oil reserves in 28% and the country oil reserves in 6%.

The largest oil and gas producer in Argentina is Repsol-YPF, now YPF afer the nationalization of the company in 2012. The next two largest oil producers in Argentina are Perez Company and Petrolera Argentina San Jorge[45]. Other companies looking to expand their presence in the upstream oil sector include Argentina's Pluspetro, Petrobras, and Pan American, a joint venture between BP Amoco, Bridas, Unocal, and Total-Fina-Elf. Based on EIA (2009) data, Argentina produced around 796 000 barrels per day and is the fourth largest hydrocarbon producing country in Latin America, behind Mexico (2.9 million barrels per day) Brazil (2.05 million barrels per day) and Venezuela (2.5 million barrels per day); it has the fifth largest reserves (2.587 billion barrels) in the region, after Venezuela (296.5 billion barrels), Brazil (12.8 billion barrels), Mexico (11.6 billion barrels) and Ecuador (7.2 billion barrels per day).

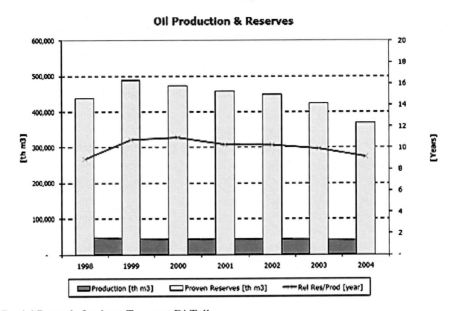

Source: Daniel Perczyk, Instituto Torcuato Di Tella.

Figure 29. Oil production and reserves in Argentina.

From Figure 29, the following can be stated: Oil production and reserves are declining since 2000, and it is expected that in the medium-term Argentina will be an oil net importer. It is important to know that over the past five years it have not been invested to a large extent

---

[44] In April 2012, the Argentinean government sent a draft bill to the Congress for the nationalization of the Repsol-YPF company.
[45] Petrolera Argentina San Jorge was acquired by Chevron in 1999.

in hydrocarbon exploration, and nowadays remaining proven oil reserves would last for 10 years at today's production levels.

The country produced an estimated 804 000 barrels per day in 2006, which is 1% higher than the production of 2009; of this amount, 663 000 barrels per day was crude oil (82% of the total produced in that year), the rest consisting of lease condensates, natural gas liquids, and refinery gain. Argentina's oil production has declined from a peak of 916 000 barrels per day reached in 1998 to 794 470 barrels per day in 2009, a reduction of 13% for the whole period (1.2% annual). The reason of this decline is that oil producers have not brought enough new capacity online to replace declining production from mature oil fields. However, it is important to note that the rate of the decline in production has eased in recent years.

Argentina consumed an estimated 470 000 barrels per day of oil in 2006, leaving net oil exports of 334 000 barrels per day. In 2008, the country consumed 594 000 barrels per day and, in 2009, a total of 580 000 barrels per day, an increase of 23% for the whole period 2006-2009 (7.3% per year). The bulk of the country's oil exports go to Brazil's central-east coast.

Table 24. Argentina oil information (Thousand barrels per day)

	Argentina 2008	Central and South America	World	Rank	Argentina 2009
Total oil production	782.03	7 411	85 509	24	794.47
Crude oil production	661.05	6 281	73 670	25	653.93
Consumption	594.00	6 091	85 234	28	580.00
Net export/imports(-)	188.03	1 320	--	173	214.47
Refinery capacity	626	6 608	85 460	30	626
Proved reserves (Billion barrels)	2.59	110	1 330	30	2.59

Source: EIA and OGJ.

In December 2006, ENARSA, a State-owned company, launched a joint offshore exploration program with Repsol-YPF in the Cuenca Colorado Marina region, in order to increase the oil reserves of the country. It is important to know that oil accounts for 51.5% of Argentina primary energy supply.

Oil Export and Import

Argentina exported 188 030 barrels per day in 2008, and 214 470 barrels per day in 2009. In 2010, the country exported 35.8 million barrels of crude oil, an average of slightly less than 100 000 barrels per day, which was much lower that the level of oil exported in previous years. The United States and Chile each accounted for about one-third of exports, followed closely by China. Argentina is also exporting oil to Uruguay and Paraguay. Argentina exported to the United States in 2010 a total of 29 000 barrels per day of crude oil, and 5 000 barrels per day of petroleum products.

Outputs from Argentina's refinery capacity do not satisfy all internal fuel demand. As a result, Argentina imports significant volumes of finished products, including an average of 19 000 barrels per day from the United States in 2010.

Oil Refineries

According to OGJ, Argentina has ten refineries with a combined 627 075 barrels per day of crude oil refining capacity, nearly half of which is controlled by Repsol-YPF. The major refineries are Repsol-YPF's La Plata (189 000 barrels per day), Shell's Buenos Aires (110 000 barrels per day), Repsol-YPF's Lujan de Cuyo (105 500 barrels per day); and Esso's Campana (87 000 barrels per day). These refineries produce petroleum products primarily for the domestic market. Most of these refineries have been significantly upgraded over the past several years, mostly to meet new environmental standards and streamline operations but also to be able to produce lighter products and enhance octane as the country switches to unleaded gasoline.

However, despite the modernization of these refineries, most of them were optimized for lighter low-sulfur Argentinean crude oils and, for this reason, are unable to convert heavy crude oils economically.

Oil Pipelines

Argentina's three major crude oil pipelines all start at Puerto Hernandez in the Neuquen Basin. Two pipelines are domestic, transporting crude oil north to the Lujan de Cuyo refinery near Mendoza and east to Puerto Rosales on the Atlantic. The 429 km, 115 000 barrels per day Estenssoro-Pedrals pipeline (former Transandino pipeline), is Argentina only international oil pipeline, climbing over the Andes to a refinery in Chile. Argentina also supplies Paraguay and Uruguay with crude oil via tanker.

Energy Investment

In recent years, the situation of the energy sector in Argentina is worsening, and it urgently needs to be tackled through heavy investment in exploration and production projects. If Argentina's economy keeps on growing around 5% a year, then there will be a need to invest US $4.5 billion a year (2% of Argentina's GDP), in oil and gas exploration and production, according to the outcome of a study carried out by the Buenos Aires Technology Institute[46]. The purpose is to avoid an energy crisis that forced the government to ration gas and power supplies in the future. According to government sources, the country's shortages reflect a global energy crisis, and are a side effect of the country's strong economy, which expanded by more than 8% for a fifth-straight year in 2007[47]. However, analysts say that structural bottlenecks are the result of an energy rates freeze for residential users that the government adopted to protect Argentinean purchasing power amid the country's 2001-2002 financial meltdown. The rates freeze has deterred energy company investments. By means of comparison, the price of medium tension electricity in Argentina is about US $30 per MWh,

---

[46] Faced with rising electricity demand (over 6% annually) and declining reserve margins, the government of Argentina is in the process of commissioning large projects, both in the generation and transmission sectors. To keep up with rising demand, it is estimated that about 1 000 MW of new generation capacity are needed each year. An important number of these projects are being financed by the government through trust funds, while independent private initiative is still limited as it has not fully recovered yet from the effects of the Argentina's economic crisis.

[47] In 2008, the increase was 8.7%; in 2009 was 6.8%; and in 2010 was 0.90%.

while in Chile and Brazil exceeds US $100 per MWh, according to a study elaborated by energy and economic consultant Francisco Mezzadri. Overall, Argentina utility rates are some 50% below those seen in other nations, he said.

Finally, it is important to single out the following: The Argentina's government launched, in 2008, an ambitious offshore exploration project. The State-owned energy company, Enarsa, has announced plans to tender new deep-water offshore exploration contracts in the near future. In a move that could reverse recent declines in reserves, YPF announced a US $500 million five-year plan to survey the potential of uncharted oil and gas blocks that have not yet been assigned to other companies.

Electricity Generation

Up to December 2005, Argentina's electrical system was divided in two isolated systems: Wholesale electric market (MEM), covering the northern and central part of the country and Patagonia wholesale electric market system (MEMSP), covering the southern part of the country. In December 2005, it was commissioned a transmission line, linking Choele Choel and Puerto Madryn power plants. This project interconnects MEMSP and MEM with 354 km of 500 kV line.

It is important to know that private and State-owned companies carry out generation in a competitive, mostly liberalized electricity market, with 75% of total installed capacity in private hands. The share in public hands corresponds to nuclear generation and to the two bi-national hydro power plants Yacyretá (Argentina-Paraguay) and Salto Grande (Argentina-Uruguay). The generation sector is highly fragmented with more than ten large companies, all of them providing less than 15% of the system's total capacity. Power generators sell their electricity in the wholesale market.

On January 2006, it was signed a contract for the construction of the second step of the Patagonia interconnection, which will link Puerto Madryn in the Chubut province, with Pico Truncado in the Santa Cruz province. This line will allow increasing the interconnection between both systems.

According to Daneil Perczyk, the final step of this link is the line Pico Truncado-Rio Gallegos, both in the Santa Cruz province (264 km from Rio Turbio). Works began in 2006. This interconnection would allow installing new coal-fired power plants near Rio Turbio field (50 MW) and near Rio Gallegos (500 MW).

Argentina produced in 2007, according to EIA sources, a total of 109.51 billion kWh, which represented around 11% of the total regional electricity generation produced in that year, and around 1% of the total world's generation electricity. In 2008, the country produced 115.42 billion kWh, an increase of 5% respect to 2007. In 2010, the total electricity generated in the country reached 115.08 billion kWh, which is almost the same that the total electricity produced in 2008.

Argentina consumed in 2008, a total of 104.73 billion kWh, which represent 91% of the total electricity produced by the country in that year. The electricity generation capacity of Argentina in 2008 was 30 GWe. In 2008, the electricity distribution and transmission losses were 17 950 MWh, which represent 15.6% of the total electricity generated per hour in that year. In 2009, these losses dropped to 13%; this represents a reduction of 2.6% respect to 2008. This level of losses is lower than the regional average but higher, in 3%, to international standards. The electricity access of the Argentinean population in 2008 was 97% (100% access in the case of the urban population, and 70% access in rural area). A total of 1.1 million of Argentina's rural population have no access to electricity in 2008.

Table 25. Electricity generation in 2007 and 2008 (Billion kWh)

	Argentina 2007	Central and South America	World	Rank	Argentina 2008
Net generation	109.51	1 004	18 795	29	115.42
Net consumption	99.21	843	17 139	29	104.73
Installed capacity (GWe)	29.11	237	4 468	26	30

Note: In 2006, Argentina imported 3% of the total electricity consumed by the country in that year. Source: EIA.

Looking Forward

The newly published Argentina Power Report from BMI forecasts that, by 2013, the country will account for 10.25% of Latin American regional power generation. The BMI forecasts a growth in regional generation to 1 320 TWh by 2013, representing a rise of 16.9% respect to 2008.

Latin American thermal power generation in 2008 reached 453 TWh, accounting for 40% of the total electricity supplied in the region. The forecast for 2013 is 523 TWh, implying 15.5% growth, trimming the market share of thermal generation to 39.6% - in spite of environmental concerns that should be promoting renewables, hydroelectricity, and nuclear power. By 2013, the country is expected to account for 16.4% of thermal generation.

Between 2008 and 2018, BMI are forecasting an increase in Argentinean electricity generation of 24%, which is one of the lowest for the Latin American region for that period[48]. This equates to 14.6% in the period 2013-2018 up from 8.2% in the period 2008-2013; this represents an increase of 6.4%.

An anticipated increase of 27.1% in hydro power use during the period 2008-2018 is one key element of generation growth. Thermal power generation is forecast to rise by 19% between 2008 and 2018, with nuclear consumption set to increase by 66.7%.

It is important to know that among the challenges for the coming year regarding energy policy matters is the promotion of oil field development, given the disincentives the companies faced in previous years.

This decision involves either price increases in the internal market with the accompanying high social and political costs, or perhaps the State will again undertake important energy investment decisions. One of these decisions is the systematic reduction of the use of oil for electricity generation in the energy mix of the country in the coming years, and the increase use of hydrogen in the transport sector.

---

[48] Argentina is now ranked third in BMI's updated power sector Business Environment Ratings, remaining behind Chile in spite of its market size and low energy import dependency but overtaking Colombia.

With respect the environment, there is also the challenge of tackling industrial as well as urban air pollution through concrete programs, which will involve the design of power plans to encourage the use of clean or alternative energies for electricity generation, such as gas, nuclear energy, wind, and other renewable energy sources.

BOLIVIA

Petroleum had been known to exist in Bolivia since the colonial period but serious exploration did not begin until 1916. In that year, foreign firms probed for oil, marking the start of a long and sometimes bitter relationship between foreign oil companies and the Bolivian government.

Hydrocarbons, primarily natural gas, account for roughly 10% of Bolivia's gross domestic product, 30% of government revenues, and 40% of export earnings. The State-owned oil and private companies claimed to invest around US $800 million in Bolivia's hydrocarbon sector in 2010, an increase of over 30% from 2009 investment level.

Privatization of the Oil Sector

The government nationalized the oil industry for the first time from 1916 to 1920, denationalized it from 1920 to 1937, and nationalized it again in 1937 under the control of YPFB, where it remained until 1989. A revision of the country's petroleum code in 1952 allowed foreign companies to drill for Bolivian oil. Nevertheless, the only successful company, Bolivian Gulf a subsidiary of Gulf Oil, was nationalized in 1969 in an acrimonious dispute with the government. Two foreign firms, Occidental International and Tesoro Petroleum, held service contracts with YPFB in the late 1980s. Bolivia privatized again its oil sector in the mid-1990s. Formally YPFB divested most of its assets, though the company retained responsibility for negotiating and monitoring contracts with foreign oil companies. A regulatory authority over the oil sector was established under the control of the Hydrocarbons Superintendent.

Following the privatization process, foreign companies took control over the bulk of Bolivia's oil sector. The largest of such companies included Petrobras and Repsol-YPF.

Oil Production, Consumption, and Reserves

Oil production peaked in the early 1970s but declined throughout the rest of the decade and into the 1980s. Production dropped from 47 000 barrels per day in 1973 to only 21 000 barrels per day in 1988; this represents a reduction of 55%. This reduction is the result of price fluctuations, obsolete machinery, minimal exploration, YPFB mismanagement, and declining reserves, among others. As part of the new energy policy, the government divided YPFB into three autonomous subsidiaries in 1985, and reduced its payroll by one-third. One of YPFB's major goals was to accelerate oil exploration and improve its inadequate reserves-to-production ratio. Oil proven reserves were estimated at 470 million barrels in 2009.

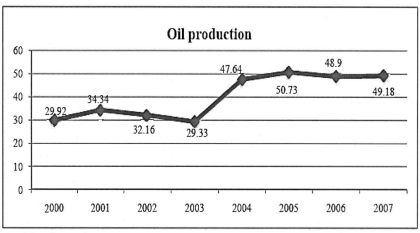

Source: Index Mundi.

Figure 30. Oil production in Bolivia during the period 2000-2010 (Thousand of barrels).

**Table 26. Bolivia's oil production, consumption and reserves in 2008 and 2009
(Thousand barrels per day)**

	Bolivia 2008	Central and South America 2008	World 2008	Rank 2008	Bolivia 2009
Total oil production	51.50	7 411	85 509	61	47.09
Crude oil production	38.88	6 281	73 670	57	35.90
Consumption	62.00	6 091	85 234	88	60.00
Net export/import (-)	-10.50	1 320	-	109	-12.91
Refinery capacity	41	6 608	85 460	88	41
Proved reserves (Billion barrels)	0.47	110	1 330	41	0.47

Source: EIA.

Historically, Bolivian oil consumption and production had been strongly correlated. Domestic production satisfied most of the country's demand, with a small surplus devoted to exports. From Figure 30, the following can be stated: After the low peak in the production of oil in 1988, the production increased to 29.92 thousand of barrels per day in 2000. In 2004, the oil production was 47.64 thousand barrels per day, an increase of 59.2% respect to 2000. The oil production in 2007was 49.18 thousand barrels per day, an increase of 3.1% respect 2004. However, following the sector's reorganization, oil production declined between 2007 and 2009, and Bolivia transitioned from the status of a net exporter to a net importer of oil. Bolivian oil production rebounded appreciably in 2010 but the level reached was 7% below the one reached in 1973. Statistics from the State-owned oil company suggest that increased production of natural gas liquids more than offset declines in crude oil production.

According to EIA estimates, Bolivia produced 47 090 barrels per day of oil (including crude oil, condensates, natural gas liquids, and refinery gain) during 2009, a decrease of 4.3% respect to 2007. Bolivia consumed about 60 000 barrels per day of oil in 2009.

From Table 26, the following can be stated: The production of oil in Bolivia increased from 29 920 barrels per day in 2000 to 50 730 barrels per day in 2005 an increase of 69.6%.

From 2006 to 2009, the oil production dropped from 48 900 barrels per day in 2006 to 47 090 barrels per day in 2009, a decrease of 3.8%. During the whole period, the oil production increase 57%. However, the level of the production of oil in 2010 (42 910 barrels per day) is 7% lower than the level reached in 1973.

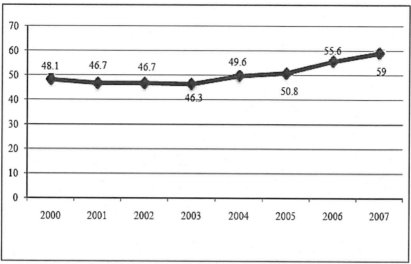

Source: Author compilation from different public sources.

Figure 31. Level of oil consumption in Bolivia during the period 2000-2007 (Thousand barrels per day).

From Figure 31, the following can be stated: Oil concumption in the country increased from 48 100 barrels per day in 2000 to 59 000 barrels per day in 2007 (22.7%).

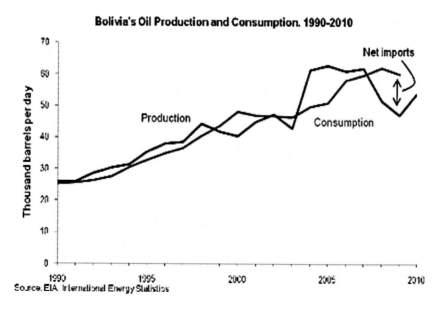

Figure 32. Bolivia's oil production and consumption during the period 1990-2010.

In order to satisfy the demand of different oil products, Bolivia imported 10 500 barrels per day in 2008, and 12 910 barrels per day in 2009, an increase of 23%.

From Figure 32, the following can be stated: The level of oil production since 2007 is below the level of consumption forcing the government to import oil from other countries in order to satisfy the demand. It is important to single out that during the period 1990-2010, oil production was sometimes above consumption (1992-1999, 2003-2007) and sometimes below (1999-2003, 2008-2010) and, for this reason, the government is adopting additional measures in order to increase oil production in the coming years.

Finally, according to official Bolivian statistics, more than half of the country's oil production is driven by two oil fields – Sabalo (36.6% of the total oil production) and San Alberto (20.6% of the total). Tarija, which claims those two fields, dominates liquids production (70% of the total), followed by the departments of Cochabamba (15% of the total), Santa Cruz (12% of the total), and Chuquisaca (3% of the total).

Oil Exploration

In the 1980s, oil exploration in Bolivia remained highly regulated by the government. For exploration purposes, the country was divided into four regions, three of which were higher risk areas; in the fourth region, reserves were unknown, YPFB had exclusive rights for exploration. The YPFB's region was located in southeastern Bolivia. YPFB, however, issued contracts for foreign oil companies to explore portions of its own select region. In September 1988, Occidental signed a thirty-year contract with YPFB for exploration and production in a 2.5 million-hectare area, encompassing the Madre de Dios and Lapachos regions of La Paz, Beni, and Pando departments.

Bolivia's known fossil fuel endowment is largely concentrated in southern and eastern departments, which have been controlled by opposition parties that demand greater autonomy from the federal government, partly in order to increase investment in and revenues from the hydrocarbon sector, and partly because of political dispute from the federal government. Seventy-five percent of Bolivia's oil was drilled in four Santa Cruz oil fields; La Peña, Monteagudo, Caranda, and Camiri, with the balance provided by fields in the departments of Chuquisaca and Tarija. A major oil field, Vuelta Grande, began production in 1989, providing upwards of 5 500 barrels per day[49].

During April 2005, Bolivia's government submitted seventy six exploration and production contracts signed with oil companies since 1997 to be either ratified or rejected by Congress. The government announced that none of the contracts had been signed by the government and were therefore subject to congressional approval. The contracts were to be reviewed under the terms of the new hydrocarbons bill. Bolivia's constitutional court ruled on April 7, 2005, that Congress must approve all oil production contracts signed in the country, even though contracts had been signed in the past few years without Congress' approval.

The private company Transredes currently own and operates 2 700 km of liquids pipelines. However, in line with the Bolivia's nationalization plan started in 2006, YPFB will seek to become the majority partner in all projects originating in Bolivia. The government approved plans for the construction of new thermoelectric generation power plants for export

---

[49] It is important to stress that most oil fields had large reserves of associated natural gas.

of electricity in the 2000s. Thus, in July 2003, for example, the Spain company Red Electrica[50] announced a project for constructing a transmission line to link La Paz, Bolivia and Puno, Peru. This project seeks to provide cheaper energy to that part of Peru. In September 2003, a Brazilian company, Furnas, announced that together with Pan American Energy, is studying the development of a megaproject for the construction of a 2 000 MW thermoelectric power plant, and the construction of a 1 500 km transmission line that would link Bolivia and Brazil.

Investment in the Oil Sector

The Bolivia's government, through YPFB and the Hydrocarbons Vice Ministry, completed the auction process of three new oil licenses in the country through two separate oil licensing rounds, according to a statement made by general advisor to YPFB's Vice-presidency of international business and contracts Alberto Palacios. Bolivian oil company Petrogas presented an offer for the 490 000 ha Rio Beni exploration block in Beni, Pando, and La Paz departments. As the block is located in areas that have not been explored previously and is far from existing hydrocarbons infrastructure and oil pipelines, most exploration should take place through wildcat wells. Rio Beni consists of work commitments worth   US $3 million during the first three-year phase of a seven-year initial exploration period. Each work units equals roughly US $5,000 and gives the company freedom to decide what specific exploration works it will undertake, as long as it spends the amount of money pledged.

Bolivian oil company Matpetrol S.A. won the 7 500 ha Villamonte marginal oil production field in southern Tarija department after offering US $459,000. There are no working units or exploration commitments involved in this contract. Villamonte production is currently plugged, and has some areas and formations with potential for exploration activities.

The Hydrocarbons Vice Ministry awarded the Cobija exploration block in Pando department to the US Texas Victoria Oil Company Inc. Exploration commitments for Cobija block include the spending of US $4.5 million. Like Rio Beni, Cobija block has not been previously explored.

The government plans to unveil policies to encourage new investment and stimulate hydrocarbon exploration and production. There have been proposals to fully reimburse private producers for their exploration costs, if they find new reserves of oil or natural gas or increase the price paid to private firms for each barrel of oil produced. Foreign investment in the sector has stagnated as profit margins have narrowed and the international price of oil has diverged from the price that the Bolivian government is willing to offer.

Oil Refineries

The country has two major refineries, both located in Santa Cruz and Cochabamba departments, which produce a diverse range of petroleum products; two small oil refineries are also located in Santa Cruz department. The refineries entirely meet the country's demand for gasoline, kerosene, 55% of domestic diesel consumption, 20% of liquefied petroleum gas

---

[50] The Spanish company was nationalized in April 2012.

consumption, and jet fuel. However, the country still must import some petroleum products, especially diesel, for a total of 12 910 barrels per day in 2009, due to a lack of suitable domestic refining capacity. According to the nationalization decree of May 2006, YPFB obtained a majority stake in these two refineries.

According to EIA sources, Bolivia's refining capacity is roughly equivalent to its current crude oil output. YPFB Refinación S.A. is the State-owned subsidiary that operates the country's two largest refineries. Nearly 60% of Bolivia's 2010 refinery output came from the Gualberto Villarroel refinery in Cochabamba, which has 25 000 barrels per day of crude oil refining capacity, according to *OGJ* sources. The Guillermo Elder Bell refinery in Santa Cruz processed over 15 000 barrels per day in 2010. YPFB has announced plans to boost capacity from 43 600 barrels per day to 57 000 barrels per day over the next few years. The government also reports output from two much smaller refineries in Santa Cruz, Oro Negro, and Parapetí refineries.

Oil Pipelines

The State-owned YPFB Transporte controls the majority of Bolivia's petroleum transportation network. It operates more than 2 000 km of pipelines – capable of carrying crude oil, condensate, natural gas liquids, and intermediate products – that connect centers of production with the departments of Cochabamba, Oruro, and La Paz.

Transredes, majority-owned by Shell and Prisma Energy, operates Bolivia's domestic oil transportation network. The 692 km northern system transports crude oil and condensates from Carrasco to the cities of Santa Cruz and Cochabamba. The 982 km southern system connects Yacuiba to Santa Cruz, carrying crude oil and LPG. The 499 km central system links Santa Cruz with Cochabamba. Transredes also operates a small, 18 000 barrels per day, crude oil pipeline between Cochabamba and Arica in Chile. The pipeline operates only occasionally. CLHB S.A. Nacionalizada, another component of the national oil company, operates a separate network of petroleum product pipelines that total about 1 500 km. An international oil pipeline connects the northwestern terminus of the domestic pipeline network with Arica. In the south, the YPFB Transporte network terminates at the border between Yacuiba in Bolivia and Pocitos in Argentina.

Electricity Generation

Currently, there are eight generation companies in the interconnected system, all of them privately owned. The three largest companies alone represent 70% of the total generation. The largest company serving the national interconnected system is the Bolivian Electricity Energy Company, which serves the region surrounding La Paz and is the biggest company in the sector. The other two are Guarachi Electricity Firm and Corani Electricity Firm.

Transmission in the national interconnected system is in the hands of just two companies Transportadora de Electricidad, previously owned by Spain's Red Electrica but nationalized in April 2012 by the government, and ISA Bolivia, which was created in 2005. ISA Bolivia, which runs 53% of the transmission network in Bolivia, is a subsidiary of Interconexión Eléctrica S.A., a corporation controlled by the government of Colombia. The entry in this sector is institutionally restricted. As for distribution, the six existing companies enjoy a geographic monopoly in their concession areas. The largest company is Electropaz, which is majority-owned by Spain's Iberdrola.

The electricity sector in Bolivia was privatized in the early 1990s and was unbundled into generation, transmission, and distribution. The electricity supply is dominated by thermal generation (60%), while hydro power (40%) has a smaller share in its generation mix compared to other South American countries. It is important to single out that the electricity coverage in rural areas in 2008 was among the lowest in the Latin American and the Caribbean region (see Table 13). For this reason, the current government is adopting specific measures to increase the current coverage. Without any doubt, this task represents a major challenge in the future and requires the joint efforts from both the public and private sectors.

Like in other countries of the region, Bolivia's electricity sector consists of national interconnected and off-grid systems. The national interconnected system connects major population centers and represents 83% of the installed capacity. The system provides electricity to the largest cities and operates in the departments of Cochabamba, Santa Cruz, Oruro, Potosí, and Chuquisaca[51]. Its grid covers the central and southern parts of the country. The population in the northern and western parts of the country remains largely unconnected to the national grid, either served by the off-grid system or having no access to electricity at all[52]. The off-grid system consists of numerous self-producers and independent power plants located in rural or isolated areas.

In 2008, the total installed capacity was 1.5 GW. Bolivia's electricity export and import activities are fairly limited. Imports from Brazil amount to less than 0.01 TW per year and have so far been devoted to supply the city of Puerto Suarez, in the department of Santa Cruz.

According to the World Bank, in 2010 the total electricity generation was 5 734 MWh; using oil as fuel the total electricity generation was 819 MWh; this represents 14% of the total electricity generation of that year. The electric power consumption per capita was 519 kWh. In 2010, electricity losses were 830 MWh, which is 14% of the total, a little bit higher that the recognized international acceptable electricity losses but lower than regional average.

In 2008, total access to electricity in Bolivia was 78%, one of the lowest in Latin American and the Caribbean region. Urban access was 98%, while rural access remained as low as 38%. Around 2.2 million of Bolivians have no access to electricity. To reduce this figure to the minimum possible in the coming years, the Bolivian government is implementing the "Living with Dignity" program, which aims to give access to the power service to all the urban areas till 2015 and to all the rural areas till 2025.

According to the demand projections prepared by the Bolivian competent authorities, the generation capacity reserve will fall below the recommended 10%, if no new capacity is developed in the coming years. Service quality as measured by interruptions was much better than the Latin American and the Caribbean average in 2005. In the period November 2004-October 2005, there were a total of 141 transmission interruptions (up from 86 transmission interruptions in the previous period), with a total duration of 71.2 hours. A total of 57% of the interruptions were due to weather conditions, while 17% derived from facility operations. In 2005, the average duration of interruptions per subscriber was five hours (the highest since 1998 although far below the fourteen hours average for Latin American and the Caribbean

---

[51] The departments of Beni, Pando, and Tarija and the eastern region of Santa Cruz are not integrated in the national interconnected system.
[52] In 2008, around 38% of the Bolivian population, 2.2 million people had no access to electricity.

region), while the average number of interruptions per subscriber per year was seven (the highest since 1995 but also below the 13% average for whole Latin American and the Caribbean region).

Looking Forward

One of the main elements of the new policy for the energy sector is the extension of the coverage of rural electrification by implementing alternative energy in rural areas and expanding electrical interconnection lines.

It is also planned to construct new thermoelectric generation plants for export of electricity and the construction of a transmission line to link La Paz, Bolivia and Puno, Peru. The objective of this project is to provide cheaper energy to that part of Peru. In September 2003, a Brazilian company, Furnas, announced that together with Pan American Energy is studying the development of a megaproject for the construction of a 2 000 MW thermoelectric plant and the construction of a transmission line that would link Bolivia and Brazil.

The Bolivian government plans to invest in nearly one GW of capacity additions, mostly hydro power by 2015. The government has expressed a desire to increase its reserve margin, or the cushion between available capacity and peak load from around 10% in order to enhance system reliability and minimize disruptions.

BRAZIL

Energy Reform

The first Brazilian oil law dates from 1938, when the National Petroleum Council (CNP) was created and oil and gas resources were declared the property of the federal government. The CNP regulated oil exploration and production, as well as imports, exports, transport, and distribution of oil and oil products within the country. In 1953, Brazil national oil company, Petrobras, was created as a monopoly for research, exploration, refining, and transport of oil and oil's products. It ranges from being a strategic instrument of the State within the global geopolitical context to performing as a modern, competitive, and integrated energy enterprise. As a policy arm of the government and a key element in its foreign policy, Petrobras has also been used by the government as a means to promote energy integration in Latin America, and especially in South America (Landau, 2007).

In 1975, foreign investment in oil exploration and production was allowed, but it did not materialize to any great extent, mainly owing to the country's adverse geology, the low quality of Brazilian oil, and economic uncertainties. In 1988, the Brazilian Constitution eliminated risk contracts. Finally, in 1995, the government began liberalizing the oil industry. A constitutional amendment authorized the government to deal with public or private companies to promote activities in oil research and exploration, oil refining and transport, and imports and exports of oil and oil's products. The National Petroleum Agency (ANP) was then created, whose functions included regulation, supervision, and control of the oil industry.

Its activities include improvement of market competition and protecting consumer interests as to price, supply, and quality of fuels.

In the 1997, a new oil law was signed, breaking the monopoly of Petrobras and of its regulatory role, which was turned over to the new national hydrocarbons agency. It also ended the State monopoly and opened the sector to private investment. Petrobras, in which the State has 30% ownership and 55% political rights, has shown itself to be extremely competitive and efficient. Under the new law, in addition to Petrobras, a total of forty two other companies have started operations in the Brazilian market, through concessions for oil exploration. Oil product prices were liberalized in January 2002. It is important to single out that since 2004 Petrobras has been buying exploration concessions in other countries in Africa, such as Equatorial Guinea, Nigeria, and Libya, and bought Shell distribution assets several countries in the Latin American region, such as Colombia, Paraguay, and Uruguay (Arriagada, 2006).

A major priority for Brazil in the energy sector is to satisfy growing energy demand fuelled by population and economic growth, and to balance this effort with environmental priorities, energy affordability, accessibility, security, and efficiency. For this reason, the energy policy now being implemented as well as the formulation of future policies, should be monitored and evaluated in the light of both sustainable development needs, and their effectiveness in ensuring efficient expansion of energy services without affecting the environment.

In Brazil, energy policy and policy frameworks for sustainable development focus on guaranteeing to the whole Brazilian population, universal access to energy, particularly electricity, encouraging energy efficiency, and the use of renewable energy sources for electricity generation. The aim of this policy is not only to satisfy the foreseable increase in the electricity demand but to reduce the CO_2 emissions.

The objectives in implementing a new institutional and regulatory framework in the energy sector in Brazil are the following:

a) Ensure a secure and reliable supply of electricity;
b) Encourage economic efficiency in all segments of the energy sector, notably through maximization of competition (where feasible), design of appropriate regulatory arrangements, and continuity of relevant system integrative functions;
c) Support further development of economic hydroelectric sites;
d) Create conditions that support continuation of the privatization program and make new investments attractive to the private sector, in particular through appropriate allocation of risks.

After the liberalization of the electricity market in 1995, a regulatory agency (ANEEL) was established in 1996 and a national transmission system operator was created two years later. ANEEL was created for oversees concessions, bids, and inspection of utilities services and competition for electricity system expansion, to solves conflicts between agents, and to establish power accessibility targets for each distribution utility. A wholesale electricity market was created in September 2000 and it was put under ANEEL authority in 2002. In 1996, the federal government regulated the status of two new players in the power generation system. These players are the following: Independent power producers and self-generating firms. As a result, the new model created three business segments in a semi-competitive framework:

a) Generation companies operating in an open marketplace, making both spot and contract sales to eligible customers (initially, distributors and heavy users);

b) Transmission companies guaranteeing open access and operating under a set tariff framework, allowing a regulated return on assets;

c) Distribution companies having both eligible customers (large energy intensive users that have permission to purchase electricity from their choice of power provider at a market price), and non-eligible customers (users that purchase from the distributor under regulated tariffs).

In addition to ANEEL, other two regulatory agents were created to oversee the operation of the power sector:

1. The Wholesale Energy Market[53], created in 1998, consisting of four distinct regions with system independent marginal costs and real time spot prices, aimed at free negotiation between players and the independent system operator (ISO). The ISO is the dispatch authority that prioritizes dispatch on a low marginal cost basis, and is in charge of coordination and control of the operation of interconnected systems. The ISO is a non-profit private organization including transmission utilities, international electricity traders, and eligible consumers;

2. Ministry of Mines and Energy (MME).

In this new model, the ISO controls the physical dispatch of the power system, according to the declared availability of each generator. The objective to be reached is the optimization in the use of hydro power resources in space (avoiding deleterious competition between hydro power plants) and time (considering the opportunity cost of using or stocking water).

ANEEL has had a primary role in promoting the construction of new transmission lines, having awarded contracts for a total of more than 10 782 km of lines since September 2000. Tractebel Energia became the biggest privately owned company in Brazil, with an installed capacity of more than 5 GW, following the acquisition of a former federal generator that was privatized (Electrosul). Several other foreign utilities (mainly US and European utilities) are also present in the Brazilian electricity market.

It is important to note that since the beginning of 2003, the government has been discussing a new model for the Brazilian power sector that will be driven by the following three main principles:

a) Electricity should be made available to all Brazilians;

b) The MME should ultimately be responsible for energy planning;

c) Assets from private investors or private-public partnerships will be managed by a new agent that, once created, will sign long-term contracts with power generators and final consumers.

---

[53] The Wholesale Energy Market is a non-profit private civil organization with compulsory members (power generators higher than 50 MW), and non-compulsory members (self-generators and co-generators not connected to the transmission electrical grid). It coordinates spot market operations according to the rules defined by ANEEL.

The government expects that investors who win long-term contracts will benefit from a captive market, and thus will have the incentive to accept this arrangement. There seems to be a gradual shift from the model built in the 1990s, based on an open market with third party access, to a variation of the "single buyer" model, in which a new single State agent is responsible for operating a single power pool, acting as a kind of trader between power producers and consumers (Tolmasquim et al., 2002).

According to Isbell (2009), Brazil biggest energy challenge will be to avoid the temptation to follow so many other oil and gas producers down the road of energy nationalism, particularly once oil prices begin to rise again in the future (as they most surely, eventually, will), in a risky and desperate attempt by the State to monopolize the country's rents from hydrocarbons. So far, the government pragmatism on economic policy, in general, and energy policy, in particular, suggest that Brazil will continue to the current policy already adopted. However, significant oil discoveries in the Santos and Campos Basins, together with the spike in oil prices in 2008, 2009, 2011, and 2012, have generated demands from certain quarters in Brazil to significantly alter the national hydrocarbons legislation, a development which would likely change the Brazilian policy on oil and gas production currently in force. Such demands are unlikely to thrive in the current low price environment, but should prices rise significantly again in the future, the Brazilian government will face intense pressure, not only to tighten fiscal conditions on oil production but also to limit foreign and private sector access to oil and gas, and possibly even to take over Petrobras altogether.

Finally, it is important to stress the following: According to EIA sources, the Brazilian government released the proposed regulatory framework for the pre-salt reserves in August 2009. The framework consists of four pieces of legislation. The first two laws were signed in July 2010. The first law creates a new agency, Petrosal, to administer new pre-salt production. The second allowed the government to capitalize Petrobras by granting the company five billion barrels of unlicensed pre-salt oil reserves in exchange for larger ownership share. The other two bills, establishing a new development fund to manage government revenues from pre-salt oil and laying out a new production sharing agreement system for pre-salt reserves, passed through the Congress in December of 2010. In contrast to the earlier concession-based framework, Petrobras will be the sole operator of each production sharing agreement and would hold a minimum 30% stake in all pre-salt projects.

The Brazilian Energy System

The Brazilian energy system has been characterized by a rapid increase in energy demand, particularly electricity, and an accelerated switch from traditional non-commercial fuels to indigenous commercial fuels and electricity. The emphasis on indigenous energy sources started in the late 1970s and early 1980s, as a result of policies designed to replace high cost oil imports. The recent discovering of new oil reserves will reduce significantly the dependence of the country of the import of oil, which cover around 25% of the country energy needs. It is expected that due to the new oil reserves discovered, the country will not need to import oil for domestic consumption in the future.

Technological innovation and policies encouraging domestic exploration and production of oil have led to a sharp decrease in oil imports and a rapid increase in oil reserves over the past two decades, with significant impacts on the energy dependence and security of the country. The reduction in oil imports resulted from technological innovations not only in oil exploration but also in ethanol production, in which Brazil is a world's leader. In the past years, oil and oil's products are reducing their share in the total primary energy balance, while natural gas and coal are increasing their share. Technological innovation and policies have also helped to improve, to a certain extent, the diversity of fuels in energy use.

In January 2007, according to MEM sources, the number of oil power plants operating in the country was 568 with an installed capacity of 4 446 MW, which represent 4.4% of the total. Other power plants operating in the country are shown in Table 27.

Table 27. Number of power plants operating in Brazil in 2007

Source	Number of power plants	Installed capacity (MW)	% Total
Hydroelectricity	633	73 678	72.1%
Gas	101	10 798	10.6%
Oil	568	4 446	4.4%
Biomass	269	3 693	3.6%
Nuclear	2	2 007	2%
Coal	7	1 415	1.4%
Wind	15	237	0.2%
Total	1 595	96 294	94.3%

Source: MEM.

Main Energy Programs

To ensure universal access to energy, particularly electricity, several programs have been adopted by the Brazilian government. These programs are the following: a) Energy Program for Small Communities (PRODEEM); and b) National Electricity Conservation Program (PROCEL). In addition to these two programs, in 1992, the Brazilian National Program for Rationalization of Oil Products and Natural Gas Use (CONPET) was established. These three programs have been promoted by the government and are well accepted by the Brazilian society. However, it is important to single out that until now they have yielded modest results, especially in the case of CONPET.

In addition to these programs, private participation in the development of the energy sector is increasing through the flourishing of energy service companies, particularly after the establishment of a compulsory federal program requiring investments by utilities in energy conservation at the clients' facilities.

Oil Reserves

According to *OGJ*, Brazil has 12.9 billion barrels of proven oil reserves in 2011, the second-largest in South America after Venezuela. The offshore Campos and Santos Basins, located off the southeast coast, hold the vast majority of Brazil's proven oil reserves[54].

---

[54] According to Ernst and Young, more than 93% of Brazil oil reserves are located offshore, while about 80% of the country natural gas reserves are offshore. The waters off the State of Rio de Janeiro (which include most of the

Brazil with 0.9% of world's oil reserves is the largest energy oil importer in the region. These imports meet merely one quarter of domestic needs; however, the remaining three-fourths come from domestic production. Recent deep-water discoveries have made further increased the ability of the country to quickly deliver affordable oil flows. The existence of these oil reserves augurs a brilliant future for the national petroleum industry.

Furthermore, as Petrobras has developed into a world-class petroleum company, discovering as much as 50 billion barrels of oil (along with large amounts of gas) in the country offshore zones and developing a niche as one of the world's leaders in ultra-deep water drilling, Brazil has also become one of the only countries in recent times to have moved from oil-import dependency to self-sufficiency, while maintaining a good chance of becoming a significant net oil exporter in the not-so-distant future.

Finally, it is important to stick out that exploration for oil and gas continues apace, and thus major new discoveries are possible, particularly in the Amazon region and offshore, increasing the current level of oil reserves of the country. In relative terms, oil reserves have increased faster in Brazil than in many other oil producing countries.

Oil Production, Consumption, Export, and Import

Domestic production of oil has grown rapidly between 10% and 11% annually since 1980. Notably, in the late 1990s the Marlim oilfield, discovered in the Campos Basin in 1984, became Brazil most important oil field, accounting for 35% of Brazil's total production and pushing up the domestic oil supply. The successful increase in oil production results from technological innovations developed by Petrobras through specific programs for oil exploration in ultra-deep-water fields.

It is important to stress that Brazil's oil production has risen steadily in recent years from 1.56 million barrels per day in 2003 to 2.055 million of barrels per day in 2010, according to EIA[55]; this represents an increase of 31.7% for the whole period. According to IEO (2010), the largest increase in non-OPEC total liquids production is expected for Brazil, with projected growth of 4.9 million barrels per day by 2035 from its 2007 level of 2.3 million barrels per day. Of that increase, 2.6 million barrels per day is attributed to conventional liquids production.

Based on its January 2011 Short-Term Energy Outlook, EIA forecasts Brazilian oil production to reach three million barrels per day in 2012. Brazil liquids consumption averaged 2.52 million barrels per day in 2009, more than the production of oil in that year. However, and according to different expert's evaluation, Brazil will become a net oil exporter of crude oil in the decade 2010-2019.

From Figure 33, the following can be stated: Brazil oil production increased during the period 2003-2010 from 1.5 million barrels per day in 2003 to a little more than two million barrels per day in 2010, an increase of 33%.

---

prolific Campos and Santos Basins) account for about 80% of Brazil's oil reserves and about 45% of the country natural gas reserves.
[55] According to Petroleo Brasileiro SA, the Brazilian oil production in 2010 was 2.004 million of barrels per day.

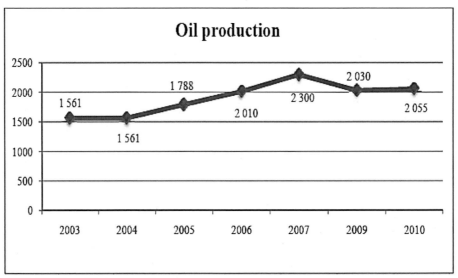

Source: EIA (2010) and Index Mundi.

Figure 33. Oil production in Brazil during the period 2003-2010.

Brazil is the only country in the Hemisphere that has significantly reduced not only its excessive dependence on external sources of fossil fuels but also its very dependence on fossil fuels themselves.

With respect to import dependence, Brazil has managed to reduce its overall imports at a rate of 2.6% per year. As a result of the expansion of the national domestic oil production, dependence on oil imports has decreased from 81% in 1980 to 47% in 1990 and to10% in 2002 (/STI/PUB/1247, 2006)[56]. Petrobras invested US $12 billion through the year 2010 in order to develop their oil industry, and increase oil production with the purpose of satisfying its energy needs and to eliminate the need to import oil in the near future.

The strong growth in Brazil oil production results, in part, from short- and mid-term increases at producing oil fields for which expansions are in progress. It also results, in part, from recent and expected discoveries in the Campos and Santos Basins, including the massive Tupi and related Guara and Iara discoveries, which both add to production in the mid- and long-term and suggest the presence of other large oil fields in the same formation. The vast size of the sub-salt potential in Brazil, as well as national economic strategy and industrialization goals, has led Brazil to pursue new petroleum legislation.

The legislative change most pertinent to production potential is the requirement that the State oil company, Petrobras, be the sole operator and a minimum 30% equity holder for all sub-salt fields. Although Petrobras has repeatedly proven itself a leader in deep-water development and is known to have the technical capabilities to develop sub-salt prospects, it is not expected to have the resources (financial, manpower, etc.) to develop its new oil reserves completely on its own. The different IEO (2010) price cases assume different investment terms offered by Brazil to foreign investors and hence different rates of sub-salt development.

---

[56] In 2011, the country does not imported oil to satisfy the domestic energy needs.

Finally, it is important to single out the following: Most Brazilian oil is produced in the southeastern region of the country, particularly in Rio de Janeiro and Espírito Santo States. More than 90% national oil production is offshore in very deep-water and consists of mostly heavy crude oil. Five fields in the Campos Basin (Marlim, Marlim Sul, Marlim Leste, Roncador, and Barracuda) account for more than half of the national crude oil production. These Petrobras-operated fields each produce between 100 000 and 400 000 barrels per day. International oil companies also play a role in Brazilian oil production. Parque de Conchas oil field operated by Shell and Frade oil field operated by Chevron are expected to achieve production levels of 100 000 barrels per day and 68 000 barrels per day, respectively.

It is important to single out that a consortium of Petrobras, BG Group, and Petrogal, discovered the Tupi field in 2007, which contains substantial reserves that occur in a pre-salt zone 6 000 m below the ocean surface under a thick layer of salt. Following Tupi, numerous additional pre-salt finds were announced in the Santos Basin, such as Iracema, Carioca, Iara, Libra, Franco, and Guara. Additional pre-salt discoveries were also announced in the Campos and Espirito Santo Basins. Estimates for the total pre-salt resources vary. Some analysts place total extent of pre-salt recoverable oil and natural gas reserves at more than 50 billion barrels of oil equivalent. These pre-salt discoveries have triggered a reassessment of the Brazilian regulatory model and a restructuring of the government role in the oil industry, bringing uncertainty for investors seeking to efficiently exploit the opportunities. The Brazilian government is looking to:

a) Attract the international capital to fund the development of these complex resources;
b) Create a national development fund for infrastructure, education, housing, and social services;
c) Build a strong, technologically sophisticated domestic oilfield services industry.

According to EIA sources, the Tupi pilot project, which has a production capacity of 100 000 barrels per day, began operations in October 2010. In its 2010-2014 business plan, Petrobras plan to invest US $33 billion in pre-salt exploration and production activities to achieve an oil production target of close to four million barrels per day by 2020. More than a quarter of this target is to come from pre-salt oil. Brazil pre-salt announcements immediately transformed the nature and focus of Brazil oil sector, and the potential impact of the discoveries upon world's oil markets is vast. However, considerable challenges must still be overcome in order to bring these reserves to fruition. The difficulty of accessing oil reserves, considering both the large depths and pressures involved with pre-salt oil production, represent technical hurdles that must be overcome. Further, the scale of the proposed expansion in production will also stretch Petrobras exploration and production resources and national infrastructure.

According to Index Mundi, Brazilian oil consumption during the period 2000-2009 increased from 2 166 290 barrels per day in 2000 to 2 522 000 barrels per day in 2009; this represents an increase of 16% for the whole period (2% per year as average). Figure 34 shows the consumption of oil during the period considered.

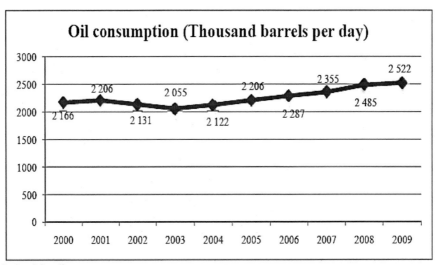

Source: Index Mundi.

Figure 34. Oil consumption in Brazil during the period 2000-2009.

From Figure 34, the following can be stated: Oil consumption increase from 2 166 000 barrels per day in 2000 to 2 522 000 barrels per day in 2009; this represents an increase of 16.4% for the whole period.

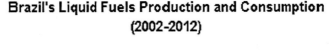

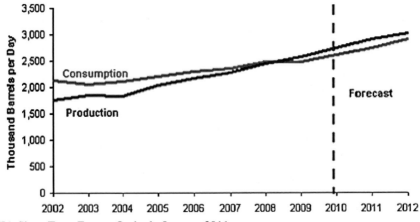

Source: EIA Short-Term Energy Outlook, January 2011.

Figure 35. Oil production and consumption in Brazil during the period 2002-2012.

From Figure 35, the following can be stated: Between 2002 and 2008, national oil production was not enough to satisfy the demand, forcing the government to import oil. After 2008, oil production has been higher than the level of consumption, leaving some amount of oil for export. It is foreseen that oil production will continue to growth, leaving an increase amount of oil for export.

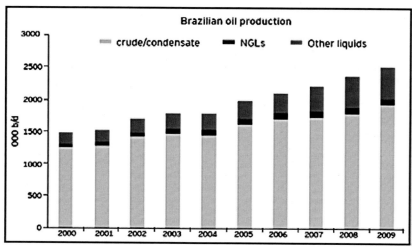

Source: EIA.

Figure 36. Brazilian oil production during the period 2000-2009.

Among its extremely ambitious plans, Brazil invested around US $56 billion from 2005 through 2010 in order to ensure the production of 3.4 billion barrels per day in the coming years in order to satisfy the foreseeable electricity demand. Brazil is also the third largest energy consumer in the Western Hemisphere, behind the USA and Canada, the 12th world's largest oil producer and the largest emitter of CO_2 in the region. While Brazilian exports of oil and its by-products may attain significant levels as of 2015, it is probable that, due to exponential growth of domestic demand, the surplus theoretically available for export or at least part of it would be consumed within the country itself. In the coming years, there will be an increase dependence on light oil refined abroad, since it cannot for the most part be processed in Brazilian refineries. The obvious solution would, therefore, seem to lie in energy integration, at least within the South American context. Brazil could exercise regional leadership towards energy integration but until today the result achieved are somehow limited, and indications are that in this respect the government will continue to adopt a conservative posture on this issue (Landau, 2007) and will be present in all regional energy integration process that could be promoted by countries of the region in the future.

It is important to stress that over the next twenty years domestic oil demand is expected to increase approximately 1.9% per year, with oil demand in 2020 expected to reach about 4 million barrels per day.

Oil Refineries

According to *OGJ*, Brazil has 1.9 million barrels per day of crude oil refining capacity, corresponding to 82% of national total primary capacity, spread amongst thirteen refineries, located in the south and southeast regions of the country. Only two refineries are not located in this region; a large refinery in Bahia State (Relam) and a small refinery for onshore production in the Urucu field in Amazonia (Reman). Petrobras operates eleven facilities, the largest being the 360 000 barrels per day Paulinia refinery in Sao Paulo.

The refining capacity in Brazil is relatively simple, meaning that the country must export some of its heavy crude oil production and import light crude oil; domestic crude oil constituted 79% of total domestic refinery feedstock in 2009. To meet burgeoning domestic demand, Petrobras plans to increase its Brazilian refining capacity to 3.2 million barrels per day by 2020. Under the company's 2010-2014 business plan, Petrobras will build five additional refineries to meet this goal. These facilities will be designed to process heavier grades of crude oil, increasing the share of Brazilian oil processed in these refineries to 91%.

In a joint venture PdVSA and Petrobras, a US $2.5 billion heavy oil refinery will be constructed in Pernambuco, Brazil. Petrobras will also participate in the exploration and production of super-heavy oil in the Orinoco Oil Belt in Venezuela.

With respect to the Brazilian refineries, it is important to note that domestic crude oils are mainly heavy and have a high acid content. Although the average oil refining efficiency has improved, increasing from 66% in 1980 to 73% in 2000, the production profile of national refinery park stock still includes almost 20% low value added products, especially residual fuel oils. Brazil Long Term Energy Plan for 2000–2022 envisages new refineries producing only up to 9% of heavy crude oil products and optimizing medium and low distillates (Tolmasquim et al., 2002).

Furthermore, the projected investment in existing Brazilian refineries for the next ten years, which is mostly focused on bottom of the barrel units (especially delayed coke and residual fluid catalytic cracking) and treatment units, is expected to reduce the average yield from heavy crude oil products from 23% in 2001 to 12% by 2011, while increasing the proportion of heavy acid Brazilian oils in the average refinery raw material input (Szklo et al., 2004).

Investment in the Oil Sector

Brazil has the ability to attract new capital to develop its oil fields. Unlike other countries, Brazil has a history of attracting new capital for oil development working with partners, and is not dependent on the oil industry for the bulk of its government revenues. This allows for greater reinvestment in the future. Higher reserves, high production, a greater focus on exports, and a politically popular and stable government, make Brazil an excellent trade partner.

According to World Energy Investment Outlook 2003, investment in power generation over the next thirty years should reach US $156 billion, most of which will go into the construction of 120 GW of new power plants. Development of Brazil transmission and distribution systems will require investment in the order of US $175 billion. Insufficient investment in the transmission and distribution network was one of the causes of the electricity crisis in 2001, and this will be one of the major challenges during the next thirty years.

The government policy designs and goals include the expansion of national heavy crude oil refining capacity. Petrobras invested around US $5.5 billion to increase its refining capacity to about 1.9 million barrels per day today, according to a plan approved by the government. Petrobras plans also to expand its oil and gas operations outside Brazil. In May

2003, Petrobras purchased an Argentinean company, Perez Company, and has gas and oil facilities and projects in other countries, including Bolivia[57], Cuba, and Venezuela.

It should be noted that the approved plans foresees investments by US $34 billion in exploration of new fields over the next years. In addition, Brazil will spend US $224 billion in five years on doubling its capacity for oil production and export despite cautious business optimism on the future global outlook for crude oil prices. State-run Petrobras unveiled the spending plans as Chief Executive Officer Sergio Gabrielli set out the company's strategy to build capacity in the run-up to 2020, when Brazil is expected to reach an oil production of four million barrels per day.

According to different experts' opinions, Brazil outlandish spending plans anchored Petrobras business strategy to a prevailing optimism that oil prices would remain between moderate to higher brackets in the foreseeable future, and would not fall so much as to discourage major investment. Skeptics in the industry believe all long-term and large investment in the oil industry remains high-risk, unless the spender feels comfortable about unloading today's cash for tomorrow's returns irrespective of inflation and other factors. On the other hands, Petrobras officials said 95% of the planned outlay would be spent within Brazil, a reference to national plans to limit the company's presence in joint venture projects abroad. Brazil discovered massive offshore oil fields, prompting the country to revise not only oil industry spending plans but also defense expenditure to beef up military protection for the offshore fields. Petrobras expects to raise US $58 billion through loans and equity sales to assume these new costs. A planned US $25 billion share offering this year would make it the biggest stock sale in the Western Hemisphere in at least a decade. Petrobras production targets do not include output from projects the company has not started yet, including the Franco oil field it plans to buy from the government in July with stock. The government said that it found 4.5 billion barrels of recoverable light oil at Franco, the largest discovery since Petrobras found Tupi oil field in 2007.

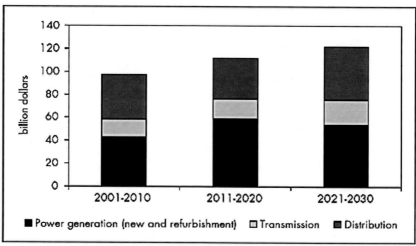

Source: Eletrobas.

Figure 37. Electricity sector investment in Brazil during the period 2001-2030.

---

[57] In Bolivia, the government nationalized in 2010 Petrobras' possession in the energy sector creating a difficult political situation with Brazil.

The corporation is also planning to raise its refining capacity to 3.2 million barrels a day by 2020 from about 1.9 million barrels a day at present, an increase of 68%. Brazil is looking to the rest of Latin America and beyond as potential markets for crude oil and oil refined products.

According to Figure 37, Brazil will invest around US $60 billion during the period 2001-2010 in new and refurbishment of power plants and around US $50 billion in transmission and distribution projects. More than US $120 billion are expected to be invested during the period 2021-2030 for the construction of new power plants, for the refurbishment of exiting power plants and in distribution and transmission projects.

The positive drivers of the Brazilian business dynamic going forward are Brazil political and economic stability, expected massive investments in local and national infrastructure, particularly in oil and gas, and huge partnership/supplier opportunities. However, as noted by IHS Global Insight, as well as other analysts, there are some potential pitfalls. These are:

1. *Recent successful share offering but with greater State ownership.* The recent successful share offering gives Petrobras the necessary funding for the first phase of its aggressive development plan. In addition, the rights offer adds substantial acreage and potential reserves to the asset base, adds to long-term production growth and increases the company's operational flexibility by broadening its development options. However, in the recent share offering, the government bought almost two-thirds of the shares. As a result, the Brazilian government now directly or indirectly controls 64% of all Petrobras common shares and about 48% of all shares, including preferred shares. The free float of Petrobras shares is now down to about 52%, as opposed to 60% before the share offering;

2. *Political stability and geopolitics.* The positive business implications of the political stability of the Lula years and the prospects of political continuity with his successor, Dilma Rousseff, will likely offset any worries that foreign policy objectives and/or ideology could be detrimental to or conflict with commercial objectives. Similarly, the government has pledged to use the new oil revenues for the public good;

3. *Tax and regulatory structure.* The current fiscal structure, which applies to existing discoveries, is a tax/royalty regime. The regime operates through three mechanisms:
    a) A flat royalty, typically of 10%;
    b) A special participation tax, which is a sliding scale levy set with reference to field location, field vintage, and field production;
    c) A corporation tax levied at 34%.
   While the intention is that this regime will be ultimately superseded with a production sharing contract based system for newly licensed acreage, the system has yet to be passed into law and it does not appear that this will be applied to the resource that forms the transfer of rights;

4. *Local service, labor and infrastructure constraints.* There are existing bottlenecks in equipment and skilled personnel availability, which are not expanding in step with acreage and production growth targets. The high local content provisions of the rights offer (55% through 2016 and 65% through 2019) will further reduce the flexibility to import equipment and manpower. Importantly, existing rig tenders are running a year behind schedule and Petrobras implied drilling plan for the rights offer areas could lead to significant mid-term rig shortages;

5. *Investment requirements.* The scale of the required investment in national infrastructure is enormous, with estimates approaching almost US $1 trillion over the next ten years. Almost half of the required investment is expected to be dedicated to oil and gas, including exploration and development of the massive pre-salt resources, expansion and upgrading of the country's refining and petrochemical sector and expansion of the energy transportation and distribution infrastructure. The numerous large and complex projects will present huge opportunities for suppliers and partners. However, the potential cost and execution risks are large as well;

6. *Technical challenges, production logistics, and operational risks.* The best prospects lie in ultra-deep-water, essentially at the technology frontiers. The water depth challenges are further complicated by high pressures and low temperatures and by the difficulties in drilling through the thick salt layer and by the high CO_2 content in many of the reservoirs. In addition, there are gas monetization and transport issues, such as moving gas to shore rather than flaring, as well as issues with floating production storage and offloading unit logistics. Similarly, the recent spill in the Gulf of Mexico highlighted some of the risks in deep-water that will need to be mitigated through the implementation of operational best practices and leading incident response procedures.

Electricity Generation

Between 1990s and 2000s, electricity production in Brazil increased at an average annual rate of 4.6%, while installed capacity grew only by 3.1% per annum. As a consequence, reserve margins were low and the whole system became too dependent upon the annual rains. The energy crisis in 2001 was solved through a rationing program for a period of ten months, which had a profound negative effect on the electricity sector and the Brazilian economy in general. The crisis highlighted the need for Brazil to diversify the fuel mix in order to reduce the strong dependence on hydro power (Deutsche Montan Technologie GmbH, OLADE and CIEMAT, 2005).

Brazil has the largest electricity market in South America, with a power consumption that is more than double the combined consumption of Argentina, Bolivia, Chile, and Uruguay. Its installed capacity is comparable to that of Italy and the United Kingdom, although with a much larger transmission network.

The Brazilian power system is composed of two large interconnected systems. The first corresponds to the south, southeast, and middle-west regions and the second, to the northeast and part of the north region. Since December 1998, a 500 kV and a 1 000 MW, 1 000 km line interconnects these two systems. Only 3.4% of the country electricity production is located outside the SIN, in small isolated systems located mainly in the Amazonian region.

According to EIA sources, the country has in 2011 an installed electricity capacity of 100 GWh. In 2009 a total of 461 000 MWh was produced. The electricity consumption in 2009 was 421 000 MWh, which represent 91% of the total electricity generated in that year. The electricity distribution and transmission losses in 2009 were 71 285 MWh, representing around 15% of the total electricity generated in that year. Distribution and transmission losses in 2010 were around 16% of the total, which is below the distribution and transmission losses average for the Latin American and the Caribbean region, but 6% above international standards. Brazil is still a net importer of electricity, mostly from Argentina but import dependence is falling.

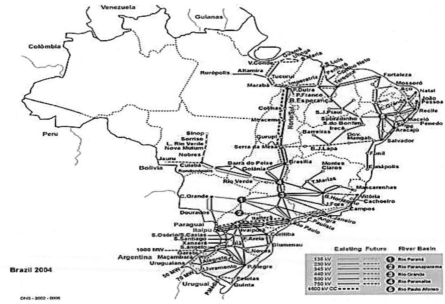

Source: CNS.

Figure 38. Brazil electrical grid in 2004.

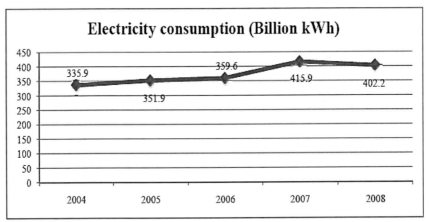

Source: EIA.

Figure 39. Electricity consumption in Brazil during the period 2004-2008.

From Figure 39, the following can be stated: The electricity consumption in Brazil during the period 2004-2008 increased from 335.9 billion kWh in 2004 to 402 billion kWh in 2008; this represents an increase of 20% for the whole period or 4% average per year. Electricity demand is expected to grow an average of 3.6% in the next few years, leading to total estimated consumption of 504 TWh and an average per capita consumption of 2 527 kWh.

In Brazil, capacity addition traditionally lagged behind demand growth. Electricity demand is expected to continue to grow at a quick pace. Between 1980 and 2000, electricity demand increased on average by 5.4% per year while GDP grew by 2.4% on average per year. Investment is, therefore, needed to boost generation and transmission capacity because there is limited excess supply, despite the reduction in demand following the energy rationing program implemented in 2001 in response to the energy crisis that affected the country.

Brazil is the country with one of the highest electricity access rate in Latin American and the Caribbean region. The power sector in Brazil serves more than fifty million customers, which corresponds to about 98% of the households, who have access to reliable electricity (100% in urban areas and 88% in rural areas in 2008). A total of 4.3 million of Brazilian have no access to electricity in 2008 (see Table 13).

Interruption frequency and duration are very close to the averages for the Latin American and the Caribbean region. In 2005, the average number of interruptions per subscriber was 12.5, while duration of interruptions per subscriber was 16.5 hours. The weighted averages for Latin American and the Caribbean as a whole were thirteen interruptions and fourteen hours, respectively.

In Brazil, large government-controlled companies dominate the electricity sector. Federally-owned Eletrobras holds about 40% of capacity (including 50% of the Itaipú dam), with State-companies CESP, CEMIG, and COPEL controlling 8%, 7%, and 5% of generation capacity respectively.

Currently, about 27% of the generation assets are in the hands of private investors. Considering the power plants under construction, as well as the concessions and licenses already granted by ANEEL, this figure is expected to grow up to 31% in the medium-term and to reach almost 44% over five or six years. Private capital participation in the generation business will likely represent 50% of the installed capacity in the years to come.

However, under the new sector regulatory model, there are about 40 transmission concessions in Brazil. Most of them are still controlled by the government, with subsidiaries under federal company Electrobras holding 69% of total transmission lines.

Looking Forward

The combination of vast untapped potential oil and natural gas resources with a favorable regulatory framework, positions Brazil as one of the most attractive oil country in the world today. A stable market-driven regulatory framework has been in place in Brazil for over ten years, resulting in the increased participation by global industry players in exploration and production activities.

As a result of recent major discoveries, oil and natural gas potential reserves in Brazil are now recognized as one of the largest in the region. Since 2002, over 9 billion boe have been discovered in more than fifty new oil and natural gas fields, according to Petrobras. Recent exploratory activities have led to the expansion of drilling activities in the Campos Basin, the opening of new frontiers, such as Espírito Santo and Santos Basins, as well as the discovery of highly promising accumulations in the pre-salt layer. According to BP Statistical Review of World Energy (2009), Brazil oil and natural gas reserves were among the fastest growing in the world between 1988 and 2008, increasing at a rate of 7.8% from 2.8 billion boe of proven reserves in 1988 to 12.6 billion boe of proven reserves at the end of 2008. In addition, daily oil and natural gas production in Brazil grew at a rate of 6.6%, from 1.033 million boe per day in 1998 to 1.9 million boe per day at the end of 2008. It is important to know that Brazil has 7.5 million km² of sedimentary areas across more than forty sedimentary basins, of which twenty nine are considered to be the main basins for oil and natural gas exploration and production activities.

Approximately 96% of these sedimentary areas are not yet subject to concession agreements. Industry experts have estimated the potential prospective resources yet to be discovered in Brazil to be between approximately 70-100 billion boe.

Finally, it is important to single out that there are several energy projects that are financed by the IDB and the World Bank in Brazil in order to enhance the energy sector. The main projects under implementation are the following:

1. *Inter- American Development Bank (IDB)*
   The IDB is supporting, since 2008, several projects and contributing to various technical assistance initiatives in the power sector in Brazil. The most relevant projects are:
   a) The Celpa Capital Investment Program: This Program aims to expand and improve distribution electrical system allowing the company to provide electricity to new customers, mostly in rural areas, allow productivity gains and reduce costs, and improve quality and reliability of its network distribution. The IDB supports this US $400 million project with a contribution of US $75 million loan;
   b) ATE III Transmission Project: In February 2008, the IDB approved a US $95.5 million loan for the ATE III Transmission Project, a US $402 million project for the development, construction, erection, commissioning, operation, and maintenance of approximately 459 km transmission lines from the State of Pará to the State of Tocantins.

2. *The World Bank*
   The World Bank, since 2008, is supporting three rural poverty reduction projects that include the provision of access to electricity services:
   a) *Rural Poverty Reduction Project in Pernambuco:* US $60 million loan (10% electricity component);
   b) *Rural Poverty Reduction Project in the State of Ceara:* US $50 million loan (10% electricity component);
   c) *Bahia State Integrated Project – Rural Poverty:* US $54.35 million (16% electricity component).

Colombia

The Energy Industry

The oil industry in Colombia has its origin in 1905, with the signature of two well knows concessions called "Barco" and "De Mares", and subsequently consolidated with the discovery and further development of the giant La Cira – Infantas field in 1918. The oil industry in Colombia can be characterized as follows:

a) *1918–1969:* Period of market forces and demand, where technological innovation and capital resources played an important role as engines of exploratory activity. In Colombia, the property of all underground resources belongs to the State. During this period several fields of over 200 million barrels of oil each were found, for an accumulated total of 4 182 million barrels of oil. Towards the end of this period, the State owned company Ecopetrol was founded (1951), as a result of the reversion of La Cira - Infantas concession, operated by an Exxon affiliate. Ecopetrol is the largest oil producer in the country, representing about one-third of total national production. Ecopetrol has a target to increase oil production above 800 000 barrels per day in a bid to maintain the country's self-sufficiency in oil in the near future, and to reach one million barrels per day in 2020. To reach this goal, Ecopetrol drilled 100 exploratory wells and spent US $3 billion on exploration and US $6.3 billion on development. Oil demand in Colombia is forecast to climb 3.8% per annum through 2020. The consumption of oil in Colombia during the period 2003-2009 is shown in Figure 43;

b) *1970–1994:* This was a period marked by nationalism and deregulation, when a new association contracts was established (1974); the State-take was increased under several consecutive contractual schemes, leading to an almost complete loss of competitiveness for the contract. This period was related to a number of important reserve discoveries (over 500 million barrels of oil per field), and intensive exploratory activity. The discovery of giant fields such as Chuchupa (1973), Caño Limón (1983), Cusiana (1988), and Cupiagua (1993) placed Colombia in the spotlight for the most important oil multinationals, despite the unfavorable contractual terms. Thereby a significant increase in exploratory activity took place. During this period, 5 169 million barrels of oil reserves were discovered, and fresh capital and technology became key contributions of foreign investors. The hydrocarbons sector was restructured and the National Hydrocarbons Agency was created in 2003. New contracting mechanisms were developed and the State-take reduced, creating favorable conditions to increase investment. Small companies and independent investors played a crucial role in exploratory activity in the country, particularly in the later years, as a result of high oil prices. Along these years, 631 million barrels of oil were discovered, mainly in small fields and particularly in the eastern plains basin (Los Llanos). The number and size of discoveries got smaller since 1993, with yearly discoveries lower than 100 million barrels and even to 50 million barrels of oil, recently. The most important discovery in this period was the Guando field in 2000, with reserves close to 100 million barrels of oil (Echeverry et al., 2008).

Energy Reform

Colombia has had a liberalized energy market since 1995. The structure of the Colombian energy market is based on Laws 142 (Public Services Law) and 143 (Electricity Law) of

1994. The Ministry of Mines and Energy is the leading institution in Colombia's energy sector. Within the Ministry, the Unit for Mining and Energy Planning is responsible for the study of future energy requirements and supply situations, as well as for drawing up the National Energy Plan and Expansion Plan. The purposes of both laws are:

a) Creation of a competitive market as a means to promote efficiency;
b) Promotion of private participation in order to strengthen competition and to incorporate other sources of capital;
c) Flexible operating and expansion planning by means of establishment of indicative planning to guide the decision making process;
d) Regulation of natural monopolies to prevent abuse against customers;
e) Rational rather than political procedures to set tariffs and an efficient subsidy allocation;
f) Re-structuring of utilities to introduce modern and sound management principles;
g) Granting budgetary, administrative, and financial autonomy to State owned utilities so that they can operate in a competitive environment;
h) Surveillance and control of market participants to ensure efficiency, quality, and continuity in the electricity service provision.

The Regulatory Commission for Gas and Energy (CREG) is in charge of regulating the market for the efficient supply of energy. It defines tariff structures for consumers and guarantees free network access, transmission charges, and standards for the wholesale market, guaranteeing the quality and reliability of the service and economic efficiency. Among others, CREG is responsible for providing regulations that ensure the rights of consumers, the inclusion of environmental and socially sustainable principles, improved coverage, and financial sustainability for participating entities.

The provision of public services (water, electricity, and telecommunications) to final users is supervised by the independent Superintendence for Residential Public Services.

Colombia has sixty six registered electricity producers. Private companies own 60% of the installed generation capacity and account for 43% (measured in number of consumers) to 49% (measured in kWh sales) of energy supplied to the interconnected grid. Just three companies control altogether 52% of total generation capacity.

Transmission in the national interconnected system is carried out by seven different public companies, four of which work exclusively in transmission. The remaining three are integrated companies that carry out all the activities in the electricity chain (i.e., generation, transmission, and distribution). The largest company is Interconexión Electrica S.A., which belongs to the government.

Currently, there are twenty eight commercializing companies, twenty two distribution and commercialization companies, eight companies that integrate generation, distribution and commercialization, and three companies fully integrated. The three largest players in commercialization are Union Fenosa (with Electrocosta and Electrocaribe), Endesa in Bogotá, and Empresas Públicas de Medellín[58].

In July 2002, the government signed a law revising its hydrocarbons royalty's scheme in a bid to attract more foreign investment in oil and gas exploration. The law cuts royalties on

---

[58] Medellin's Public Enterprises.

recent discoveries of oil fields producing less than 125 000 barrels per day to between 8% and 20% (depending on daily output) from the long-standing flat rate of 20%. To put this into context, only the country's largest fields, the Cusiana-Cupiagua fields[59], exceeds 125 000 barrels per day. The purpose of the revision is to better compensate foreign oil companies for the country's instability and risk of violence. The sliding royalties' formula is opposed by provinces with substantial oil reserves that depend heavily on revenue streams from oil fields.

Provinces keep 60% of the royalties with the rest going to Bogotá. The reforms have sparked a renewed interest in Colombia's upstream sector, with record levels of exploratory and development drilling.

Since the Uribe's Administration, the country is trying to reverse the decline of oil production through pro-business policies lowering the government share of taxes and royalties to 50%, and decreasing the share of exploration contracts in the hands of Ecopetrol to 30%.

In the hydrocarbons sector, the main objective of the energy policy adopted by the government is to increase oil reserves, since during the past years there have been no new oil discoveries and, for this reason, the reserves have dropped significantly.

This new policy permits the production period of partnership contracts with Ecopetrol to be extended, so that crude oil production can continue until the economic limit of the reservoir is reached and for contracts to give separate treatment block by block.

Through these measures, the government hopes to position Colombia as one of the most competitive countries within the region in terms of oil contracts. Other policy objectives include reducing the subsidies on gasoline, strengthening the fight against fuel contraband, completing the deregulation process for the liquid fuel chain in order to encourage new participants to become involved, as well as competition (Deutsche Montan Technologie GmbH, OLADE and CIEMAT, 2005).

The government took the decision of reforming Ecopetrol with the purpose of increasing their efficiency and productivity. Colombia transferred regulatory tasks to a new National Hydrocarbons Agency and announced, in July of 2006, that it would privatize 20% of Ecopetrol.

These measures are meant to bring about strong increases in exploration and production, as about 80% of Colombia has never been explored for oil. The principal regional partner in this effort is Petrobras, a leader in exploration and the fourth-largest producer in Colombia after Ecopetrol, British Gas, and Occidental (Arriagada, 2006).

Finally, it is important to stress the following: Much of Colombia's crude oil is lighter and sweeter than that of other major Latin American oil producers ranging between 28° and 36° API.

All oil production is undertaken by Ecopetrol in contracts of association with foreign companies. Ecopetrol is legally responsible for exploration, extraction, production, transportation, and marketing oil for export. Agencia Nacional de Hidrocarburos (Hydrocarbons National Agency) is the national regulatory agency.

---

[59] The largest field in the country is the Cusiana/Cupiagua complex operated by British Petroleum. The field has a combined reserve of 1.6 billion barrels of oil equivalent. The crude oil from that field is light sweet crude with 36.3° API gravity and 0.26% sulfur content.

Oil Reserves, Production, and Consumption

According to *OGJ*, Colombia had 1.9 billion barrels of proven crude oil reserves in 2011, the fifth-largest in South America[60]. These reserves are expected to increase with the exploration of several new blocks that were auctioned in 2010. Colombia has vast untapped oil potential reserves and its crude oil tends to be of a better quality than the oil from most of its Latin American neighbors, with its three export crude oils ranging from 20° to 36° API (Lynch, 2003a).

Taking into account the energy consumption of the country and its oil production it can be stated that Colombia, for the time being, does not depend of any other country to satisfy its energy needs. In Colombia, the State owns all hydrocarbon reserves. Government control is exercised in the oil and natural gas sectors through two State-own companies Ecopetrol and Ecogas[61].

The scarcity or moderate scenario entails a reserve rise of about 2.3 billion barrels. It would require discovery of one billion barrels; another 1.3 billion barrels would be drawn from better recovery from existing wells. Any potential increase in production relies on the results of recent and future exploration, and a number of enhanced oil recovery (special technology) projects, as well as the Llanos Heavy Crude Oil project. The Rubiales project also plans to raise output from 22 000 barrels per day in 2007, to 100 000 barrels per day by 2010, subject to the authorization of an ambitious upgrading project.

The government aims to raise oil reserves by 250 million barrels per year to a target of 4 billion barrels by 2020. That's twice as much as Colombia uses, so the country could resume substantial export of oil in the future. Such a dramatic rate of oil reserve increase is quite ambitious, given that, over the past decade, reserves rose only 40 billion barrels per year on average.

The National Hydrocarbons Agency calculates that investment of US $2 billion per year would be required to raise reserves to 4 billion barrels. This level of investment should be feasible at the current pace of foreign direct investment into the oil sector of the country. Foreign direct investment into the oil sector soared to US $3.5 billion in 2007, from less than US $2 billion in 2006, and it could reach US $5 billion in 2011 (Echeverry et al., 2008).

Colombia has been producing modest volumes of heavy oil, defined as having an API gravity of 22 degrees or less, since at least 1945, and has been producing lighter oil since 1921. Output has been erratic, largely due to the remote and difficult location in which much of the oil is located, both geographically and geologically. A pronounced peak in output in 1999 was due to a combination of just three light oil fields (Cano Limon, Cusiana, and Cupiaga in the Llanos Basin) all reaching maximum output at around the same time. No other light oil fields of this magnitude have ever been found, although over 200 smaller fields are also producing in the country.

---

60 The total of proven oil reserves in the country differ depending the sources used. According to EIA (2010), the total proven crude oil reserves in 2010 reached the figure of 1.36 billion of barrels. The production of oil in 2009 reached the amount of 680 000 barrels per day; the oil production in 2008 was 600 000 barrels per day. On the other hand, the total proven reserves of crude oil in Colombia are at 2.05 billion barrels, according to an independent evaluation presented by the Mines and Energy Ministry on May 2010. According to the Mines and Energy Ministry's Director of hydrocarbons, the total reserves, including proven, probable, and possible had reached 3.1 billion barrels.

61 Empresa Colombiana de Gas (Colombian Gas Company).

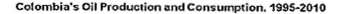

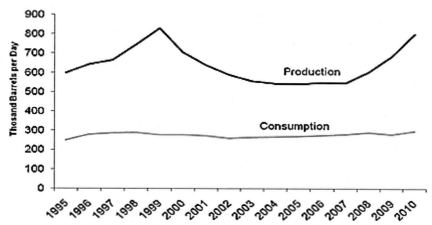

Source: U.S. Energy information Administration.

Figure 40. Oil production and consumption in Colombia during the period 1989-2009.

Oil is currently Colombia's leading export and source of foreign income, constituting a third of the country's foreign revenue. However, the production of oil since 1999 started to decline reaching a minimum in 2008. After that year, oil production increased significantly and this trend is expected to continue in the coming years. If this situation changes in the coming years, many observers believe that Colombia will lose its standing as an oil-exporting country by the beginning of the current decade. This is a critical issue for the country because oil sales from 1993 through 2003 accounted for over a quarter of overall exports (Arriagada, 2006). The main cause of the turn down has been natural declines at its existing oil fields and a lack of sizable new oil reserve discoveries.

As can be seen from Figure 40, the level of oil production is higher than the level of consumption during the period 1995-2010. According to Figure 40, the difference between the level of oil production and consumption after 2007 is widening again in a significant manner, as happened during the period 1995-1999, ensuring the satisfaction of any increase in the consumption of electricity that could occur in the coming years, without the need to invest important resources in the increase in the electricity generation capacity.

Table 28. Oil production in Colombia during 2008 and 2009

	Colombia 2008	Central and South America	World	Rank	Colombia 2009
Total oil production	602.67	7 411	85 591	28	685.82
Crude oil production	588.36	6 281	73 670	27	670.65
Consumption	288.00	6 091	85 234	43	279.00
Net export/import(-)	314.67	1 320	--	177	406.82
Refinery capacity	286	6 608	85 460	49	286
Proved reserves (Billion barrels)	1.51	110	1 330	34	1.36

Source: EIA.

Prior to 2008, Colombia's oil production had remained largely flat for several years, producing 530 000 barrels per day during 2003-2007 (see Figure 40). The country produced an estimated of 685 820 barrels per day of oil in 2009, up from around 602 670 barrels per day in 2008; this represents an increase of 14% (see Table 28). The peak in oil production was reached in 1999, when Colombia's oil production was 830 000 barrels per day.

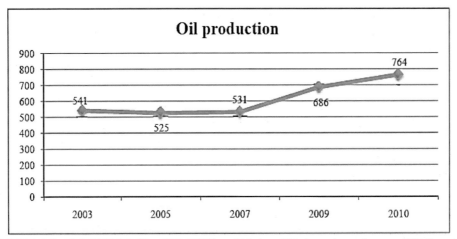

Source: Index Mundi, ECOPETROL, OGJ (2009) and National Hydrocarbons Agency (2010).

Figure 41. Oil production in Colombia during the period 2003-2010.

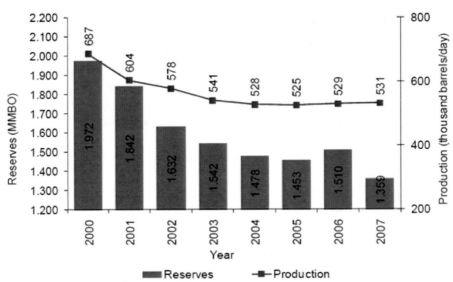

Source: ECOPETROL, Agencia Nacional de Hidrocarburos and other sources.

Figure 42. Crude oil production and reserves in Colombia during the period 2000 – 2007.

From Figure 42, the following can be stated: Oil reserves are declining from 1,972 billion barrels in 2000 to 1,359 billion barrels in 2007; this represents a reduction of 31% and this trend is expected to continue in the coming years. The oil production declined also in the same period from 687 000 barrels per day in 2000, to 531 000 barrels per day in 2007; this represents a reduction of 22% but after 2007 the oil production started to increase again from 531 000 barrels per day to 764 000 barrels per day in 2010; this represents an increase of 43.9%. After 2010, oil production continues to increase reaching more than 800 000 barrels per day.

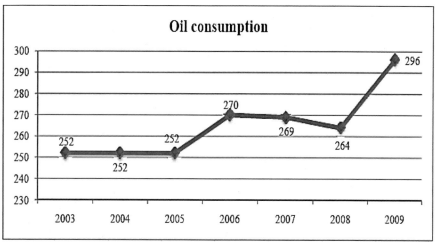

Source: Index Mundi and OGJ (2009).

Figure 43. Oil consumption in Colombia during the period 2003-2009.

Finally, it is important to stresss the following: Over the period 2004-2007, the average annual production levels have been maintained, efficiently confronting their natural decline, through aggressive programs to optimize mature fields production, mainly by Ecopetrol and its partners. However, during this period reserve replacement has been insufficient for maintaining the levels present at the beginning of the decade. This, in conjunction with the deficit created over the previous years, generates a worrying imbalance. Discovered reserves in 2007 amounted to 44 billion barrels, compared to an annual average of 320 billion barrels in the 1980s, and 109 billion barrels in the 1990s (Echeverry et al., 2008).

It is important to stress that the country produced 764 000 barrels per day of oil in 2010, up from 686 000 barrels per day in 2009, an increase of 10%[62]. EIA forecasts that Colombia's oil production will increase in the next two years: in the June 2011 edition of the Short Term Energy Outlook, EIA projects that Colombian oil production to rise to 910 000 barrels per day in 2011, and to surpass the one million barrel per day mark during the third quarter of 2012.

During the period 2003-2009, oil consumption increased from 252 000 barrels per day in 2003 to 264 000 barrels per day in 2008; this represents an increase of 5%. In 2009, the consumption was 296 000 barrels per day, leaving an important amount of oil for export[63].

---

[62] The National Hydrocarbons Agency reported that Colombian production reached 923 000 barrels per day in May 2011.

[63] About half of Colombia oil production is exported to the USA.

Oil Fields

According to government sources, there are eighteen sedimentary basins in Colombia, covering a total of 1 036 400 km^2 with about 200 200 km^2 under actual exploration and production activity. Only seven of these basins, 44% of the total, have so far entered into commercial oil and/or gas production. These are: the Upper, Middle, and Lower Magdalena Valleys, Llanos Orientales, Putumayo, Catatumbo, and Guajira Basins. The hydrocarbon resource potential of these seven basins is estimated to be 26 billion barrels of oil equivalent, while the potential of the remaining eleven basins is estimated to be 11 billion barrels of oil equivalent.

The discovery of the Guando oil field in June 2000, has given government officials reason for optimism of reaching their goal of continuing to be an oil exporter in the future. Guando oil field, located in the Upper Magdalena Basin 90 kilometers southwest of Bogotá, is the third largest oil field of the last twenty years in Colombia, and the largest since BP's discoveries at the Cusiana-Cupiagua oil fields in 1989. Proven oil reserves are 118 million barrels. The discovery was made by a joint venture between Canada's Nexen and Brazil's Petrobras.

According to EIA sources, the bulk of Colombia's crude oil production occurs in the Andes foothills and the eastern Amazonian jungles. Meta department, in central Colombia, is also becoming an important production area, predominately of heavy crude oil. The largest oil field in the country is the Rubiales field, located in that department. Low levels of production began at Rubiales oil field in the late 1980s but increasing investment and the completion of a new pipeline have allowed production rates to rise in recent years. Production at Rubiales oil field exceeded 100 000 barrels per day in December 2009, up from only 12 000 barrels per day in June 2007, an increase of 773%. According to the Colombian government, the Rubiales oil field could contain around 500 million barrels of oil. The crude oil produced at the Rubiales oil field is very heavy (below 15° API), so a diluent (such as naphtha) must be added to it in order for the crude oil to flow through pipelines.

Other large oil fields include Cupiagua/Cusiana, Cano Limon, Suroriente, and Guando. In the past, the Cusiana/Cupaigua complex and Cano Limon represented the bulk of Colombia's oil production but steep declines have reduced production at each to less than 50 000 barrels per day. In April 2004, Occidental extended its contract for Cano Limon investing US $263 million into the field over a period of six years. Other important oil fields in Colombia include the Suroriente field, operated by a consortium led by Petrotesting Colombia; the Guando field, operated by Petrobras and Nexen, and the Orito block, operated by Canada's Petrobank Energy and Resources.

Colombia has numerous, smaller oil fields spread throughout the oil-producing regions of the country. Vast unexplored and potentially hydrocarbon-rich territories remain in Colombia, which shares many of the geological features of its oil-rich neighbor Venezuela. During the past several years, some of the companies that signed exploration and production contracts with Ecopetrol include, Chile's Sipetrol, Colombian-based Argosy Energy International, Petrominerales, a subsidiary of Petrobank, Petrobras, Nexen, US-based Mercantile Oil and Gas, Occidental, and Russia's Lukoil.

There has also been renewed interest in Colombia's offshore basins. In 2005, BHP Billiton signed an agreement for exploratory drilling in the Fuerte Block off Colombia's

Caribbean coast. The government has also begun seismic studies of offshore blocks in the Pacific Ocean, which industry analysts believe could hold significant oil reserves.

In February 2002, meaningful discoveries were made in the Capachos and La Hocha oil fields that could add 250 million barrels of crude oil to Colombia's oil reserves. Capachos is situated 199 km east of Bogotá, in the Piedemonte region in the eastern province of Arauca, and is operated by Repsol-YPF, Total-Fina-Elf, and Ecopetrol. La Hocha is located 233 km south of Bogotá in the Upper Magdalena Valley region in the southern province of Huila, and is operated by Hucol, a Saudi-Colombian joint venture. Other recent discoveries include oil fields in the Casanare-Arauca area and near the upper River Magdalena, both with estimated reserves of 100 million barrels of oil each. Another promising basin is Putumayo, in southern Colombia, which Ecopetrol estimates could hold 2.4 billion barrels of oil. Exploration of the area faces daunting challenges as it is in the center of the country's cocoa cultivating region, an area contested by rebels on the right and left. Ecopetrol believes that the Llanos and Magdalena Basins have good prospects for oil exploration. The company is hoping that development of sixteen potential sites in the two basins will raise crude oil reserves by 2.8 billion barrels. The sites could hold between 200 million and 900 million barrels of crude oil each. The Niscota oil field in Piedemonte could hold reserves as high as 900 million barrels, and Ecopetrol believes the field could be producing 250 000 barrels per day by the end of 2011. However, in 2003, BP failed to find commercially-viable oil reserves in the Niscota block after spending US $45 million and drilling to 6 330 m.

Exploration is underway in the Upper Magdalena Valley. Several companies, including Petrobras and Hucol are drilling high-risk wells in the region.

Finally, in March 2003, Ecopetrol officials announced that they had discovered one of the largest oil deposits in over a decade, the Gibraltar-1 in the Siriri Block. They estimated that the area contained 200 million barrels of oil. However, following criticism of the study by industry analysts and government officials, Ecopetrol released a revised estimate of potential reserves in the Gibraltar-1 field in 2004 that showed that only 15 million barrels of oil could be the realistic figure.

Investment in the Oil Sector

Since 1999, Colombia's government has been adopting measures to make the investment climate more attractive to foreign oil companies in order to increase oil production. As result of these measures, Colombia has revived its once flailing energy sector over the course of the past decade, developing into one of Latin America's foremost destinations for investment, particularly in the oil and gas sector, and securing a steady supply of electricity for its growing population.

Most of the Colombian oil industry runs through joint ventures between Ecopetrol and foreign companies, some of which have heavily financed the construction of the current oil pipelines. Investment from these multinational corporations has led to the creation of the oil infrastructure that exists in Colombia today. BP-Amoco and Occidental Petroleum are two of the largest foreign companies in the Colombian oil sector. BP-Amoco, which has invested about US $3 billion in Colombia to date, operates the Cusiana-Cupiagua oil fields (source of nearly half of Colombia's production) on behalf of a group of companies that includes Ecopetrol (50% interest), BP-Amoco (19%), Total (19%), and Triton (12%). Regrettably, output from the Cusiana/Cupiagua oil fields has been dropping from a peak of 440 000 barrels per day reached in 1999. The Cano-Limon oil field, located in Colombia's eastern plains, is the second leading oil field but is also in decline. The crude oil from this field is also of high quality, with an API gravity of 29.5°. Occidental Petroleum has a 35% working interest in the Cano-Limon oil field.

According to the Colombian government, investment in Colombia's booming oil and mining sectors is expected to jump from US $62 billion between 2008 and 2015 from a previous estimate of US $50 billion; this represents an increase of 24%. Latin America's No. 5 oil producer[64], and the world's 26th exporter, has seen an influx of US dollars from energy firms hungry to snap up resources in the Andean nation, where there has been a dramatic fall in rebel violence. "Between 2008 and 2015, investment could rise to US $54 billion in the petroleum sector and US $8 billion in the mining sector," according to National Planning Department sources[65]. "The investment in exploration will allow a sustained rise in hydrocarbon production that could reach 1.5 million barrels per day from 2018 going forward." Colombia's average oil production rose 29% in 2009, producing 685 820 barrels per day (531 000 barrels per day the year before). The country has produced an average of 764 000 barrels per day in 2010, an increase of 17%, according to the information provided by the National Hydrocarbons Agency. Colombia will auction more than two hundred oil blocks in order to double crude oil reserves during the coming years.

Ecopetrol has begun efforts to expand refining capacity in the country. The company approved a US $3.8 billion expansion of the Cartagena refinery in late 2009, which would increase capacity to 165 000 barrels per day and improve the quality of produced refined products. Ecopetrol is also embarking on an expansion plan at the Barrancabermeja plant of US $1 billion, which would increase its capacity to 300 000 barrels per day and improve the refinery's ability to process heavier crude oils.

Changes to laws related to hydrocarbons exploration since 2000 have helped Colombia secure more exploration contracts with foreign companies. Ecopetrol has signed seventy seven exploration contracts between 1999 and August 2002 only. In August 2002, Argosy Energy International became the first company to sign a contract under the so-called "Adjacent Prospects Contract Model" adopted by Ecopetrol to provide greater incentives for oil exploration, and has been awarded rights to a 20 000-hectare area called "the Guayuyaco prospect", in Putumayo. This type of contract structure grants Argosy a 70% share of any discoveries (up from 35%), and cuts royalties from the current 20% to a sliding scale that starts with 8% for the first 5 000 barrels per day. Argosy places recoverable reserves for its block between 170 million barrels and 230 million barrels, of which between 60 million barrels and 90 million barrels are held in five areas that have already been identified using 2D and 3D seismic data, electric well logs, and production figures from nearby fields. The company drilled the first well in 2003. Argosy is also active in oil exploration in Colombia through its Santana and Río Magdalena contracts (Lynch, 2003a).

On the other hand, according to the Hydrocarbon National Agency, the number of exploration contracts awarded doubled between 2004 and 2009 and, in 2010, ninety five blocks - a 50% increase over the previous year - were licensed in the "Open Bid Round," which was dominated by Ecopetrol and small Colombia-focused independents, such as

---

[64] Mexico, Brazil, Venezuela, and Argentina are the first four producer countries in the region (2009-2010).

[65] Only in 2009 and 2010, the oil sector received US $2.95 billion and US $3.5 billion in foreign direct investment, respectively.

Pacific Rubiales, Gran Tierra, and Petrominerales. These smaller companies have been drawn by the country's attractive regulatory framework - despite the lack of large oil discoveries- and have managed to increase Colombia's total oil production by tapping many small fields. Several major international oil companies are also still operating in Colombia but their portion of total production is shrinking. The reasons of this lack of interesting of the large international companies in the oil sector in Colombia is that mostly small fields that have been discovered in Colombia in recent years often do not offer the scale of production and reserves that attracts these type of companies.

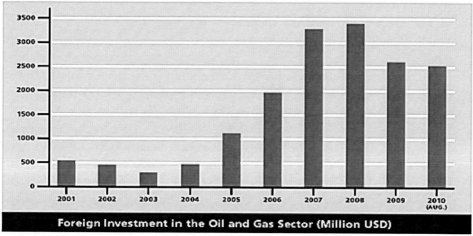

Source: Bank of the Republic of Colombia (Banco de la República de Colombia).

Figure 44. Foreign investment in the oil and gas sector in Colombia during the period 2001-2010.

From Figure 44, the following can be stated: During the period 2004-2008, there was an important increase in investment in the oil and gas sector in the country moving from around US500 million in 2004 to almost US $3,500 million in 2008, an increase of sevenfold. However, this trend changed in 2009. In the last two years the level of investment dropped to US $2,500; this represents a decrease of US $1,000 million in that period.

It is important to know that it will be very difficult to meet a volume close to the million barrels per day target hoped for by Ecopetrol for 2020 whilst oil production stay below 800 000 barrels per day. Furthermore, most of the new oil will be much heavier than that already being produced. Perhaps an oil production between 800 000 barrels per day and 850 000 barrels per day as a target for 2015 could be a more realistic goal, under the condition that the level of oil production increase each year in 18 000 barrels per day. The goal to produce one million barrels per day by 2020 could be a more realistic option, if the level of oil production follows an increase path during the period 2015-2020. To reach one million barrels per day in 2020, oil production need to increase, from the 2010 level of 764 000 barrels per day, a little more than 23 000 barrels per day as average.

In December 2009, Colombia's officials said that "foreign investment in its oil sector will surpass US $3.5 billion next year as the Andean country enjoys a "miniboom" that has made it Latin America's No. 5 oil producer." Foreign investment in Colombia's oil industry in 2009 was US $3.4 billion, led by Canadian companies, such as Pacific Rubiales, according to the National Hydrocarbons Agency.

In June 2010, Colombia conducted its latest oil sector bidding round, which included two hundert and twenty eight exploratory blocks. The round featured both known hydrocarbon-rich areas as well as frontier regions, such as offshore blocks in the Caribbean Sea and the Pacific Ocean. However, the National Hydrocarbons Agency only awarded seventy six total licenses in well-established areas in the round.

Additional key investments and recent announcements in Colombia's oil sector are briefly described in the following paragraphs:

a) Occidental Petroleum operates two fields with Ecopetrol. Last year it said it expected its total production to rise to 135 000 barrels per day by 2011, with La Cira Infantas oil field output climbing from 15 000 barrels per day to 50 000 barrels per day but said its Cano Limon oil field may struggle to remain steady at around 95 000 barrels per day;

b) Ecopetrol, Petrobras and Exxon-Mobil have said they are going to start drilling in 2010 in offshore blocks in the Caribbean as part of the US $400 million in investments companies are expected to pump in projects in the area;

c) Canada's Pacific Rubiales invested US $853 million in 2010, for the development its Rubiales and Quifa projects in Colombia's eastern plains. The company is now one of Colombia's major oil producers with output at 100 000 barrels per day;

d) APCO Oil and Gas International agreed to buy 50% interest in Colombia's Turpial Block for US $4.8 million. APCO will also buy 20% of Llanos 32 Exploration and Production Contract from TC Oil and Services;

e) Canada's Petrominerales Ltd, a unit of Petrobank Energy and Resources, has informed that one of its sites in Colombia was now producing 6 000 barrels per day and its A-2 site at the Corcel Block was now producing more than 10 000 barrels per day;

f) A unit of Indian energy firm Reliance Industries signed a deal with Ecopetrol for two offshore blocks in Colombia. Ecopetrol will take 20% stake in the Borojo North Block 42 and the Borojo South Block 43 with the Indian unit holding the rest;

g) Canadian firms Brownstone Ventures and Quetzal Energy Brownstone Ventures have entered into an agreement with Montecz SA and NCT EG Energy Group C.A. to participate in the Block LLA 27 in Colombia's eastern plains;

h) U.S. firm La Cortez Energy has signed a letter of intent to buy Avante Colombia, which has a 50% share in Rio de Oro and Puerto Barco exploration projects operated with Ecopetrol in the Catatumbo region;

i) Ecopetrol has signed an agreement with US Company Chicago Bridge and Iron as the leading contractor for a US $1.4 billion upgrade of the Cartagena refinery;

j) California-based Petro Vista Energy and New Horizon Energy recently announced they had begun drilling at La Maye block, the first of two exploration wells they plan to drill. New Horizon operates the block with Petro Vista owning 25% interest;

k) Canada's Alange Energy Corporation announced a US $20 million purchase of 19.27% more interest in Colombia's Cubiro production block, which has estimated reserves of 400 million barrels of crude oil.

Oil Refineries

There are five petroleum refineries in Colombia, four of which connect production fields to the Caribbean export terminal at Covenas, but two of them (Barrancabermeja and Cartagena) account for about 98% of all refining capacity. Ecopetrol is responsible for managing all aspects related to the petrochemicals industry, as well as management of the two Barrancabermeja and Cartagena refineries. A summary of Colombia's oil refineries is shown in Table 29.

Table 29. Colombia's oil refineries (2010)

Refinery	Location (Department)	Capacity (Barrels per day)
Barrancabermeja	Santander	205 000
Cartagena	Bolivar	80 000
Empresa Colombiana de Petróleos (Apiay)	Meta	2 250
Tibu	Norte de Santander	1 800
Orito	Putumayo	1 800
Total		285 850

Source: Ecopetrol.

According to *OGJ*, Colombia had 290 850 barrels per day of crude oil refining capacity in 2010. The largest of the five refineries, all owned by Ecopetrol, is the Barrancabermeja-Santander facility, with a capacity of 205 000 barrels per day. The second major refinery is Cartagena[66] with a refinery capacity of 80 000 barrels per day. In 2006, Switzerland's Glencore International and Ecopetrol launched an US $3.8 billion expansion of the Cartagena refinery. The project, scheduled for completion by 2010-2011, will increase output from 80 000 barrels per day to 165 000 barrels per day and upgrade the facility to produce refined products that meet higher specifications. Output from Cartagena refinery will go to meet domestic needs. Any excess production will be shipped to the Unites States and some Caribbean countries.

In 2008, Ecopetrol awarded a tender to Foster Wheeler company to upgrade the Barrancabermeja refinery, improving its ability to process heavy crude oil, increase its production of cleaner fuels, and expanding its distillation capacity to 300 000 barrels per day. Completion of a new cracking unit at the Barrancabermeja refinery will increase output of fuels by 30 000 barrels per day and liquefied petroleum gas by 10 000 barrels per day. The increased capacity will enable Colombia to meet domestic demand for transportation fuels (86 000 barrels per day) and liquefied petroleum gas (24 000 barrels per day) with output from the Barrancabermeja and Cartagena refineries.

---

[66] In May 2009, Ecopetrol assumed complete ownership of the Cartagena refinery after purchasing the stake formerly held by Glencore.

Oil Pipelines

Ecopetrol, in addition to its responsibility for exploring, extracting, processing, and marketing of oil, is also responsible for its transportation through Colombia's oil pipelines. Colombia possesses an extensive network of eight oil pipelines linking production areas to the main refineries and to shipping ports, all of them owned by Ecopetrol. The main pipelines are: Ocensa, Cano Limón, Alto Magdalena, Colombia Oil, TransAndino, Mariquita-Cali, Ballena-Barrancabermeja and Barrancabermeja-Neiva-Bogotá. In all, there are 6 881 km of oil pipelines.

The Caribbean port city of Coveñas, in the Córdoba department, is the terminus point for four of the eight major Colombia's oil pipelines. The 774 km Oleoducto Caño Limón-Coveñas transports oil from the oil fields in the eastern Arauca province via Zulia State in Venezuela to Coveñas for export, while the 757 km Oleoducto Ocensa, with a capacity of 615 000 barrels per day, transports oil to Coveñas from the Cusiana and Cupiagua oil fields in Casanare and Boyacá departments. Other major oil pipelines that feed oil toward Coveñas include the Oleoducto del Alto Magdalena, which runs north from Huila department along the Magdalena River valley, the Oleoducto Central de Los Llanos, which funnels oil from the basins of Casinare and Meta departments into the Oleoducto Ocensa (as well as supplying crude oil to the Apiay refinery), and the 481 km Oleoducto de Colombia, which parallels the Oleoducto Ocensa from the Magdalena valley to Coveñas. The other major pipeline, the TransAndino pipeline, serves to move Ecuadorian and Colombian oil from the Orito field in the Putumayo Basin to the Pacific port city of Tumaco in Nariño department. Ecopetrol operates the Oleoducto Caño-Limon Coveñas in partnership with US firm Occidental Petroleum and runs the Oleoducto Ocensa together with BP (Lynch 2003a).

Environmental Considerations

Colombia was one of the first Latin American countries to implement legislation requiring environmental impact assessments for implementing energy projects (Law 2811). Inderena, the first Colombian environmental protection agency, was responsible for administering the environmental impact assessments requirements. The Law required developers to prepare impact statements and environmental and ecological studies as a step to obtain environmental licenses. The purpose of licensing was to prepare an environmental plan that showcased activities aimed at mitigating environmental impact.

Between 1991 and 1993, Colombia's Department of Natural Planning appraised the effectiveness of the environmental impact assessments, and found that the existing regulations gave government officials too much discretion over the manner in which environmental impact assessments were conducted. Following the appraisal in 1993, the Colombian Congress phased out Inderena and created the Ministry of the Environment through Law 99. The Ministry of the Environment is now Colombia's highest environmental authority. The Law established a system of shared responsibility for environmental impact assessments. Law 99 requires an environmental license for the execution of projects and the establishment of industries or development activities that may cause natural resource or environmental damage. By 1997, the environmental license became the main regulatory mechanism in Colombia.

Electricity Generation

The electricity sector in Colombia is dominated by two energy generating sector: Hydro power (over 60%) and thermal power (over 30%). Despite the country's large potential in new renewable energy technologies, mainly wind, solar, and biomass, large hydro power and thermal power plants dominate the current expansion plans. The construction of a transmission line with Panama, which will link Colombia with Central America, is underway.

The electricity sector has been unbundled into generation, transmission, distribution, and commercialization since the adoption of the sector reform in 1994. About half the generation capacity is privately owned. Private participation in electricity distribution is much lower.

Electricity supply in Colombia relies on the national interconnected system and several isolated local systems in the non-interconnected zones. The national interconnected system encompasses one third of the national territory and non-interconnected zones covers the remaining two thirds.

In Colombia operates thirty thermal power plants which feed electricity into the national interconnected system. On the other hand, the non-interconnected zones are mostly served by small diesel generators, many of which are not in good working conditions. At the end of 2005, installed net effective capacity was 13.4 GW, with the following share by source: Thermal (gas): 27.41%; thermal (coal): 5.2 %.

The share of thermal participation in electricity generation has increased since the mid-1990s. This has happened in response to the 1992/1993 crisis caused by El Niño-Southern Oscillation associated droughts, and the high reliance of power generation on hydroelectric installations that lacked multi-year storage capacity. As a result of the new policies adopted by the country, the dominance of hydro power in the generation portfolio has been reduced from 80% in the early 1990s to less than 65% today. The expansion path involves adding 1 500 MW of new capacity, half of it with thermal sources by 2011. This will entail total investments of US $258 million per year.

Total electricity production during the period 2000-2010 increased from 45 TWh in 2000 to 50.31 TWh in 2010[67]; this represents an increase of 12%. Electricity demand grew by approximately 1.2% annually in the period considered. Between 2010 and 2019, experts are forecasting an increase in Colombian electricity generation of 39.1%, which is above average for the Latin American region. This equates to 17.6% in the 2014-2019 period, down from 18.2% reached in 2010-2014. An increase of 20% in hydro power use during 2010-2019 is one key element of generation growth. Thermal power generation is forecast to rise by 47% between 2010 and 2019.

In 2010, the electricity consumption per capita was 976.8 kWh. The export of electricity during the period 2000-2008 is shown in Figure 47.

As can be seen from Figure 47, Colombia started of exporting electricity in 2001. The electricity exported in 2001 reached 27 million kWh. In 2008, the electricity exported reached 876.7 million kWh; this represents an increase of 32.4 fold. The peak was reached in 2007 with 1 682 million kWh.

---

[67] BMI forecasts that Colombia will account for 5.04% of Latin American regional power generation by 2014, with a theoretical generation surplus that may still require imports on occasion, particularly if drought conditions impact the vital hydro power segment.

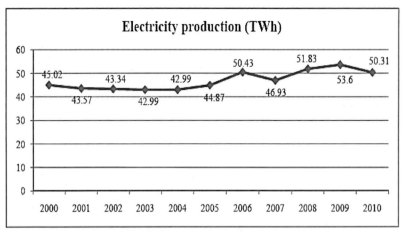

Source: Source: Index Mundi and EIA (2010).

Figure 45. Electricity production in Colombia during the period 2000-2010.

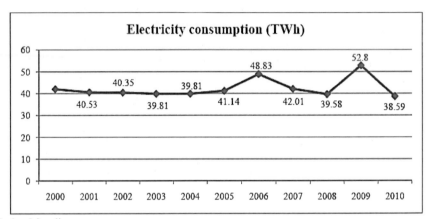

Source: Index Mundi.

Figure 46. Electricity consumption in Colombia during the period 2000-2010.

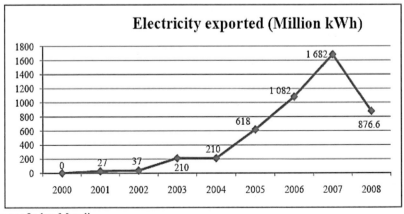

Source: Source: Index Mundi.

Figure 47. Electricity exported by Colombia during the period 2000-2008.

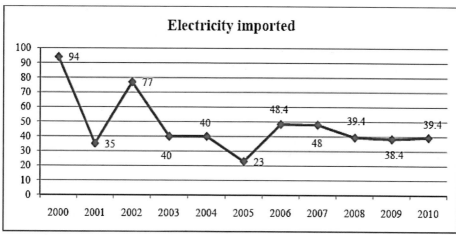

Source: Index Mundi.

Figure 48. Electricity imported by Colombia during the period 2000-2010.

Colombia imported only very small volumes of electricity from Venezuela and Ecuador. During the period 2000-2010, import of electricity dropped from 94 million kWh in 2000 to 39.4 million kWh in 2010, a reduction of 42% for the whole period (4.2% reduction average per year).

In the past years, the interconnected electricity system served 94% of the population (100% in urban areas and 76% in rural areas) according to World Bank data. The population without access to electricity was, in 2008, three million of persons[68].

Losses in transmission and leaks are still a concern, even if the total amount has decreased in the past years. Distribution and transmission losses in 2010 were, according to World Bank data, of 20%, which is above the average in the Latin American and the Caribbean region and two times the international standards.

Looking Forward

According to Viscidi (2010), the government should continue to plan a long-term strategy for meeting the country's electricity demand. In addition, Colombia should develop more long-term contracts for power generation and rely less on the spot market. Given the more limited transportation options for natural gas - compared to more fungible crude oil - and the importance of natural gas in the energy matrix, the government should provide incentives for the production of natural gas, which is currently under the same regulatory regime as oil. The government could also provide price incentives for the use of renewable energy sources for electricity generation, such as tax breaks or a carbon tax.

---

[68] According to Viscidi (2010), the interconnected grid supplies power in 2010 for about 96% of the population; some 1.8 million people has limited access to electricity.

Cuba

Cuba depends on fossil fuels to generate electricity consuming in 2008 around 7.6 million tons of oil (Arrastria Avila, 2008). At the same time, the country lacks sufficient proven indigenous fossil energy resources to support sustainable long-term economic and social development. For this reason, the discovery of new fossil fuel reserves is vital for the future of the country.

Currently, the Cuban energy situation is characterized by a deficit in access to affordable energy services (especially in remote rural areas), the lack of finance for energy imports, the control of the State of oil production and distribution[69], and the need of energy infrastructure improvements and expansion.

The oil industry in Cuba dates back to 1881 with the discovery of a naphtha field near Motembo, in the central part of the island, about twenty years after its commercial discovery in the USA. However, oil start to be commercially exploited early 1930s but it was only after 1960 that a systematic and detailed prospecting program began, comprising geological and geophysical studies, and the drilling of deep wells for stratigraphic and prospecting purposes. The breakup of the Soviet Union and the loss of Soviet oil shipments in the 1990s, forced Cuba to increase its exploration activities and develop its oil resources.

Energy Reform

Analysis of the energy resource situation in Cuba shows that fossil fuels will maintain, in the short and long-term, their significant contribution to the national energy balance, mainly because of the use of domestic oil and associated gas for the generation of electricity. The Cuban oil and gas industry has been one of the most dynamic industries within the Cuban economy in the past decade, making important progress in prospecting and extraction, as well as in the development of infrastructure for fuel transport. The discovery of light crude oil and natural gas reserves in the Cuban Economic Exclusion Zone (EEZ) of the Gulf of Mexico is expected to be a reality in the near future[70]. However, until now no significant oil and gas reserves have been found. The last effort to find these reserves in 2012 failed and the well was declared an "dry hole".

Structural changes and reforms stated in the Law on Foreign Investments were carried out in the energy sector to allow the participation of private capital in energy industries. Foreign investment was implemented both in electricity generation and in the exploration and production of petroleum and associated gas. By the end of the 1990s, oil production was shared equally between CUPET, the State-owned oil company, and some foreign companies.

---

[69] It is important to stick out that Cuba does not have a Ministry of Energy within the government official institutions but have plans to create such ministry in the future.

[70] These offshore oil reserves are estimated to be almost eight times larger than the onshore oil reserves.

The Energy Situation

During the period 1960-2004, Cuban oil production increased rapidly from 3% of total energy consumption in late 1960s, to more than 20% of total energy consumption in 2004. During the 1970s and 1980s, the energy sector development in Cuba were characterized by strong economic and social development, although based on inefficient technologies, supplied by the former Soviet Union and by other socialist countries, with high level of energy consumption. However, the situation of the energy sector became critical during the 1990s with the collapse of the former Soviet Union, the main Cuba's oil supplier country. As a consequence of this situation, Cuba experienced a major economic crisis across all sectors, particularly transport, industry, and agriculture, which virtually collapse (Arrastia Avila, 2008), due the termination of its favorable trade relationships with all member States of the Council for Mutual Economic Assistance.

As a result of this crisis, Cuba was forced to slash its energy imports, which affected in a significant manner the country's capability to satisfy its energy requirements. This situation provoked a very difficult economic situation with a 35% decreased in it Gross Domestic Product in early 1990s[71]. The search for energy solutions became the primary activity of national State institutions, and of many specialists, technicians, and workers. Significant actions were taken to increase production of domestic crude oil and associated gas, with the purpose of using it for electricity generation in thermoelectric power plants. These actions were included in the Development Program of National Energy Sources adopted by the government in 1993 (Lopez and Perez, 2000). The above program was developed and approved to counteract the growing shortage of financial resources for purchasing oil after the collapse of the former Soviet Union and bearing in mind the new global market conditions. The main objectives of this program were the following:

a) To increase the use of domestic crude oil and associated gas in electricity generation, as a substitute for imported oil;
b) To achieve higher efficiency in the use of bagasse and other crop residues of the sugar industry, allowing the industry to provide itself with its energy requirements and to increase the electricity delivered to the national electric system;
c) To extend the use of hydro power, waste based (industrial, agricultural, and urban) energy sources, solar, wind, and biogas as energy sources for electricity generation.

The program was divided into two phases, demarcated by results and not by periods. The first phase focuses mainly on the increase in the production and use of domestic crude oil and associated gas, the increase on energy efficiency, and in the raise in the contribution of sugarcane biomass to the country's energy mix. In addition, several measures were taken to improve energy efficiency, the modernization of thermoelectric power plants, and a decrease in total electricity losses during transmission and distribution, investments in infrastructure for fuel transport, increase fuel diversification by extending the use of renewable energy sources for electricity generation and a reduction in the dependency on oil imports.

---

[71] During the 1980s and 1990s, subsidized Soviet oil allowed Cuba to resell up to 50 000 barrels per day on the spot market and keep the difference.

As result of the energy crisis in the 1990s, it is important to stick out the following: Total electricity losses in 1996 grew to 23.2% of generated electricity, as a consequence of inadequate maintenance, lack of investment in the distribution network, and 'theft' of electricity. Starting in 1997, measures to reduce transmission losses were adopted, such as monitoring of the transmission system or the installation of new electric meters to control distribution losses in the residential area, among others. By 2003, these measures brought the level of total electricity losses down to the same level as those in 1990, i.e., 17.5%, which is still high according to international standards. In 2010, the level of electricity losses was 16.8%. Plans were adopted to reduce these losses to 14% at the end of 2011. These actions combined were expected to add an additional 700 000 ton of oil equivalent of domestic fuel annually.

The second phase was planned to begin when sufficient financial resources would be available for energy infrastructure development. However, it is important to stress that the main short and medium-term limitations inhibiting development of the Cuban energy sector are the scarcity of hard currency for normal operations, and the lack of finance needed to undertake new investments, maintenance work, modernization, grid extensions, among other indispensable investments.

The lack of financial resources is one of the main problems hindering the investments in the energy sector. Another problem is the impossibility for the US oil companies of participating in any activities related to the oil and gas sector development in Cuba or in the sale of oil equipment for the exploration of the oil sector in the island.

The adoption of the different measures mentioned above was the most important step towards a new approach to energy development in Cuba. The results obtained in crude oil and gas exploration and extraction activities were particularly positive, as were those concerning partial recapitalization and modernization of the country's electricity generation plants, the opening of the energy sector to foreign investment[72], and changes in the structure of energy imports. However, the results already achieved are still far from what the country need to improve significantly its energy sector.

Security on Energy Supply

In recent years, several problems concerning the security of the national energy supply were identified. These problems can be summarized as follows:

1. A shortage of hard currency to finance the purchase of imported fuels, to carry out new investments in oil fields, and to the implementation of programs for the rational use of energy;
2. High dependency on imported oil;

---

[72] Investment in the Cuban energy sector has been primarily used to modernize thermal power plants, to improve electric transmission lines with the purpose of reducing electricity losses, to expand drilling and extraction of crude oil and associated gas, to improve fuel transport infrastructure via oil and gas pipelines or by sea transport, and to increase oil refinery and storage capacities. More than 500 km of oil and gas pipelines were built between 1998 and 2002. Harbor facilities and a supertanker station, including an oil treatment facility to improve quality, were also constructed to supply crude oil to the thermal power plants located in the western and eastern parts of the country, i.e., areas far from the production sites (United Nations and the IAEA, 2008).

3. Electricity generation is heavily dependent on oil and gas (95%). Ten major energy facilities, two of them using gas as energy sources, produce a high percentage of the electricity used in the country. The high sulphur content of domestic crude oil has adverse effects, both environmentally and operationally, decreasing the availability and efficiency of thermal power plants, increasing in unplanned downtimes because of breakdowns, shortening operating times between maintenance cycles, and increasing the resources needed for maintenance;

4. Problems related to fuel transport, particularly coastal transport, which have sometimes caused temporary shortages of energy and interruptions in energy services resulting from rainstorms and tropical hurricanes;

5. The extension of transmission lines throughout the country, because of the country's geographical position, making the lines susceptible to damage from tropical storms and hurricanes;

6. Old energy infrastructure and lack of adequate maintenance and repair services.

Oil Production, Consumption, and Reserves

According to EIA International Energy Statistics, Cuba has oil proven reserves estimated of 124 million barrels as January 2010. The oil production in 2009 reached 48 340 barrels per day, a reduction of 29% from the level reached in 2007, and the consumption was 169 000 barrels per day in the same year.

Cuba produces about 95% of its power using fossil fuels, a very high percentage when compared with other countries. In 2007, the domestic production of crude oil, 68 000 barrels per day, accounted for about 40% of total consumption and the rest was imported from Venezuela (102 000 barrels per day in 2007[73]). From the total supply of fuel oil, about 50% is used for power generation and 50% for transport and other uses.

Table 30. Liquid fuel production and consumption in Cuba in 2007

Liquid fuel supply 2007		
Liquid fuel sources	Barrels per day	% of total
Domestic production	68 000	40%
Imports	102 000	60%
Total supply	170 000	100%
Liquid fuel uses	Barrels per day	% of total
Power generation	85 700	50%
Transport	84 300	50%
Total uses	170 000	100%

Source: Belt (2009).

---

73 In 2009, Cuba continues importing from Venezuela more than 120 000 barrels per day.

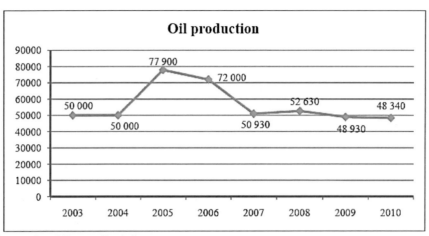

Source: International Energy Statistics.

Figure 49. Oil production in Cuba during the period 2003-2010.

From Figure 49, the following can be stated: Oil production increased during the period 2003 to 2005 from 50 000 barrels per day in 2005 to 77 900 barrels per day in 2010; this represents an increase of 56%. However, the oil production started to decline from 2006 to 2010. The production peak within the period was reached in 2005 with 77 900 barrels per day.

Table 31. Cuba's oil data 2007-2009 (Thousand barrels per day)

Cuba	2007	World	Rank (2009)	2008	2009
Total oil production Production of crude oil (including lease condensate), natural gas plant liquids, and other liquids, and refinery processing gain (loss).	50.93	84 392	60	52.63	48.93
Crude oil production Includes lease condensate.	50.54	72 989	54	52.25	48.23
Consumption Consumption of petroleum products and direct combustion of crude oil.	154.00	86 142	61	162	181
Net exports/imports(-) Net Exports = Total Oil Production – Consumption. Negative numbers are Net Imports.	- 103.07	--	40	- 109	-132.07
Refinery capacity Crude oil distillation capacity as of January 1.	301	85 355	48	301	301
Proved reserves As of January 1.	0.124	1 317	57	0.124	0.124

Source: International Energy Statistics.

As can be easily seeing in Table 31, until 2009 the level of import of oil (132 070 barrels per day) is 2.7 times higher than the oil domestic production (48 930 barrels per day) for that year. At the same time, it is important to note that the production of petroleum products has largely depended on the international political situation, which has generally favored imports over domestic refining until the beginning of the 1990s. This situation has changed in favor of domestic refining, especially in the light of the oil supply agreement with Venezuela, which resulted in a 40% increase in refining in 2003 over the previous year[74] (Statistic National Office, 2004).

Cuba's oil consumption is closely related to its economic activities. Despite various conservation and efficiency measures adopted after 1991 to reduce oil consumption, most of the decrease is related to the decline in economic activity after that year. According to International Energy Statistics, Cuba's oil consumption reached 169 000 barrels per day in 2007. In 2008, the oil consumption decreased to 162 000 barrels per day, a decrease of around 5% respect the level reached in 2007. In 2009, Cuba consumed 181 000 barrels per day, an increase of 12% respect to the level reached in 2007.

In Cuba, oil is also used in transportation, fertilizer plants, the cement industry, nickel refining, and other mining operations.

Up to 1998, the total primary energy supply in Cuba had been dominated essentially by two fuels: oil and biomass. The share of oil was, and still is today, the dominant fuel in the energy balance supply of the country. It grew significantly from 52% in 1970 to 75% in 1985. By 2003, the oil share was around 76%, almost the same than in 1985. In 2007, this share was 85%, an increase of 9% repsct to 2003. With the aim of reducing the share of oil in the energy balance of the country, a plan entitled "National Energy Sources Development Program" was adopted by the People Power National Assembly in 1993. The objective of the plan was to reduce Cuba's energy imports and obtain maximum benefits from domestic energy sources. The document identified efficiency as the first national source of energy.

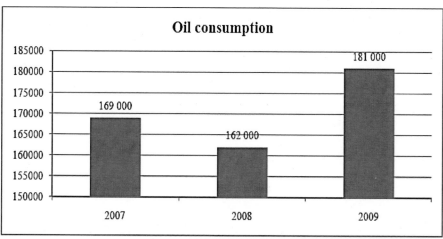

Source: International Energy Statistics.

Figure 50. Oil consumption in Cuba during the period 2007-2009.

---

[74] Around 50 000 barrels per day are resold in world markets, giving Cuba the advantage of obtaining subsidized supplies for domestic use and reselling a portion. This form of aid resembles was given also to Cuba by the former USSR in the 1980s and in the 1990s.

During the period 1990-2000, it was possible to increase domestic production of crude oil for electricity generation nearly six fold, but the sugarcane industry, however, was not in a position to supply the electricity planned. The main reason was a steady reduction in the use of sugarcane biomass owing to the limited availability of sugarcane, due to a lack of financial resources and fertilizers, problems with the industry efficiency, and the closure of an important number of sugar mills[75]. A restructuring process in the sugar sector, postponed because of its social implications, was finally implemented in 2002. Nearly half (45.5%) of the 156 sugar mills in the country were closed, and half the area devoted to sugarcane cultivation was used for other crops to substitute for food imports, and for timber-yielding trees[76.] After professional retraining and/or reorientation, 25% of the sector's labor force was assigned to other productive activities. The decision to close almost half of sugar mills due to the international low sugar price and heavy losses in the production of sugar at the beginning of the 2000s definitively was, without any doubt, a wrong strategic decision. With this decision, Cuba lost its long experience in the production of sugar acquired during so many years, starting in the second half of the 1800s and during the whole 1900s and the contribution of the sugar mills in the co-generation in a moment of electricity generation crisis. The increase in the international sugar price in the 2000s and at the beginning of the 2010s have no direct effect in the Cuban economy due to low level of sugar production, one of the lowest in the whole history of sugar production of the country. This situation is provoking the loss of millions of dollars each year, in a moment when the lack of hard currency is the main limiting factor for the economic and social development of the country.

According to a report prepared by the United Nations, the IAEA, and Cubaenergia in 2008, Cuba lacks sufficient proven indigenous fossil energy resources to support sustainable long-term economic and social development. This situation, however, might change in the near future due to the ongoing oil exploration programs in the Gulf of Mexico. Several reports estimate proven oil reserves in this area to be around 4.6 billion barrels[77]. However, it is important to know that almost all-Cuban crude oil is heavy with high sulfur content. For this reason, Cuba needs to find light crude oil in order to achieve its goal of self-sufficiency in the future.

Oil Exploration

Prior to the 1940s, oil and gas exploration and production in Cuba were confined primarily to shallow drilling and recovery associated with numerous oil seeps in western and central part of the country. Since the mid-19th century, some of these oil seeps, such as the heavy tars (asphalt) of Cárdenas Bay, and the light condensates (naphtha) of Motembo, among others, have been exploited for commercial purposes. Shallow exploratory activity carried out by US and Cuban companies in the 1940s and 1950s, eventually resulted in the discovery of several small commercial oil fields in La Habana, Matanzas, and former Las

---

[75] During the restructuring process of the sugar industry in 2001-2002, significant co-generation capacities were retired totaling 278 MW.

[76] A second restructuration of the sugar industry was carried out at the end of 2011, leaving only 56 sugar mills in operation. A total of 45% of the labor force was assigned to other productive activities.

[77] The current oil reserves are 124 million barrels. However, the United States Geological Survey estimates that Cuba holds reserves of 4.6 billion barrels of oil, and 9.8 billion barrels of natural gas in its Gulf of Mexico waters. That's nearly two-thirds the amount in the Arctic National Wildlife Refuge.

Villas provinces, located in the central part of the island. Eventually commercial fields were developed, the most important of which were Jatibonico and Jarahueca. With the exception of the Cristales Field, most of the oil discovered during this period was high sulphur heavy crude oil with over 5% sulphur and an average gravity of 18° API.

US companies and private investor syndicates, in association with Cuban partners, were the main participants in the oil and gas upstream sector during the 1950s. Standard Oil of New Jersey (Esso) and Standard Oil of Indiana (Amoco) conducted various geological and geophysical studies, as well as exploratory drilling work in central and eastern part of the island without any success in the 1950s. Cuban oil production in 1958 was less than 50 000 tons annually, approximately the equivalent of 1 000 barrels per day.

During the 1960s, exploration results were also poor, with only several small oil discoveries made. Results changed during the 1970s, with Soviet assistance and the discovery of the Varadero Oil Field in 1971. Until today, two large sedimentary basins have been identified with important oil reserves: the north basin which is part of the Florida-Bahamian Plate, and the south basin, which is part of the Caribbean Plate. Most discoveries in the north basin have been low gravity (heavy), high sulphur (sour) quality crude oil, along with associated natural gas along a 150 km stretch of the coastal and onshore region between Guanabo and Corralillo. The south basin has seen some exploratory work in the past in the Gulf of Guacanayabo, Gulf of Ana María, and Jardines de la Reina, with no promising results yet. In the case of the south basin, the predominant type of oil found is of the so-called "medium and light crude oil". Since 1991, exploration activities in these two zones have been carried out with the participation of foreign companies from Angola, Brazil, Canada, China, India, France, Malaysia, Norway, Spain, Sweden, Venezuela, Vietnam, and Russia. In the north basin, fifteen exploratory wells have been drilled. As a result of this effort, new oil fields have been found in this basin, particularly in the area of Varadero and Puerto Escondido, both in production at the moment. The most recent oil field discovery was in 1994; it is still in the exploration phase and its reservoir is being delineated. In the south basin, four oil fields have been identified, and several wells have been drilled but without economic success. Currently, crude oil exploration and drilling activities are being intensified. New extraction techniques have been introduced to increase the production of wells (Statistic National Office, 2004).

It is important to knowledge that in the 1990s, the economic exclusion zone located in the deep waters of the Gulf of Mexico was open to foreign investment. It has been estimated, through geological studies that were carried out by the US government in this zone, that resources could exceed 4.6 billion barrels of oil. The economic exclusion zone, covering 112 000 km^2, has been divided into 59 blocks of 2 000 km^2 each, which are currently under tender (Delgado, 2004).

It is important to single out that the study of other areas with oil extraction potential and the drilling of new wells will continues during the coming years with the participation of foreign companies but using more efficient and productive techniques available in the market. Based on 2003 extraction rates for crude oil and gas, and considering hypothetically that all reserves found until now can be extracted, it is estimated that onshore reserves will last about 22 years, and offshore reserves around 155 years.

During the September 2003 visit to Cuba of Brazil's President, Petrobras announced a new oil technology agreement with CUPET. This announcement represented Petrobras's return since its major exploration setback in 2001.

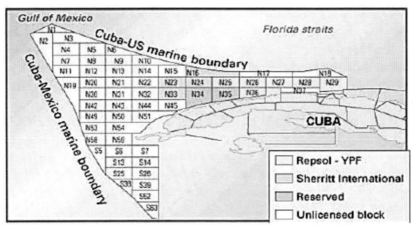

Source: Unión Cuba Petróleo. Cited in the *Oil and Gas Journal*, August 18, 2003.

Figure 51. Cuba's 59 offshore sections and the operating companies.

In 1998, Petrobras, in association (60/40) with Canada's Sherritt International, announced their first Cuban offshore wildcat project (block 50), 32 km north of Cuba's Ciego de Avila province at Key Felipe, a coral formation off Key Coco/Key Guillermo. At that time, Petrobras' geological surveys estimated the potential of oil reserves at 500 million barrels. After three years of work, US $15 million dollars, and reaching the 4 000 meters depth, they declared the well a dry hole.

According to CUPET, Cuba hopes to perforate, after the arrival of a platform contracted in China in 2011, a total of five wells in its zone of the Gulf of Mexico, twenty two of them under risk contract with the Statoil and Norsk Hydro companies (Norway) in partnership with Repsol (Spain) and OVL (India), company that also works single in other two blocks, PdVSA (Venezuela), Petrovietnam, Petronas (Malaysian), and Sonangol (Angola). It is important to stress that the participation of Norsk Hydro Company is an indication of the importance and potential of the project, because this company is recognized in industry circles for their deep-water exploration technology and operational expertise.

Investment in the Oil Sector

Investment in the Cuban energy sector has been primarily used to modernize thermal power plants currently in operation, to improve electric transmission lines, to expand drilling and extraction of crude oil and associated gas, and to improve fuel transport infrastructure via oil and gas pipelines or by sea transport.

The country had eleven large, old, and quite inefficient thermoelectric power plants generating electricity for the entire island. Most of the plants were twenty five years old or more and, for this reason, and due also to a lack of proper maintenance, these plants are not functioning a full capacity most of the time. Until 2006, there were frequent blackouts, especially during peak demand periods. There were also a high percentage of transmission losses along the electrical distribution grid.

From 1996 to 2002, average investments in the energy sector were about 298 million pesos[78] per year, which in 2002 represented almost 13% of the total annual investments in the country for that year (IEO, 2007).

Without any doubt, the lack of financial resources is one of the main problems hindering the investment process in Cuba and affects the energy sector, in particular. Although private sector foreign investments have emerged in recent years, they are insufficient to meet the needs of the energy sector and are concentrated in specific areas. The expansion of private investment in the energy sector in the country during the coming years would require the revision of the regulatory framework in force (United Nations and the IAEA, 2008).

It is important to stress that Cuba anticipates tripling in the next six years its capacity to refine petroleum from 120 000 to about 360 000 barrels per day with the support of Venezuela and China, their two main economic partners in the energy sector. The plan includes the expansion of two refineries and the construction of another one in the coming years. The oil refine capacity of the island at the moment is about 301 000 barrels per day but the investment program approved will increase substantially this capacity of refinement by 2017. In addition, the expansion program will guarantee a product of high quality, which responds to European environmental standards, according to public statement made by the manager of PdVSA-Cuba, Hector Pernia, in an interview with the Venezuelan press. According to Mr. Pernia, the plans include the extension of the refinery of Cienfuegos (260 km southeast of Havana), that Cuba and Venezuela modernized and operates since 2007, in order to increase its refinement capacity up to 150 000 barrels per day from the current capacity of 65 000 barrels per day in two years. China will also participate in the extension of energy industry in Cuba by dredged the port of Cienfuegos, by the construction of a liquefied gas plant, as well as in a construction of network of gas pipelines with an extension of 320 km. China's National Petroleum Corporation had signed a US $6 billion agreement to invest in an oil refinery, located in Cienfuegos province jointly owned by Cuba and Venezuela, in Cuba's drilling explorations, and in the development of its oil industry[79]. In February 2005, China's Sinopec signed a production sharing agreement[80] with CUPET to explore Pinar del Rio province's north coast onshore and coastal areas.

In addition, CUPET and China National Petroleum Corporation signed a MoU that could open the economic zone of Cuba in the Gulf of Mexico for oil research in the future. Cuba and Venezuela also have expressed their intention of constructing a new refinery in the province of Matanzas, 100 km to the east of Havana, with a refine capacity of 150 000 barrels per day, and to increase from 22 000 barrels per day to 50 000 barrels per day the refinement capacity of another refinery located in Santiago of Cuba, 900 km to the southeast of the

---

[78] Cuban Pesos is the national currency. The Convertible Cuban Pesos (CUC) is the national currency that can be used for foreign currency exchange. One CUC is 24 Cuban Pesos. However, the official exchange between CUC and Cuban pesos is 1 to 1 for trade and business activities.

[79] Caribbean analysts see the latest Chinese investment in Cuba as another example of the increasing role China has been playing in the search for oil in the Latin American and the Caribbean region.

[80] A production sharing agreement is a contractual format used by many countries and generally accepted by major international oil companies. These are contracts in which an international oil company assumes all risks and expenses and works as a contractor to the national oil company. In the event of a commercial discovery, the foreign oil company is allowed to recover its expenses and share in profits from the field's production. The term or duration of the contract, along with costs and production share are negotiable, and vary according to the complexity and level of risk of the work. The foreign oil company generally pays a 30% corporate tax on its profits to the host government. The foreign company is also allowed to dispose of its share of production by exporting it or selling it to the national oil company at world price levels.

capital. Other two refinery plants in Havana and Cabaiguán (center of the island) will increase their refinement capacity up to 33 000 barrels per day. It is expected that after the implementation of the plan the capacity of refinement of the island will be increased to up 360 000 barrels per day.

It is important to know the following: PdVSA announced the signature of a contract on the constitution and administration of the mixed company Venangocupet, with the participation of entities of Cuba and Angola. According to a press note circulated in Cuba, the company was created for the production, transport, technical exchange, and refinement of crude oil, and includes the Venezuelan Corporation of Petroleum, the Cuban company Cupet and the Angola's Sonangol. Venangocupet will operate in the fields mature Migas and Melones, located in the State of Anzoátegui, Venezuela. The initial production capacity is 20 000 barrels of crude oil per day with the possibility in the future to extend it up to 60 000 barrels of crude oil per day.

Finally, the Canadian firm Sherritt announced in March 2011 that it is expects to invest US $100 million in Cuban oil operations, up from US $53 million last year. The rise is mainly due to eight new on-shore wells planned for this year in the zone under exploration of the company.

Dependency on Oil Import

After the collapse of the former Soviet Union and despite national energy conservation efforts realized in this period, especially concerning crude oil and petroleum products, the Cuban dependence on imports did not decrease after 1990s. The principal energy imports of Cuba have been crude oil and petroleum products. Overall, net imports increased steadily from 1970, reaching 71% of the total primary energy supply in 1985. During this period, crude oil and petroleum products were imported from the former Soviet Union at preferential prices. Net imports dropped between 1985 and 1995 to 59% of the total primary energy supply and continued to decline through 2003 when they reached 42%. In 1989, imports of crude oil and petroleum products represented almost 30% of the total imports of goods and services, about 42% of the country's exports of goods and services, and around 72% of the country's energy supply, equivalent to about 14.9 million ton oil equivalent (Memories, 2004). The net energy import dependency could have been even lower in recent years had the sugar industry not continued to be depressed and made more bagasse available for energy purposes.

Without any doubt the collapse of the socialist system in Eastern Europe, and in particular the dissolution of the former Soviet Union, was an enormous blow to the Cuban economy. In light of this economic shock, imports of crude oil and petroleum products decreased sharply. However, the collapse of the former Soviet Union was not the main cause that reduced the Cuban oil imports from this country. The decline in oil imports was the result of a trade protocol that was signed in 1990 that eliminated barter deals and preferential prices and replaced them with world's market prices and convertible currency payments. This protocol dealt a serious blow to the Cuban economy, in general, and the energy sector, in particular. Energy imports represented a striking of around 35% of Cuba's total imports before the collapse of the former Soviet Union. After signing the protocol, Cuba had no choice but to reduce its oil imports. In addition, the protocol prevented Cuba from receiving additional cheap oil for re-export, which had generated additional revenues and hard currency for the government (Alhajji and Maris, 2003).

At the same time, the supply of parts and equipment needed to maintain or expand the national electricity system fell to a minimum. This, in turn, led to an electricity shortage across the country that became critical in 1993–1994. The fuel supply to the residential sector was also greatly affected. It was necessary to halt important energy projects owing to a lack of finance, which led to the delay and even the cancellation of important investment in the energy sector, such as the modernization of thermal power plants in Havana and Holguín, and the cancellation of the construction of the Juraguá nuclear power plant in the Cienfuegos region[81].

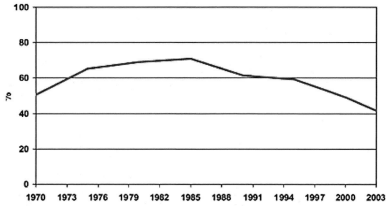

Source: Anuario Estadístico de Cuba (Statistic National Office, 2004).

Figure 52. Net energy import in the Cuban total primary energy supply during the period 1970-2003.

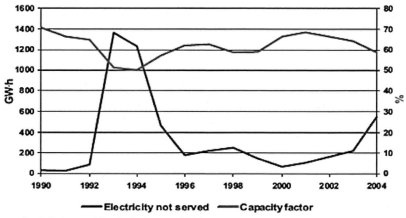

Source: Memories Ministry of Basic Industry (2004).

Figure 53. Power plant capacity factor and electricity not served.

81 During 1992 to 1996, the electricity not served reached very high levels, peaking in 1993 at twelve fold the 1990 value, mainly because of the lack of fuel. This level was drastically reduced by 1996 but owing to damage in different electric power plants, the electricity not served increased again in 2003 and 2004. Although it was five times higher in 2004 than in 1990, it only constituted 4% of the electricity demand of the country in that year.

One of the main limitations faced by the energy sector during the 1990s was the replacement of imported fuels, especially fuel oil with domestic crude oil, which has a slightly lower energy performance and high sulphur content.

The main negative effect of the use of the domestic fuel was on the operation of power plants. The use of heavy crude oil in electric generating plants reduces their capacity by almost 10%, largely by increasing the frequency and level of maintenance required, as well as the number of emergency shut downs and capacity limitations, which in turn affects the availability of electricity for final use. It is important to single out that the production of domestic crude oil has growing in line with the country's social and economic development, Cuba's total primary energy supply increased 61% from 1970 to 1989 at an annual rate of about 2.5%. During the 1990s, with the country in a critical economic situation, total primary energy supply underwent important changes, falling 38% between 1990 and 1995. By 2000, total primary energy supply had increased 15% from the lowest level experienced in 1995. However, after 2001, total primary energy supply decreased again and in 2003 was still 44% lower than the peak value observed in 1985[82] (see Figure 53). The rapid decrease of the total primary energy supply during the economic collapse period resulted mainly from a drastic drop in energy imports due to the lack of hard currency necessary to buy fuels on the world's market at non-preferential prices. Oil imports decreased dramatically even after 1995 and, by 2003, were only 67% of the 1995 level (see Figure 53).

Increase in National Oil Refineries Capacity

Investments in the energy sector have allowed not only the modernization of the main thermal power electric power plants but also their adaptation for use of domestic crude oil, leading to important savings in the import of fuels for electricity generation. In addition, modernization has also reduced the financial pressures on the national balance of payments and guaranteed that, at present, almost 100% of the electricity in the country is generated using domestic fuels. The use of domestic crude oil has also been extended to cement production, where 100% of the sector fuel needs is met using this type of fuel. More recently, domestic crude oil has also begun to be used in nickel production. With the demand for crude oil in electricity generation, in cement and nickel production, and with the expected increase in the extraction of crude oil, mainly in the economic exclusion zone of the Gulf of Mexico, Cuba is likely to have surpluses of better quality crude oil in the future. Such surpluses would enable an increase in the domestic production of petroleum products, thus increasing self-sufficiency with regard to fuels and possibly leading to the export of petroleum products at a subsequent stage.

Electricity Generation

In the case of oil, Cuba consumed 13 million tons of oil in 1989, of which, 40 million barrels, some 7 million tons were for electricity generation alone. In 1999, Cuba consumed,

---

[82] In 2003, final energy use per capita was still 2.2 times lower than in 1970. In 2003, the per capita electricity use and the per capita GDP still remained lower than the 1990 level.

for all needs including electricity generation, 6.3 million ton, of these 1.2 million was domestic crude oil, with a high content of sulphur (approximately 9%). Cuba generated in 2009, a total of 17 621 MWh using all energy sources available in the country. The country consumed in 2009 a total of 14 667 MWh of electricity, which represents 83% of the total electricity generated in the country in that year. The per capita electricity consumption in 2009 was 1 309 kWh. In 2009, the distribution and transmission losses were 2 954 MW, which represents 16.8% of the total electricity generated in the country in that year[83]. The level of electricity losses in 2009 is higher than the average losses at regional and international levels. In 2010, the electricity losses were 14.7% of the total electricity generated in the country, a decrease of 2.1% respet 2009. The intention of the government is to reduce these losses to 14% by the end of 2012.

The participation of oil in electricity generation during the period 1958-2008 is shown in Table 32. Figure 54 show the installed generation capacity, and Figure 55 electricity generation during the period 2000-2009.

It is important to single out that since 1995 the use of petroleum products for electricity generation started to diminish while crude oil started to increase, becoming the prominent type of energy source for electricity generation in 2003 (93% of the electric generating capacity was based on crude oil). In 2009, electricity generation using crude oil as fuel dropped to 77%, a decrease of 16% respect to 2008.

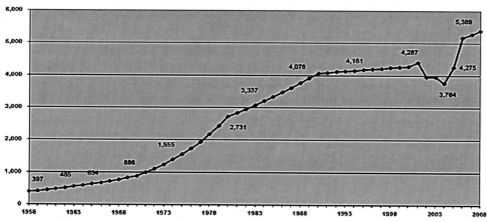

Source: Belt (2009).

Figure 54. Installed generation capacity in Cuba (MW).

Table 32. Electricity generation in Cuba (%)

	1995	2000	2002	2003	2009
Crude oil	3 451	6 297	9 759	11 613	17 709.1
Petroleum products	7 567	5 557	2 811	934	5 185.4
Crude oil (%)	31	53	78	93	77
Petroleum products (%)	69	47	22	7	23

Source: Statistic National Office.

---

[83] According to national public information, in September 2011 the level of electricity losses was only 14.4% and it is expected to reach 14% in 2012.

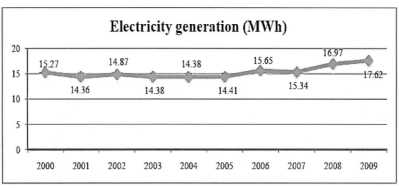

Source: Index Mundi.

Figure 55. Electricity generation in Cuba during the period 2000-2009.

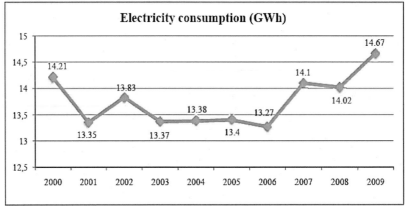

Source: Index Mundi.

Figure 56. Electricity consumption in Cuba during the period 2000-2009.

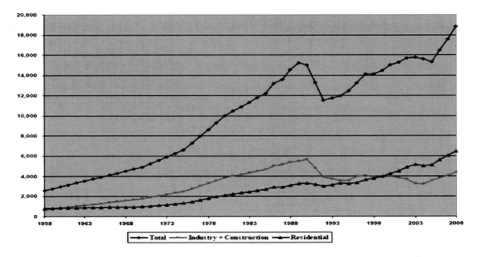

Source: Belt (2009).

Figure 57. Consumption of oil for electricity generation by sector in Cuba during the period 1958-2008 (MWh).

From Figure 57, the following can be stated: Residential sector consumed since 2000 more electricity than the industry and construction sectors together. For this reason, saving in the electricity consumption in the residential sector is an important goal to be reach in the future in order to reduce the total consumption of oil for electricity generation in the country, without affecting further the industry and construction sectors.

Finally, it is important to stress the following: National electrical system has deteriorated tremendously in the 1990s and early 2000s, due to the lack of proper maintenance, use of heavy crude oil for electricity generation, aging of the facilities and equipment, unsuitable spare parts, lack of system equilibrium, and the effect of the blackouts. An important program has been approved by the government in order to improve, step by step, the national electrical system in the coming years, by eliminating the majority of the negative factors mentioned above that are affecting the supply of electricity in the most effective and economic manner. According to some expert opinion, the estimate cost of any program adopted by the government with the aim of solving the current problems that are affecting the national electrical system could be around US $2,150 million for the next five years.

Looking Forward

The future of Cuba's oil exploration and production sector could very well be in the deep offshore Gulf of Mexico waters, along the western approaches to the Florida Straits and the eastern extension of Mexico's Yucatán Peninsula. According to some industry experts, this area is categorized as high risk from the technical geosciences standpoint. However, considering some expert reports, hydrocarbon potential exists in this area, with Cuban government sources estimating a potential of 4.6 billion barrels of recoverable reserves[84]. Given the possible presence of a sufficiently large structure, technical risks might be reduced to acceptable levels. This is the reason why some oil international companies are exploring in this area. Another advantage would be that these undiscovered reserves are likely to be of light crude oil, and not the heavy high sulfur quality that Cuba's onshore and coastal wells currently produce. It is important to stress that in the future, the Cuban government should adopt additional measures in order to reduce the participation of oil in the country energy mix, particularly for electricity generation, and to increase the use of renewable energy sources with this specific purpose.

Chile

The Energy Reform

Chile was one of the first countries in the region to privatize its power generation and distribution system. The energy reform come from the 1982 Electricity Reform Act, which

---

[84]According to the U.S. Geological Survey (USGS) report entitled "Assessment of Undiscovered Oil and Gas Resources of the North Cuba Basin 2004 (2005)," oil and gas offshores reserves were estimates in 4.6 billion barrels of undiscovered oil and 0.278 trillion m3 of undiscovered natural gas along Cuba's north coast. The high end potential of the north basin could be of 9.3 billion barrels of undiscovered oil and of 0.62 trillion m3 of undiscovered natural gas, according to the mentioned report.

was designed to break up the State monopoly Endesa[85], which was privatized in 1989 and split into fourteen different companies, including six generation companies and six distribution companies[86]. Since that year, the private sector generates 100% of the electricity consumed by the country, with twenty six companies operating generating concessions and five companies operating transmission concessions.

Chile's National Energy Commission (CNEC) has promoted a sustainable development program for energy. The four policy guidelines established were the following:

1. Private investment will be the main source of capital for energy sector expansion, and the regulatory framework must be clear and stable to attract both local and international private investment;
2. Policies must promote energy efficiency. Clean energy at the least cost is required to be competitive, and to reduce the cost of energy for the nation's exporting industrial sectors;
3. Energy development must ensure the protection of the environment. Prevention is critical and all new energy projects in Chile require an environmental assessment;
4. Social equity must be an objective of sustainable energy development. Poverty can be overcome through employment in energy development and by providing basic energy services to the poorest sectors. To this end, Chile is implementing a rural electrification program in order to increase rural access to electricity. Renewable energy sources are an excellent tool to provide electricity to remote areas where the electricity grid is inaccessible.

The strategic priorities in the power sector are the following:

1. Strengthening of the institutional framework;
2. Promotion and development of energy efficiency;
3. Optimization of the energy mix;
4. Compatibility with sustainable development;
5. Support for equitable use;
6. Preparation for contingencies.

It is important to stress that, whether due to insufficient natural gas supplies, the high price of oil or the less than adequate hydrological levels, Chile's energy sector has, in fact, faced a dangerous level of insecurity, inefficiency, and lack of sustainability. For this reason, the new Chilean energy policy has been prepared on the basis of the following three main components: a) Security; b) Efficiency; and c) Sustainability.

---

[85] Endesa is one of the largest electric power companies in the world and Spain's largest utility, as well as the leading private multinational enterprise in the Latin American and the Caribbean region.

[86] Upon privatization, Endesa went through an ambitious period of expansion throughout South America. Endesa has around 4 800 MW in installed capacity within Chile, and around 8 500 MW of installed capacity throughout South America, including Peru, Brazil, Columbia, and Argentina. Endesa is the central figure in the Chilean energy sector and, despite frequent changes of ownership, it remains at the top. Endesa's portfolio is made up of a mix of gas-fired and hydro power plants. The company also owns Endesa Eco, its renewables subsidiary, which is developing a 60 MW wind farm in Canela, the largest wind farm under development in Chile until today. Endesa also controls Ingendesa, an EPC company, created when Endesa was taken private. Ingendesa does not just supply services for Endesa but also is a vibrant player in the national market (Tarta et al., 2009).

The Energy Situation

It is important to single out that one of the characteristics of the power situation in the country is that Chile's energy supply is anything but secure. Chile dependence on imported energy had been increasing for the last thirty years. In 1980, approximately 58% of energy was supplied by indigenous production and 42% from net imports. However, in 2005 this proportion has reversed, with 71% from imports and the remainder from indigenous production and this trend not only continue until today but it will continue in the near-future. The country's own energy resources are limited and, for this reason 90% of the natural gas, coal, and oil consumed in the country come from abroad. In 2007 and 2008, Chile suffered shortage of gas supply from Argentina forcing the country to use fuel oil/diesel to power its combined cycle thermal power plants. The cost of producing thermal energy from fuel oil/diesel is substantially greater than that of natural gas and, for this reason Chile has to pay substantially more to produce the electricity its needs using thermal generation power plants with fuel oil/diesel instead of using natural gas. According to some expert opinion, the cost of powering thermal power plants in Chile rises by 80%, if fuel oil/diesel is the source fuel. There is also a significant increase in pollution levels when fuel oil/diesel is used to generate electricity.

Regarding power price, the following can be stated from Figure 58: The price of power increased about tenfold in Chile over the past three years, resulting in decreased industry competitiveness. The price increase was the result of the combination of several factors, such as droughts, gas reductions, the use of fuel oil/diesel for electricity generation, and high oil prices.

The State lays claim to all petroleum deposits, and a government agency, ENAP, is the most important Chilean company devoted to the exploration, production, and commercialization of hydrocarbons and their related products, and it is the main energy supplier in the country filling more than 40% of Chile's national energy demand. The company is the sole producer and refiner in the country. In 1990, ENAP formed an international subsidiary, Sipetrol, to seek foreign production that could offset declining domestic fields.

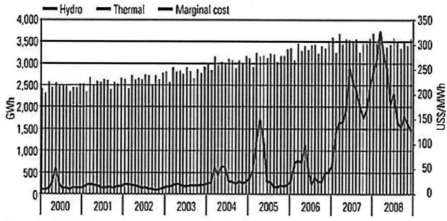

Source: Tarta et al (2009).

Figure 58. Price increase in Chile from 2000 to 2008.

Sipetrol has pursued investments in countries such as Argentina, Colombia, Ecuador, and Egypt, and holds equity in production operations in these countries with production of about 25 000 barrels per day of oil equivalent. Sipetrol is also considering expanding operations in the Middle East (US Department of Energy, 2002).

Chile's Magallanes Basin is the sole oil-producing region in the country. ENAP has developed twenty fields in the basin, the largest being the Costa Auera.

Oil Production, Consumption, and Reserves

Oil production, which began in 1945, is concentrated around the Strait of Magellanes, both onshore and offshore. Chile is a small oil producer[87] and oil production in Chile is in decline, as existing wells have matured and exploration efforts elsewhere have proven unsuccessful.

In 2006, production of oil totaled 15 100 barrels per day, which is 8% higher than the level of production for 2002 (14 000 barrels per day). In 2010, the production of crude oil reached 10 850 barrels per day; this represents a production that is 28% lower than the level of production reached in 2006.

In 2002, proven crude oil reserves in Chile was 81 050 million barrels. In 2006, according to *OGJ*, Chile had 150 million barrels of proven crude oil reserves, which is 85% higher than the one reported in 2002. In 2008, the oil reserves were the same than in 2006.

Chile consumed in 2008 an estimated of 238 000 barrels per day. In 2009, the country consumed 297 650 barrels per day, which is 25% higher than the one reached in 2008. Chile imported in 2009, a total of 286 880 barrels per day or 96% of the oil's consumption for that year. The country's main source of oil imports is Argentina, followed by Brazil, Angola, and Nigeria. Chile imports 70% of its oil's needs from these countries.

In 2008, oil was the dominant fuel in Chile, accounting for around 60% of primary energy demand, followed by hydro at 19.5%, gas at 8.4%, and coal at 11.6%. Chile's 2008 regional market share of 4.38% is set to rise to 5.02% by 2013. Thermal power generation is forecast to rise by 30% between 2008 and 2018.

Table 33. Oil production in Chile (Thousand barrels per day)

Data	2007	2008	2009
Total oil production. Production of crude oil (including lease condensate), natural gas plant liquids, and other liquids, and refinery processing gain (loss).	11.60	11.19	10.77
Crude oil production: Includes lease condensate.	2.55	2.64	3.68
Consumption: Consumption of petroleum products and direct combustion of crude oil.	282.00	298	297.65
Net exports/imports (-) Net exports = Total oil production - Consumption. Negative numbers are net imports.	- 270.40	- 287	-286.88
Refinery capacity: Crude oil distillation capacity as of January 1.	227	227	227
Proved reserves as of January 1 (Million barrels)	150	150	150

Source: EIA.

---

[87] Chile dependence on imported energy had been increasing for the past years.

Chile's oil demand has nearly doubled over the past decade, while crude oil production has declined by 28% from 2006 to 2010, forcing Chile to increase its imports of oil in 6% from 2007 to 2009.

Chile electricity generation is 99.9% produced either by hydroelectric (almost 40% of the total installed capacity) or by thermal power plants (almost 60% of the total installed capacity), run on natural gas or fuel oil/diesel[88].

Oil Refineries and Pipelines

Chile has three crude oil refineries, all of which are operated by ENAP or its subsidiary companies. The largest of these is the Petrox SA refinery (122 591 barrels per day crude oil capacity), which is located at the port city of San Vicente in the Bío-Bío region of central Chile. This refinery is supplied oil from Argentina via the Estenssoro-Pedrals (formerly the Transandino) pipeline, and accounts for about 41% of Chile's refining capacity. The second largest refinery is Refinería de Petróleo Concon (94 350 barrels per day), which is located near Santiago in the Metropolitan region. The smallest of Chile's refineries is Gregorio refinery (9 859 barrels per day), located in far southern Chile, which is supplied crude oil from an independent pipeline system local to that region. The total refining capacity of Chile's three refineries is 226 800 barrels per day of crude oil. In June 2004, ENAP signed a deal with partners Técnicas Reunidas (Spain) and Germany's Ferrostaal Group to build a US $110 million mild hydrocracker at its Bío-Bío refinery to produce low-sulfur diesel fuel. In November 2005, ENAP announced that it would add facilities at the Bío-Bío plant to produce low-sulfur gasoline as well. In June 2005, ENAP announced that it would build a US $430 million delayed cooker plant at its Aconcagua refinery. The work started in 2008.

Chile has 758 km of crude oil pipelines and 789 km of petroleum product pipelines. The most significant crude oil pipeline in Chile is the Estenssoro-Pedrals pipeline that supplies petroleum from Argentina's Neuquen Basin to the Petrox SA refinery in central Chile. Sonacol is Chile's domestic oil and products pipeline operator (US Department of Energy, 2002). The company operates Chile's domestic oil transport network (operates 467 km of crude oil and product pipelines, which link Chile's oil fields to its refineries and population centers). Sonacol also operates a fleet of oil tankers. Chile has two crude oil import pipelines.

Investment in the Oil Sector

In an effort to further the development of hydrocarbon resources in the Strait of Magallanes, the Chilean government has undertaken an aggressive international bidding process to attract private investment for up to ten blocks; seven solely for private bidders, and three in partnership with State-oil company ENAP. However, there are some limiting factors for energy development in this region.

---

[88] The country has very limited use of renewable energy sources for electricity generation, such as geothermal or wind power. The country currently has 12 000 MW of capacity and intends to reach 25 000 MW by 2020; this represents an increase of 108%. The goal of the government is to reach 10% in the use of renewable energy sources for electricity generation by 2024.

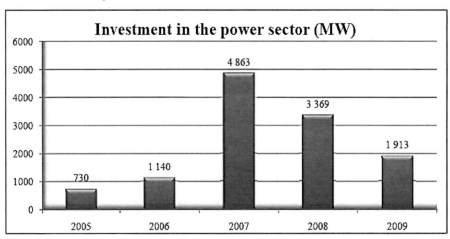

Source: National Energy Commission.

Figure 59. Investment made in Chile in the power sector during the period 2005-2009.

One of them is the size and potential reserves in the Strait of Magallanes, and the second is the fact that its geographic location would not greatly aid with energy supplies for the demand centers of Santiago and the north of the country.

In 2009, several thermal-electric power plants were under construction and planning stages, as Chile is investing to diversify its power-generating infrastructure, with the purpose of satisfying its increase power demand in the coming years.

The investments made to cover the requirements of growth during the period 2005-2009 are shown in Figure 59. The investment approved for the energy sector during the period 2008-2012 represents more than 43% of the total investment.

Electricity Generation

The Chilean electric market was liberalized in 1982. In fact, the generation, transmission and distribution of electricity activities are, since that year, undertaken by private companies. The State has only a surveillance role of the system and certain regulatory powers, especially in connection with the determination of certain tariffs.

The electric market is composed by seventy companies; twenty eight of them are generators, five are transmission and thirty seven are distribution companies. Almost 37% of the electricity of the country is produced by hydro power plants; 38.9% comes from natural gas and diesel plants; 17.4% comes from coal plants; 1.52% comes from wind and biomass sources of energy, and 3.5% from oil.

There are four separate electricity systems in Chile: the central interconnected system (SIP), which serves the central part of the county. SIP has 9 603 MW capacity or 72% of the total installed capacity of the country (13 275 MW) serving 93% of the population; the large northern interconnected system (SING), with a capacity of 3 573 MW, which serves the desert mining regions in the north. SING has 27% of the total installed capacity of the country[89]; Aysen, with a capacity of 33.5 MW, which has 0.3% of the total

---

[89] To date these two grids are not interconnected.

installed capacity; and Magallanes, with a capacity of 64.7 MW, which has 0.5% of total installed capacity, serving small areas of the extreme southern part of the country (see Figure 60). The long distances existing among the four systems make their integration very difficult.

Colbun is the second-largest player in the electricity market, with around 2 500 MW in installed capacity, and is the only major generator remaining in Chilean hands, controlled by the Matte family. Currently, around 50% of Colbun's capacity is hydro, with the other 50% coming from thermal sources. Colbun is currently working on a 144 MW hydro power plant in San Pedro at a cost of US $202 million. It is also developing a 350 MW coal-fired power plant in Coronel. In addition, it is planning some smaller, non-conventional renewable projects, the most advanced of which is a 7 MW project in San Clemente.

AES Gener is the smallest of the three big players. It currently has around 2 500 MW in installed capacity. The company suffered a severe setback when the environmental permit for its 270 MW coal-fired power plant in Campiche was invalidated by the Chilean Supreme Court.

Total installed nominal capacity in Chile in April 2010 was 15.94 GW. Of the total installed capacity, 64.9% is thermal a little bit higher than in previous years. SING is mostly thermal and, for this reason, suffers from overcapacity. Total generation in 2009 was 58.5 TWh, out of which around 58% was produced by thermal sources and consumed 55.2 TWh; this represents 94.4% of the production of that year. It is important to stress that this figure varies significantly from one year to another, depending upon the hydrology of the particular period. In addition to new hydro power projects, there are several large-scale thermal power projects in the development pipeline for Chile.

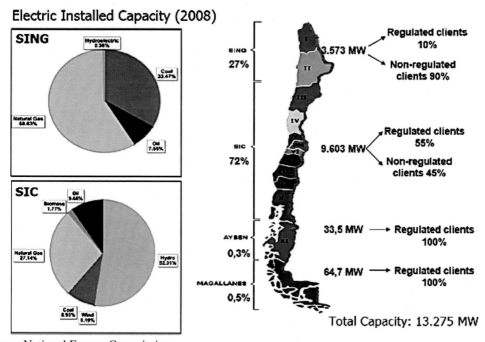

Source: National Energy Commission.

Figure 60. Electric installed capacity in Chile in 2008.

In 2010, Chile imported 72.5% of its electricity needs. The electricity consumed per capita in 2010 was 3 318.2 kWh, which is a figure still low by developed country standards. It grew rapidly (6% per year) until 2006, but since then it has been stagnated. However, it is expected that electricity demand increase at 5% per year in the period up to 2030.

Total electricity coverage in Chile was as high as 99% in 2008 (99% in urban areas and 95% in rural areas). Around 300 000 Chilean people have no access to electricity in that year. Most of the progress in rural areas has happened in the last fifteen years, following the establishment of a National Program for Rural Electrification administered by the National Fund for Regional Development. Under this Fund, there is tripartite funding of the capital costs of rural connections: Users pay 10%, companies 20% and the State provides the remaining 70%, with users expected to pay for running costs.

Distribution and transmission losses in 2010 reached 8.4% of the total electricity produced by the country in that year, which is well below the Latin American and the Caribbean average.

Looking Forward

According to the newly published Chile Power Report, the BMI forecasts that the country will account for 5.45% of Latin American regional power generation by 2013. Chile's thermal generation in 2008, represented 7.58% of the regional total. By 2013, the country is expected to account for 6.98% of thermal generation, a reduction of 0.6% respect to 2008. Between 2008 and 2018, BMI are forecasting an increase in Chilean electricity generation of 39.7%, which is mid-range for the Latin American region. This equates to 17.6% in the 2013-2018 period, down from 18.8% in 2008-2013. Chile's installed electricity capacity has grown by 72% over the past twelve years. Taking into account the very limited fossil fuels reserves that the country has until today, would be very important that the government adopt additional measures in order to increase the role of renewable energy sources for electricity generation in the coming decades, with the purpose of reducing the current dependency of fossil fuels used for this specific purpose, specially oil.

Ecuador

Oil Reserves

According to *OGJ*, Ecuador held proven oil reserves of 6.5 billion barrels in January 2010, and increase of 1.8 billion barrels from the declared proven reserves of 2009; this represents an increase of 38%. Ecuador has the fourth largest oil reserves in South America after Venezuela, Brazil, and Mexico[90], and is the fifth-largest producer of oil in the sub region after Venezuela, Brazil, Mexico, and Argentina, producing 470 000 barrels per day in 2010

---

[90] Ecuador occupies the 19th position in the list of countries according to their oil proven reserves.

down from 486 000 barrels per day in 2009 (almost all of which was crude oil)[91]. The reduction in oil production during 2009 and 2010 was 3%.

According to Arriagada (2006), Ecuador possesses 0.4% of world's crude oil reserves, which is enormously significant for the economy. Crude oil production has increased sizably since the opening of the Oleoducto de Crudos Pesados in September 2003, which removed a chokepoint on crude oil transportation in the country. However, production has fallen in recent years, as result of natural decline of oil fields in exploitation, the lack of new project development, and some operating difficulties at existing oil fields. Following drops in production by Petroecuador, a company which has drawn some criticism in the past decade over its declining efficiency and output levels, the goal of hydrocarbon energy policy is to increase oil production. In April, the government announced plans to increase oil production with the purpose of reducing the import of oil from outside the country. However, the challenge is to attract investment to achieve that goal, given the problems faced by the sector, which include the following: Opposition by Petroecuador workers to opening up jobs or projects to the private sector using partnership contracts, and the promulgation of a new hydrocarbons law, among others. During the period 2001 to 2005, Petroecuador's share of national crude oil output declined from 56% to 38%; this represents a reduction of 18%.

Oil Production, Export, and Consumption

Petroleum was first discovered in Ecuador in the early 1900s, both on and offshore from Salinas on the Santa Elena Peninsula west of Guayaquil. In the late 1980s, the vast majority of Ecuador's proven oil reserves lay in the northern part of the country between the Napo River and the Colombian border. This area formed part of a rich oil-bearing region extending from southern Colombia through Ecuador and northeastern Peru. Indeed, analysts believed that this region represented one of the richest oil-bearing areas of the Western Hemisphere. Although exploration in this region began in the 1920s, petroleum was not actually found until a consortium formed by Texaco-Petroleum and Gulf Oil companies discovered several rich fields near Lago Agrio (now Nueva Loja) in 1967. The success of the Texaco-Gulf exploration attracted other companies, and over the next two decades, more than fifty new wells began producing commercial quantities of crude oil. Ecuador's most productive oil fields are located in the northeast corner of the country. According to EIA (2010), the largest oil field is Shushufindi. Other major oil fields include Sacha, Libertador, Dorine, and Eden Yuturi. Ecuador produces two varieties of crude oil: Oriente and Napo. Both are heavy sour crude oil with APIs of 19° and between 1% and 2% sulfur content, while Oriente is a medium-heavy, medium-sour crude oil, with a 29° API and 1% sulfur content. According to Clough (2007), Ecuador increased the production of oil during the period 2001-2005 in 31% but the share of national oil production declined from 56% to 38% in that period. It is important to note that in 2009, Ecuador produced 486 000 barrels per day, down from 505 000 barrels per day a year before, a decrease of 4%, and 470 000 barrels per day in 2010; this represents 3% decrease in comparison to 2009. Since 2008, the oil production in Ecuador decreased around 7%.

---

[91] Ecuador's crude oil production increased 31% during the period 2001 to 2005. During the period 2005-2010, oil production started to decline.

In 2008, Ecuador consumed 186 000 barrels per day of oil leaving net exports of 318 580 barrels per day[92]. In 2009, the country consumed 192 000 barrels per day; this represents and increase of 3% respect 2008, In 2009, the oil net export was 239 290 barrels per day, a decrease of 25% respect to 2008, and 27% respect to 2007.

Table 34. Ecuador's oil data (Thousands of barrels per day)

Data	2007	2008	2009
Total oil production Production of crude oil (including lease condensate), natural gas plant liquids, and other liquids, and refinery processing gain (loss). Negative value indicates refinery processing loss.	511.60	504.58	485.29
Crude oil production Includes lease condensate.	511.09	504.73	485.62
Consumption Consumption of petroleum products and direct combustion of crude oil.	182	186	192
Net exports/imports(-) Net exports = Total oil production – consumption.	329.60	318.58	239.29
Refinery capacity	176	176	176
Proved reserves as of January 1. (Billion barrels)	4.517	4.52	4.66

Source: EIA.

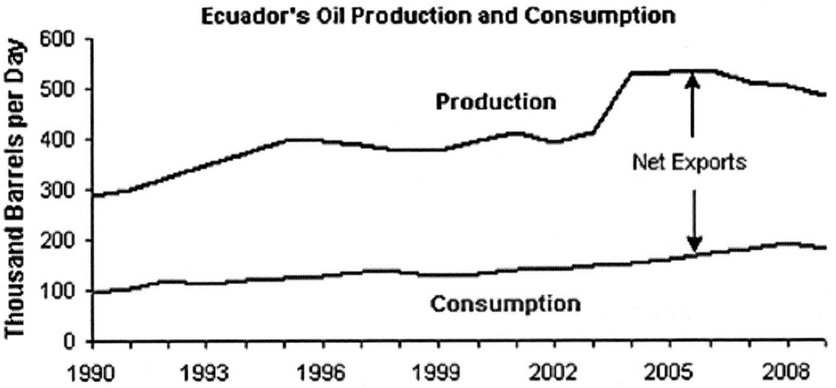

Source: EIA.

Figure 61. Oil production and consumption in Ecuador during the period 1990-2008.

From Figure 61, the following can be stated: The level of oil production in Ecuador is more than enough to satisfy the current and future oil demand of the country, leaving sufficient oil to export to other countries located outside or inside the region. However, after 2006 the level of production started to decline while, at the same time, the level of oil consumption started to increase. This situation reduced the exports capabilities of the country in the past years and the level of income in foreign currency. Due to saving measures adopted by the government to change this situation, the consumption of oil started to decline, particularly after 2008 and regretably also the production.

---

[92] With this level of oil production, the radio/production is around twenty years and likely to drop.

Several factors are limiting the increase in oil production in the country. First, many private companies have clashed with the government over contract and tax issues, especially dealing with rebates of the value-added tax (VAT) paid by oil exporters. Both Occidental Petroleum and Encana have taken legal action against the Ecuadorian government over VAT rebates. In 2004, an arbitration panel awarded US $75 million to Occidental in VAT reimbursements, an award the Ecuadorian government disputes. Second, there has been significant opposition to oil development by indigenous groups. These groups have repeatedly obstructed exploration and production activities in Ecuador's eastern region. The IIT block, which sits deep in the Amazon region, is facing particularly fierce resistance from these groups. Indigenous activists have also brought a lawsuit against Chevron-Texaco over Texaco's former oil operations in Ecuador. Protests against the oil industry have had a direct impact upon the country's crude oil production. In August 2005, protest groups shut down Petroecuador's crude oil production for a week, forcing the company to declare force majeure on its crude oil exports. In February 2006, Petroecuador shut down the Sote pipeline for several days, after protesters occupied pumping stations (EIA, 2007).

It is important to know that Petroecuador controls about half of the crude oil production in the country. The largest foreign-owned oil company is Repsol-YPF, which represents about 13% of the country's total crude oil production. Other important foreign oil producers include Andes Petroleum, a consortium led by the Chinese National Petroleum Corporation that acquired assets in September 2005, Perencol, and AGIP (an Italian firm). While Ecuador's crude oil production increased 31% from 2001 to 2005, Petroecuador's share of national crude oil output declined from 56% to 37% during that same period. In 2006, Petroecuador's share of national production jumped to 46%, following the company's takeover of the former production assets of Occidental Petroleum. In late 2007, the Ecuadorian government began attempts to transition the contracts for foreign oil companies into service agreements. Under these arrangements, oil companies typically act as an agent that produces oil on behalf of the State, receiving a fee as compensation. In early 2009, the government reportedly reached an agreement with Repsol-YPF under which the company would receive an extension of its operating contract in the country in return for accepting the new contract structure.

Future increases in Ecuador's crude oil production will likely come from development of the Ishpingo-Tapococha-Tiputini (ITT) block. The government plans to open ITT to foreign producers through a licensing round in the near future. The ITT block, located in Ecuador's Amazon region, contains an estimated 900 million barrels of proven reserves, with potential recoverable reserves as high as 1.3 billion barrels. Analysts predict that, if fully developed, the block could produce 190 000 barrels per day. However, the ITT block reportedly contains a variety of crude oil even heavier than Napo, so any oil producer would need to blend the crude oil with lighter hydrocarbons before shipping it via Ecuador's pipeline network. As an alternative to the development of the ITT block, President Correa floated the idea that the international community could pay Ecuador to not exploit the oil reserves located in this area. The country sought US $350 million per year over a ten year period, representing its estimate of one-half of the revenues that it could earn from oil production from the ITT block.

Oil Exports and Imports

According to EIA sources, Ecuador has a net oil exports estimated at 239 290 barrels per day in 2009[93]. It is important to single out that the oil sector dominates the Ecuadorian economy, accounting for almost half of total export earnings and one-third of all tax revenues. However, and despite its large oil exports, the country must import refined petroleum products due to the lack of sufficient domestic refining capacity to meet local demand. For this reason, the country does not always enjoy the full benefits of high world's oil prices because, on the one hand, these high prices bring Ecuador greater export revenues but, at the same time, they also increase the country's refined product import bill. Ecuador's energy mix is largely dependent upon oil, which represented 80% of the country's total energy consumption in 2006.

In 2009, Ecuador exported to the United States 185 000 barrels of oil per day, which represents 38% of its daily crude oil production (58% of the total oil exports realized in 2008) and around 2% of the total USA oil import. Other export destinations of Ecuadorian crude oil were Peru (15.4%), Central America (9.39%), China (12%) and Chile (5.79%). Ecuador has begun to look more towards the Asian market, particularly China, as a way to diversify its customer base. According to ECLAC, Ecuadorian oil sales account for over one-third of overall exports, an average of 36.4% from 1993 to 2003. In 2009, oil exports represented 49% of the total oil production for that year. Except for Venezuela, no other regional economy has such a high stake in oil in the region.

Finally, it is important to stress the following: Of the total domestic supply of 34 million barrels of derivate, 22.9 million (66.9%) were produced domestic (but of very poor quality) and 11.3 million (33.1%) were imported. These are mainly diesel, naphtha, and liquefied petroleum gas for respectively 36%, 35%, and 28% of the total 11.3 million barrels of refined products imports. Ecuador also exports 7.9 million barrels of refined products, mainly fuel oil and naphtha (80% and 14% respectively); these have fewer added values than the imported products (Huiskamp, 2007).

Investment in the Oil Sector

Ecuador' energy policy is in principle opposed to foreign investment in its energy sector. However, the Energy Minister announced, in May 2006, two initiatives encouraging foreign involvement in Ecuador's oil industry. In one of the initiatives, exploration rights for reserves estimated at more than one billion barrels would be awarded to foreign concerns, preferably State-owned. The other was an announcement that rights over Block 15, the area formerly controlled by Occidental, would be awarded to a State-owned foreign oil company, possibly ENAP of Chile, Petrobras of Brazil or Ecopetrol of Ecuador.

In April 2009, China reportedly agreed to loan Ecuador US $1 billion for the increase of the production of oil to be re-paid with future oil shipments (EIA, 2009). It is important to stress that Ecuador refined less than half of the petroleum it produced.

---

[93] In 2007, Ecuador rejoined the OPEC after leaving the organization at the end of 1992. Ecuador is the smallest oil producer in OPEC, with an assigned production quota of 520 000 barrels per day.

Oil Pipelines

Ecuador has two major oil pipeline systems. The first is the Sistema Oleoducto Trans-Ecuatoriano (SOTE), built in the early 1970s, and the second the Oleoducto de Crudos Pesados. The first pipeline is a 499 km, 400 000 barrels per day pipeline that runs from Lago Agrio to the Balao oil terminal on the Pacific coast. SOTE has suffered from natural disasters that severely disrupted Ecuador's oil production. In 1987, an earthquake destroyed a large section of SOTE, reducing Ecuador's oil production for that year by over 50%. In March 2008, landslides damaged SOTE, shutting operations for several days.

The second oil pipeline is Oleoducto de Crudos Pesados. The 480 km, 450 000 barrels per day runs mostly parallels to the route of the SOTE. The Oleoducto de Crudos Pesados began operations in September 2003, and its completion immediately doubled Ecuador's oil pipeline capacity. The completion of the Oleoducto de Crudos Pesados pipeline led to a sharp increase in Ecuador's crude oil production, as private companies were no longer constrained by the capacity limits of the SOTE pipeline. Use of the Oleoducto de Crudos Pesados system is mostly confined to private oil producers, with Petroecuador relying upon the SOTE pipeline. Ecuador utilizes one international oil pipeline, the Estenssoro-Pedrals; the 50 000 barrels per day pipeline connects Ecuador's oil fields with the Colombian port of Tumaco.

Oil Refineries

According to *OGJ*, Ecuador has three oil refineries, with a combined capacity of 176 000 barrels per day. The largest refinery in Ecuador is Esmeraldas (110 000 barrels per day), located on the Pacific coast. The Ecuadorian government is actively seeking ways to increase domestic production of lighter petroleum products. These plans include building new refining facilities or upgrading the Esmeraldas refinery to better handle Ecuador's heavy domestic crude oil production. In late 2008, Ecuador signed a contract with South Korea's SK Engineering to upgrade the Esmeraldas refinery. The US $200 million project would seek to conduct repairs to increase utilization rates at the facility. There have also been discussions between Ecuador and Venezuela about the construction of a new refinery in the country. The two countries established a joint company in mid-2008, with the purpose of building the facility on the Pacific coast in Manabi province. The planned crude oil distillation capacity of the refinery is 300 000 barrels per day, with an expected cost of US $7 billion. Completion of the project is foreseen for 2013.

Electricity Generation

According to EIA sources, in 2009 Ecuador produced 17 335 MWh of electricity (0.09% of world's total), out of which 7 115 GWh was produced using oil as fuel (41%). In 2009, the electricity consumption was 10 515 GWh, which represents 61% of the electricity produced in that year. In 2009, the electricity transmission and distribution losses reached 7 681 MWh or 44.3% of the electricity produced. This electricity loss is very high, according to international and regional standards. The electricity consumption per capita was in 2009, 7 881 kWh. The total electricity installed capacity in 2008 was 4.19 GW, out of which

2.4 GW was thermal (53%). It is important to stick out the following: Most electricity generation is undertaken by six State-owned companies, though there are important private producers supplying customers in the urban areas surrounding Quito and Guayaquil. A single, State-owned company, Transelectric, controls the transmission system. State-owned companies control most of the distribution sector, with the exception of Guayaquil, which is served by a municipal-owned distributor.

Table 35. Generation, consumption and electricity installed capacity in Ecuador (MW)

	Ecuador 2007	Central and South America	World total	Ecuador 2008	Ecuador 2009
Net generation	15.65	1,004	18 795 77	18.06	17.33
Net consumption	12.47	843	17 139 77	14.75	10.51
Installed capacity (GWe)	4.49	237	4 468 75	4.19	-

Source: EIA.

The distributors are highly indebted and have a poor record of paying generating companies, which contributes to Ecuador's electricity shortages during the dry season. Attempts to privatize electricity distribution have encountered resistance from provincial governments, labor unions, and rural activists. In January 2009, the government merged eleven of the nineteen power distributors, in which it had majority control, into the holding Electric National Corporation in order to reduce administrative flaws, increase productivity, and eliminate the debt among the State-owned companies.

Looking Forward

Ecuador's most important oil objectives for the coming years are the following:

a) To increase production by about 18 500 barrels per day by rehabilitating forty seven wells in the most important fields such as, Lago Agrio, Shushufindi, Sacha, Auca, and Libertador;
b) To increase production by 90 000 barrels per day in further developments of the major fields and new explorations in marginal fields. The investment required is of about US $486 million;
c) To build a new refinery to process 300 000 barrels per day.

MEXICO

Oil seeps were first documented in Mexico in 1543; the first oil wells were drilled in 1869. The first major discovery was the La Paz No 1 well in the Ebano-Panuco oil field in 1904. The oil industry was nationalized in 1938, and has since been operated by a government-owned institution called "Petroleos Mexicano (PEMEX)." The Petroleum Law of 1958 permitted PEMEX to take over all concessions held by private firms, and granted it a monopoly over the petroleum industry.

Producing oil fields are along the Gulf of Mexico coastline from the State of Tamaulipas to the State of Tabasco, with the richest concentrations around Tampico, Veracruz, and Tabasco. The majority of oil production comes from the Villahermosa district in the State of Tabasco, and the offshore wells of the Bay of Campeche. Crude oil production first reached 1 million barrels per year in 1907. Mexico production rose rapidly during the 1970s, peaking at 3 140 000 barrels per day in 1985. It stayed above 3 millions of barrels per day through the period 1985-2008. In 2009, the oil production dropped to 3 millions of barrels per day and, in 2010, dropped further to 2.6 million barrels per day; this represents a decrease of 13%[94].

Energy Reform

Historically, Mexico pursued in seeking to make oil a cornerstone of its national energy strategy. The Mexican Constitution reserves the ownership and exploitation of domestic hydrocarbons to the Mexican State. Why the oil sector is so important for Mexico? The answer is the following: The oil sector generates over 15% of the country's export earnings and, what is more important, government relies upon earnings from the oil industry (including taxes and direct payments from PEMEX) for about 40% of total government revenues. Therefore, any decline in production at PEMEX has a direct effect upon the overall fiscal balance, creating a very difficult financial situation for the government.

Pursuant to the Petroleum Regulatory Law, as amended by the energy reform, except in the case of midstream and downstream natural gas industry and coal-bed methane, the exploration, production, refining, storage, transport, and firsthand sales of domestic hydrocarbons, by-products, and basic petrochemicals are exclusively reserved to the Mexican State. Accordingly, no concessions may be granted to private parties to explore and produce hydrocarbons in Mexico. The exploration, production, and refining of oil and gas as well as production of basic petrochemicals in Mexico are, thus, conducted exclusively by PEMEX.

The energy reform includes, basically, three levels of changes aimed at creating a strong energy regulatory framework giving PEMEX management and operational flexibility and efficiency:

a) *Creation of and granting of broader authority to regulatory agencies:* The Ministry of Energy have broader regulatory authority over activities in the energy sector, including the issuance of exploration and production permits to PEMEX, and the issuance of technical standards. In addition to the regulatory powers that the Energy Regulatory Commission (CRE) already has over natural gas activities, the CRE will regulate first-hand sales of fuel-oil and basic petrochemicals, fuel-oil and basic petrochemicals pipeline transport, storage, and pipeline distribution, and biofuels pipeline transportation, distribution, and storage, including the issuance of permits for conducting such activities, the directives and price methodologies, and the approval of transportation, storage, and distribution services terms and conditions;

---

[94] Mexico has been a consistent top-five oil supplier to the USA, exporting each year around 1.3 million of barrels per day.

b) *National Hydrocarbons Agency:* A new Agency was created as a branch of the Ministry of Energy to deal with the technical regulations and survey of hydrocarbons exploration and drilling;

c) *Corporate, management and business reorganization of PEMEX:* The energy reform basically provide for the reorganization of its Board of Directors, with the purpose of giving PEMEX broader authority and autonomy from the Executive Branch, including the designation of independent members of the Board (experts in the energy sector); broader management, budgetary, indebtedness, and investment-decision autonomy from the federal government; the necessary authority to create subsidiary entities and affiliate companies, as well as participating in joint venture companies, without requiring authorization from the Executive Branch; the necessary authority to eliminate some procurement constraints giving more contracting flexibility; and the authorization to create a special strategy, investment and a procurement committees, which will be responsible for the preparation of the above-mentioned contracting rules and guidelines. Finally, PEMEX will be able to develop power co-generation projects within its facilities.

Energy Security

Mexico is an important example of how threats to the energy security of a major oil producer not only have broad ramifications for the nation itself but for the rest of the world as well.

Oil has rapidly become the most precious natural resource for the country, accounting for about 27% of total exports in 2006, compared to only 8% in 2000; this represents an increase of three folds. Oil export revenues support the Mexican economy. State-owned PEMEX contributed US $79 billion in taxes and royalties to the Mexican government budget. Oil revenues usually constitute approximately 40% of the federal budget. Petrodollars are being used to develop a middle class as well as lift millions out of poverty. Social programs in Mexico have been dramatically expanded through billions of dollars in oil income.

The Constitution of PEMEX

PEMEX is the world's sixth largest oil company and the single most important entity in the Mexican economy. The company enjoys widespread popular support as it embodies Mexican independence and sovereignty. It has a monopoly over exploration and production of all hydrocarbons, a position guaranteed by Article 27 of Mexico's Constitution, which reserves ownership of hydrocarbon resources to the State. Foreign participation in the upstream sector is limited to service and performance contract arrangements and turnkey drilling contracts. PEMEX monopoly and control over refining of crude oil and production include eight basic petrochemicals (butane, carbon black feedstock, ethane, heptane, hexane, naphtha, pentane, and propane).

PEMEX was successful in lobbying the legislature for a 40% raise in its investment budget, after years of underfunding. Significant recent investments in exploration and production by PEMEX have begun to pay off, and oil production has begun to pick up after suffering several years of declines. However, PEMEX experts believe that crude oil exports could drop by as much as one-third over the next half-decade, unless private investment increases in the areas of production and exploration

Pursuant to the Petroleum Regulatory Law, the monopoly of PEMEX is only with respect to the development of domestic hydrocarbons as an industrial chain. Likewise, the PEMEX monopoly should end whenever the company undertakes the first sale of the relevant hydrocarbon by-product or basic petrochemical; all of the activities thereafter should be within the stream of commerce with no restrictions as to the ability to participate in such activities, except for certain foreign investment limitation in liquefied petroleum gas (LPG) and fuels retail.

However, the objective to make oil a cornerstone of the Mexican national energy strategy has recently changed, and now the aims and strategies of energy policy are similar to those of any country in the world, which is seeking to secure an adequate supply of energy based on international quality standards and competitive prices. Other aims are more operational in character, given the international commitments that Mexico has undertaken in the context of free trade agreements, and these define some of the energy alternatives that need to be developed in forthcoming years.

Energy Efficiency

It is important to single out that the critical problems of the Mexican oil sector are associated with the decline in oil reserves and production, the financial standing of PEMEX, and its growing dependence on imported fossil fuels. At the same time, the efficiency of PEMEX is declining due to its falling oil reserves, inability to process heavy crude oil, comparative disadvantage in deep-water exploration and production, and high administrative costs (Arriagada, 2006).

Mexico efforts to increase energy efficiency have sparked the sustained institutional and programmatic development of various bodies, such as the National Commission for Energy Saving, the Trust Fund devoted to saving electricity, the Integrated Systematic Savings Program for households and others, which have taken the lead in formulating and applying programs for various sections of society. All these energy-saving programs together resulted, by late 2005, in a 19 650 GWh fall in consumption, or a little over 4 900 MW in deferred capacity, at both government and consumer sector levels. The targets for 2014 are savings of 40 900 GWh and 9 970 MW respectively. Crucially, this has been achieved without detriment to the quality or quantity of the services requiring energy (SENER, 2006). The most effective programs for saving energy and reducing demand are the application of official Mexican standards and other incentives, although daylight saving in summer will prove a bigger factor in 2014 (Vargas, 2007).

Oil Reserves

According to *OGJ,* Mexico had 12.9 billion barrels of proven oil reserves as of January 1, 2006[95]. In 2010, the proven oil reserves dropped to 11.7 billion barrels; this means a reduction of 9%. Most reserves consist of heavy crude oil varieties, with a specific gravity of less than 25° API. The largest concentration of remaining oil reserves occurs offshore in the southern part of the country, especially in the Campeche Basin (National Council for Science and the Environment, 2009).

Although the government and others persist in denying officially that Mexico has reached the zenith of its oil career, the shrinking of the principal deposit, Cantarell oil field, demonstrates the opposite. Various articles prepared by specialists within the oil industry indicated the fall in production from the rate of 3.83 billion barrels per day in 2004 to just 2.97 billion barrels per day in 2009; this represents a decrease of 22%. It is foresee that in 2015, imports of petrol will hit 415 000 barrels per day to cover national needs (42% of domestic consumption). The cost will be around US $13,228 million a year for an oil price of US $ 31.87. To current oil price (July 2011 OPEC's price of US $95.86), the cost will be of US $39,782 million; this represents an increase of 201%.

About one-fourth of the country total oil reserves lie in the Chicontepec region of Veracruz State, and are as yet uneconomical for PEMEX to develop. Analysts believe independent producers might be able to profitably develop Chicontepec but Mexico's Constitution bars them from doing so. To get around this legal barrier, PEMEX has announced plans for the introduction of multiple service contracts in hydrocarbons exploration whose total value could reach US $8 billion; bidding begun in the fall of 2002. PEMEX has already signed a multiple service contract with Japan National Oil Corporation covering a two-year feasibility study into joint exploration of the Chicontepec Basin. Each firm invested nearly US $3 million. The feasibility study was completed in December 2003. The basin holds what is believed to be one of the largest reserves in the world but exploration is not yet feasible given the limits of current technology. The most productive onshore field is the Samaria field, in Southern Mexico, which in 1996 yielded an average of 76 215 barrels per day of 29.30 API crude oil. Production from oil fields in the south of the country generally exceeds those in the north.

It is expected that there are substantial oil reserves located in deep-water in the Gulf of Mexico but PEMEX currently lacks the technological know-how for the complicated drilling process in that area, and the company does not have sufficient funds available for exploration and investment to reverse the decline, owing to high financial burdens placed upon the company by the Mexican government. To overcome this limitation, Mexico and the United States reached agreement to divide out a four million acre area of oil on the outer continental shelf in the Gulf of Mexico, which lies between the two countries Exclusive Economic Zone in the oil-rich western Gulf of Mexico. The agreement grants Mexico 62% of the area and the United States 38%. Although the depth of the water is around 3 330 m, with advances in deep-water drilling the area has generated considerable interest (Lynch, 2003a).

---

[95] Mexico produces three grades of crude oil: Heavy Maya-22 (which accounts for more than half of total production); light low-sulfur Isthmus-34 (about 28% of production); and extra-light Olmeca-39 (about 20% of production).

Oil Production, Consumption, Export, and Import

Mexican oil production fell 9.2% in 2008; it is down 21% from peak levels reached in 2004. In 2008, Mexico slipped to 7th place in the EIA global production ranking from 6th place in 2007. In 2009, Mexico produced 2.97 million barrels per day, maintaining its rank of producer countries but in 2010 the production dropped to 2.6 million barrels per day, a decrease of 12.5%.

From Figure 62, the following can be stated: Before 2000, the production of oil in Mexico was below three millions of barrels per day. After 2000, the production increased over three million barrels per day until 2008. Since that year, the production of oil in Mexico has been sharply declining reaching the 1986 level. Of the total oil production, about 88% was crude oil and condensate; the rest consisting of natural gas liquids and refinery gain.

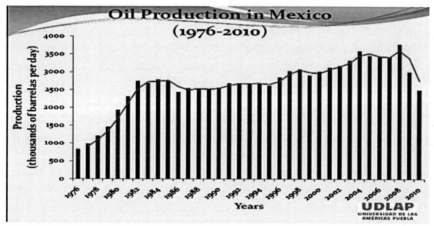

Source: UDLAP.

Figure 62. Oil production in Mexico during the period 1976-2010.

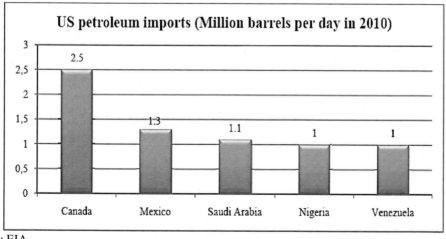

Source: EIA.

Figure 63. Top five countries exporting oil to the USA.

In 2010, Mexico exported 1.3 million barrels per day of crude oil to the USA. Mexico is consistently one of the top five exporters of crude oil to the United States, along with Canada (2.5 million barrels per day), Saudi Arabia (1.1 million of barrels per day), Nigeria (1 million barrels per day) and Venezuela (1 million barrels per day). In January 2011, Mexico exported 2 268 000 barrels per day; this represents an increase of 25% respect to 2005.

Many analysts believe that Mexican oil production has peaked, and that the country's production will continue to decline in the coming years, as shown in Figure 62, mainly driven by declining production at its super-giant Cantarell oil field[96].

The field, located in the Gulf of Campeche, is one of the largest oil fields in the world. In 2005, Cantarell produced 2 million barrels per day of crude oil or 60% of the national total for that year. The field consists of four major subfields: Akal, Nohoch, Chac, and Kutz. Production at Cantarell oil field began in 1979 but production began to decline due to falling reservoir pressure. In 1997, PEMEX developed a plan to reserve the decline by injecting nitrogen into the reservoir to maintain pressure[97]. The plan was a great success, with production at Cantarell oil field in 2004 doubling the level reached in 1995. Other expansion plans at the field should continue to add incremental production increases. Today more than three-quarters of all oil production comes from offshore sites in the Campeche Bay in the Gulf of Mexico, where the Cantarell field is located (in 2009, the production was 2.3 million barrels per day of total crude oil or 77.4% of the total production reached in that year).

In Mexico, according to IEO (2010), oil production will sinks to approximately 1.4 million barrels per day in 2025, before slowly rebounding to 1.6 million barrels per day in 2035, still 1.57 million barrels per day below 2009 level. The rebound after 2025 depends entirely on the development of potential resources in the deep-water Gulf of Mexico, which must begin some years in advance of any increase in production levels. The outlook for Mexico oil production is markedly different from the IEO (2010) projection just three years ago, in which production did not fall below 2.9 million barrels per day and a long-term recovery for 2013.

The difference between the projections is a result of declines at Cantarell field that were more severe than expected, along with diminished expectations for Chicontepec production, and more pessimistic assumptions about the level of future investment, both foreign and domestic, in Mexico deep-water production.

PEMEX has been reporting downfall in production from Cantarell since 2004. In August 2004, PEMEX announced that actual oil output from the field was forecast to decline steeply from 2006 onwards, at a rate of 14% a year. In March 2006, it was reported that Cantarell had peaked, with a second year of declining production in 2005. For 2006, the field's output fell by 13.1%, according to PEMEX data, which also predicted another decline of 15% for 2007. And in May 2008, Minister of Energy said output had fallen a further 33% to 1.07 million barrels a day, the lowest output at the field since March 1996. In January 2009, the production

---

[96] Mexico has 223 oil fields and associated gas fields and reserves from which 177 are already declining or will be in the next two years. From the forty six fields in development, twenty three are Chicontepec fields (Talwani, 2011).

[97] A group that includes BOC Gases, Marubeni, Linde, Westcoast Energy, and ICA-Fluor Daniel, built a US1 billion nitrogen plant, consisting of four 8 495 054 m^3 per day units (each of which individually would be the largest such operation in the world), which will supply Cantarell with 33 980 m^3 per day of nitrogen. The supply contract runs fifteen years and is worth US $2.7 billion. The nitrogen injection project will enable PEMEX to retrieve an additional 2.3 billion barrels of oil from Cantarell.

was around 772 000 barrels per day during a fall of approximately 38% over a year. In September 2009, the production declined drastically. The company had earlier expected production to fall continually and stabilize at approximately 500 000 barrels per day by 2012. It is expected that after 2012, the production will be maintained as 400 000 barrels per day. The downfall has adversely affected annual government budget and credit rating. PEMEX is currently developing the untapped Sihil field, located beneath Cantarell oil field, which contains an estimated 1 billion barrels of oil recoverable reserves. The production of the Sihil oil field is now stabilizing at about 500 000 barrels per day (Talwani, 2011).

The two other major oil production centers in the Gulf of Campeche are Ku-Maloob-Zaap and Abkatun-Pol-Chuc. Located adjacent to Cantarell oil field, the Ku-Maloob-Zaap complex produced 864 000 barrels per day of crude oil in 2009, an increase of 169% with respect the production reached in 2005 (Talwani, 2011). PEMEX hopes that continued development of the field will replace some of the decline in Cantarell oil field production. Off the coast of Tabasco State, the Abkatun-Pol-Chuch oil field produced 544 000 barrels per day of crude oil in 2010, an increase of 81% respect the production of 2005. However, production there has declined steadily down over 50% from 1996.

Important onshore production centers in the southern part of the country include Bellota-Jujo and Samaria-Luna. Crude oil production in the northern part of the country reached 83 500 barrels per day in 2005; the largest field in the north is Poza Rica (National Council for Science and the Environment, 2009).

The oil consumption in Mexico has been increasing in the past years from 1.5 million of barrels per day in 2003 to 2.08 million barrels per day in 2009, an increase of 39% for the whole period (an average of 6.5% increase per year).

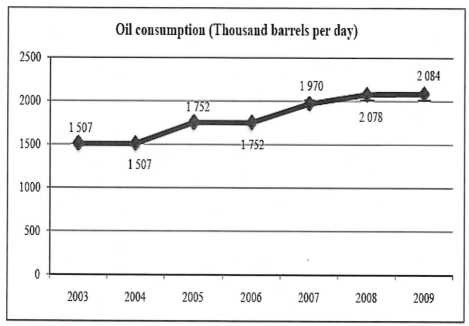

Source: Index Mundi.

Figure 64. Oil consumption in Mexico during the period 2003-2010.

Total energy consumption in Mexico by type of energy in 2008

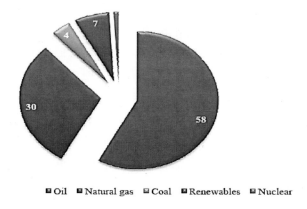

Source: EIA.

Figure 65. Energy consumption in Mexico in 2008.

As can be seen in Figure 65, oil continue to be the dominant energy source with 58% participation in the energy mix of the country, followed by natural gas, hydro power, and coal. It is expected that this energy mix will continue to be the same in the near future.

An important sign of distortion in the production model of the oil industry in Mexico relates to derivatives (refined products and petrochemicals). Production is still performed outside national territory, with the consequent impact on domestic jobs and imports of these products. It is expected that in 2015 imports of oil will hit 415 000 barrels per day or 42% of domestic consumption worth US $13,228 million a year. In terms of investment and jobs, this is like shifting the equivalent of two additional refineries to the United States.

Oil and Other Facilities

Presently there are more than 40 thermal electric power plants in Mexico that are greater than 100 MWe generating capacity, including six that are over 1 000 MWe. The largest capacity thermal electric power plant in the country is the 2 100 MWe Petecalco power plant in Guerrero State, which has recently converted from oil to imported coal as its fuel.

There are also many small diesel or internal combustion electricity generators which operate in mostly remote regions of Mexico. These plants, most of which are owned by CFE, supply a total of about 200 MWe of localized electricity for isolated industries and communities. Another form of small power production - co-generation of combined heat and power - is also being utilized in Mexico.

Co-generation has actually been available to industries for about a decade, but there has been only a relatively small amount of investment in co-generation of combined heat and power facilities. The reason of this small level of investment in co-generation is that CFE would only buy no more than 20 MWe of excess power capacity from any of these types of facilities, and would only pay the marginal cost for the electricity. Cogenerated electricity is still not yet deregulated - any electricity so generated must be directly used by the industrial facility or else sold to CFE; it cannot be sold to remote consumers via the grid.

Oil Refineries and Pipelines

According to *OGJ*, "Mexico has six refineries all operated by PEMEX, with a total refining capacity of 1.68 million barrels per day. The largest facility in the country is the 330 000 barrels per day Salina Cruz facility." PEMEX also controls 50% of the 334 000 barrels per day Deer Park refinery in Texas, USA. Despite its status as one of the world's largest crude oil exporters, Mexico is a net importer of refined petroleum products. The company has recently completed a series of refinery upgrades and additional capacity to increase refinery capacity of the country.

Mexico has 27 358 km of pipelines most of them in the central-south and eastern part of the country, connecting the cities of Salinas Cruz and Veracruz in the south-east, Mexico City in the center, and Juarez City in the north. Small net of pipelines are connecting Tijauna with other two sites in the north-west of the country.

The country's energy infrastructure needs a desperate upgrade. Over the past decade, PEMEX has slashed its maintenance expenditures throughout the country.

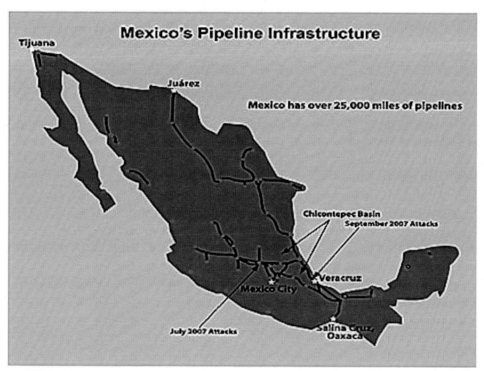

Source: PEMEX.

Figure 66. Mexico pipelines structure.

In 1997, the company had a budget of US $2.7 billion for maintenance; in 2007 the budget was only US $1 billion; this represents a reduction of US $1.7 billion or 37%. Funding decreases have become the norm at PEMEX because the federal government increasingly siphons off energy revenues to support social programs (Clemente, 2008). PEMEX has also completed a 992 km pipeline to supply the Cadereyta refinery in Querétaro State with crude oil from Nuevo Teapa, Veracruz. Construction was handled by a subsidiary of South Korean engineering firm Sun Kyung Engineering Corporation.

New Energy Investment Projects

For some time, PEMEX has been pursuing a strategic plan to offset this loss of production by launching new projects, as the decline in mature fields has been stronger than expected and new production has not been achieving forecast levels. The estimated loss sustained annually by the Cantarell oil field cannot be compensated by current efforts to increase oil production in this field.

In conjunction with this, revenue from oil has been employed to cover current expenditure rather than invest in the oil industry, and this situation has provoked budgetary inertia that has not been matched by an integral fiscal reform to bolster national finances. An integral fiscal reform would entail levying the major national and international capital that benefits from a privileged tax regime, and this has the potential to provoke political conflicts (Vargas, 2007).

It is important to stress the following: In 2008, based on the National Infrastructure Program, PEMEX, CFE, and Luz y Fuerza[98], contemplate to carry out, through domestic and international tenders, the drilling of new wells in Cantarell, Chicontepec, Burgos, and Ku-Maloop Zaap oil fields, and the construction of more than 8 000 km of oil and gas pipelines.

In the Cantarell oil field, several projects will be financed by PEMEX. The estimated budget for the projects to be implemented by 2012 varies from US $11 to US $14 billion. The project includes, among others, drilling of ninety eight wells, the construction of three marine structures, around 27 000 km^2 of 3D seismic studies, and the construction of 84 km of oil pipelines.

In the Chicontepec area, several projects will be financed also by PEMEX. The estimated budget for the projects to be implemented by 2012 varies from US $10 to US $14.5 billion. The project includes, among others, drilling of 5 421 development wells.

In the Ku-Maloob-Zaap area, several projects will be also financed by PEMEX. The estimated budget for the projects to be implemented by 2012 varies from US $6.5 to US $9 billion. The project includes, among others, drilling 164 wells, building eighteen platforms, and purchase three storage tank ships.

In the Burgos area, the estimated budget for the implementation of the foreseable projects by 2012 varies from US $7.5 to US $10.5 billion. The project includes, among others, drilling 2 681 wells (2 331 development and 350 exploration wells). A new marine terminal in Tuxpan, State of Veracruz; the construction of ten new plants for clean oil refined products will also be financed by PEMEX.

Finally, it is important to stress the following: Mexico's current relatively less-stringent environmental regulations is one of the factors that have provided an incentive for US companies to locate their power plants in Mexico in order to produce electricity for export to California. Sempra Energy Resources completed the construction of a 600 MWe power plant near Mexicali. The US $350 million power plant was built near the North Baja pipeline and became operational in 2003, and was connected to the US electricity grid via a 230 kV

---

[98] This company was closed by the Mexican government in 2009.

transmission line. Intergen is also planning to build a power plant in Baja California State. The proposed 765 MWe project, to be located near Mexicali, will supply half of the electrical output of the plant to California.

Summing up the following can be stated: The largest investment in the Mexico's oil sector will be for the further development of the country capacity for oil and gas production. As a major source of revenue to the Mexican government, PEMEX expects to invest in exploration, refining, and production (basic petrochemicals, gas, and more complex petrochemicals), more than US $76 billion. Over half of the projects have planned start dates between 2008 and 2011. The demand for imported equipment and services for the energy sector increased by 2.4% during the period 2007-2008, and this trend will continue in the coming years. The major energy-generation government agencies have been granted a budget of US $20 billion during 2009 for the maintenance and investment of energy infrastructure.

It is important to note that the lack of investment in the oil industry and its distorted productive spectrum compel PEMEX to export basic petrochemical inputs, such as naphtha and then import secondary petrochemicals and derivatives. If this situation continues in the coming years, imports of petrochemicals will account for 50% of domestic consumption by 2015.

Electricity Generation

Like PEMEX in the oil and gas industry, CFE for years has enjoyed a monopoly in the electric power sector, although reforms instituted in 1992 allow others to sell it power[99]. CFE owns most of Mexico's installed electric generating capacity (including all the nuclear and geothermal generating capacity) and generates around 92% of the country's electricity. LFC was, until 2009, Mexico's other State-owned electric utility with about 2% of the generating capacity, primarily around Mexico City.

PEMEX also generates electricity (about 3% of the total as of the end of 2001); various private sector generating facilities produce the rest. CFE's dominance is beginning to wane slightly as the company lacks the funds needed to meet Mexico's soaring electricity demand. The private sector is now beginning to secure a significant market share. For example, Iberdrola expects to have more than 2 000 MWe online, and will become the second-greatest electricity generator in Mexico.

It is important to stress that the electricity sector in Mexico relies heavily on thermal sources[100]. Expansion plans for the period 2006-2015 estimate the addition of some 14.8 GW of new generation capacity by the public sector, with a predominance of combined cycles. In 2010, the production of electricity using oil as energy source was 52 258 MWh, which represent 20.3% of the total electricity produced by the country in that year (257 455 MWh).

From Figure 67, the following can be stated: The use of oil for electricity generation has been decreasing since 2001 from around 140 000 barrels per day to around 60 000 barrels per day in 2010; this represents a decrease of 57%. The consumption of diesel for electricity generation is very low and suffered no drastic change during the whole period considered.

---

[99] The participation of the private sector represents 25% of the total electricity generation capacity installed in the country.

[100] Installed thermal capacity represents 75.3% of the total capacity installed in the country for electricity generation.

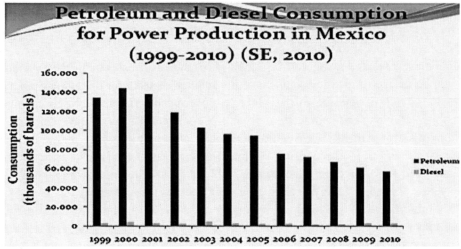

Source: UDLAP.

Figure 67. Petroleum and diesel consumption for power production in Mexico during the period 1999-2010.

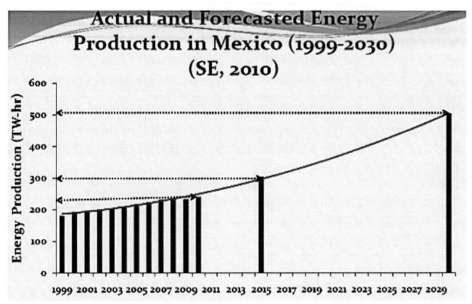

Source: UDLAP.

Figure 68. Actual and forecasted energy production in Mexico during the period 1999-2030.

According to Figure 68, in 2008 the total production of electricity was 234 TWh. It is expected that this production will increase to 300 TWh by 2015, an increase of 28% and to a little bit above 500 TWh by 2030 (an increase of 67% respect to 2015).

Installed electricity capacity in 2008 was 58 GW. The general trend in thermal electricity generation is a decline in petroleum-based fuels and a growth in natural gas and coal. In 2008, gross generation (not including co-generation and auto-generation) from conventional thermal sources was 79.2% of the total.

The expansion program contemplated by SENER for the period 2008-2017, includes the addition of 14 794 MW by the public service. Self-supply and co-generation will add another 2 490 MW in new capacity. Total public installed capacity in 2017 is estimated at 61 074 MW (5% increase respect to 2008), out of which 40% would be combined-cycles and 21% would be hydroelectric plants.

The external electricity trade is carried out through nine interconnections between the United States and Mexico, and one interconnection with Belize. These connections have primarily been used to import and export electricity during emergencies. In 2007, Mexico exported 1.3 TWh of electricity to the United States, while importing 0.6 TWh. Plans were implemented to connect Mexico with Guatemala and Belize as part of the Central American Interconnection System. The 400 kV interconnection line Mexico-Guatemala was commissioned in April 2009, has an estimated transmission capacity of 200 MW from Mexico to Guatemala, and 70 MW in the opposite direction.

Consumption of electricity during the period 2000-2010 increased from 164.7 billion kWh in 2000 to 181.5 billion kWh in 2010, an increase of 10% for the whole period (around 1% per year).

In 2008, the consumption share by sector was as follows: Residential: 26%; industrial: 59% (38% for mid-sized industry and 21% for large industry); commercial: 7%; agriculture: 4%; and services: 4%.

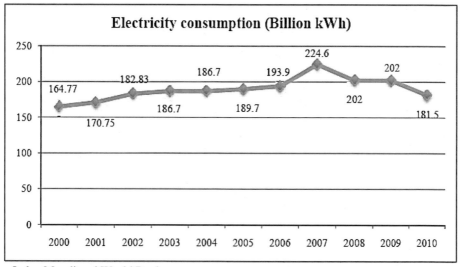

Source: Index Mundi and World Bank.

Figure 69. Consumption of electricity in Mexico during the period 2000-2010.

Electricity demand has grown steadily in the past decade and SENER forecasts that consumption will grow by 3.3% a year for the period 2007-2017, reaching 298.72 TWh in 2017. Demand growth forecasts have been revised down from an estimated 4.8% a year in the projections from 2006, to a 3.3% a year due to the expected effects of the current economic crisis on energy demand.

In 2008, the reserve margin in the national interconnected system was 45.8%, while the operating reserve margin was 21.3%. It is estimated that both reserve margins will remain high during the 2009-2013 period. However, from 2014 the reserve margin is expected to decrease to 29.2%, with the operating reserve margin reaching 8.3%. Those values would be about 25% and 6% respectively in 2017.

The commissioning of the Agua Prieta II, Norte II, Norte III, Noreste, and Valle de Mexico II and III is essential to avoid power deficits in the northern and central parts of the country. However, irrespective of the reserve margins in the national interconnected system, there are restrictions in transmission capacity that generate bottlenecks or the need to import power.

In 2008, total electricity coverage in Mexico was 97%, being almost 100% in urban areas and around 95% in rural zones. However, around 3.2 million of people have no access to electricity in that year. In 2008, the average number of interruptions per subscriber was 2.3 for CFE and 4.2 for LFC. The duration of interruptions per subscriber was 2.2 hours for CFE and three hours for LFC. In 2010, the total electricity losses was 41 939 MW, which represent 16.3% of the total electricity produced in the country in that year. In 2010, the consumption of electricity in the country reached 214 342 MWh, which is 83% of the total electricity produced in the country in that year.

Finally, it is important to know that the Federal Electricity Commission has no independent system operator that administers electric dispatching on an economic basis, and the Energy Regulatory Commission's ability to serve as an economic regulator is sharply limited by its mandate, staffing levels, and budget.

Looking Forward

Significant effort continues to be devoted by the Mexican competent authorities to prospecting and drilling for oil. In line with the PEMEX business plan for exploration and production, the crucial objective is to maximize the economic value of reserves and resources of crude oil in the long-term. The following aims remain fundamental to this:

a) Continue prospecting to assess oil potential and incorporate reserves throughout the country;
b) Step up prospecting for offshore light crude oil[101];
c) Develop fields in heavy crude oil areas;
d) Reactivate prospecting in mature oil fields;
e) Develop exploration and production in Chicontepec oil field;
f) Develop the processing and handling of heavy crude oil;
g) Activate exploration and production in deep-waters.

The oil policy of the present government will focus on speeding up the exploitation of current oil deposits, and an active search for new onshore and offshore reserves. If everything

---

[101] In early 2008, the government loudly complained about the need to venture into deep-water, and about how PEMEX needed to access technology to recover Mexico's "treasure" in deep-water but no one suggested that the government figure out a way to involve the international oil companies (who know how this is done). Further, in its legislative proposals, the government included very little to facilitate deep-water exploration and production with the purpose of increasing oil production. However, it is important to stress that in 2012 the governments of Mexico and the USA signed an agreement to explore deep-water areas of the Gulf of Mexico, with the purpose of finding new oil reserves in this area.

necessary were done to upgrade probable and possible reserves to the status of proven reserves, this would result in a total proven reserves of over 33 000 million barrels, which at a rate of output of 2.6 million barrels a day reached in 2010, it would mean almost 35 years of energy autonomy. This, however, would entail the need for massive investment and intense prospecting and development over the next eight to ten years (Vargas, 2007).

With respect to electricity infrastructure projects, a total of US $35 billion will be allocated during the coming years to improve electricity generation, transmission, and distribution. Electricity generation will have the most resources devoted to it, encompassing over 60% of electrical infrastructure projects.

The current Mexico's strategy for electrical generation covers the following main elements: Expand the infrastructure for generation, transmission, and distribution of electricity to meet expected increases in electricity demand; diversify electricity generation sources, emphasizing the use of renewable energy sources with this purpose; increase electricity service coverage, particularly in rural areas; and improve public service quality regarding electricity supply.

PARAGUAY

The first exploration well drilled for oil in Paraguay was carried out in 1947 and the latest in 2005. In the intervening fifty eight years, an additional forty seven wells were drilled by several international oil companies who carried out preliminary seismic and exploration drilling, and two private Paraguayan companies. During that same period, 12 085 km of 2-D seismic data acquisition was conducted. A recent survey acquired an additional 950 km of 2-D data.

Paraguay does not produce oil. The oil companies that conducted the exploration of oil in the country in past years did not continue with their exploration efforts for the following reasons:

a) They did not satisfy the parameters of the geologic model of large producing wells that they were pursuing;
b) They lacked the computer technology to interpret their exploration results as can be done today;
c) They had other interests to pursue in the Gulf of Mexico, the North Slope in Alaska, and the North Sea in Europe;
d) There was limited infrastructure in the Chaco region, a large sedimentary basin located in northwestern Paraguay and southeastern Bolivia;
e) Paraguayan politics at that time were not encouraging for investment by foreign corporations in the oil sector.

Oil Reserves

With no proven crude oil reserves, Paraguay relies entirely on imports to meet its crude oil and petroleum products demand.

Oil Production and Consumption

Paraguay consumes the equivalent of around 31 000 barrels of oil per day as refined products such as gasoil, gasoline, lubricants, airplane fuel, etc. It is hoped that with drilling activities by CDS Energy in 2009, there will be success in finding oil in commercial quantities that can be produced for refining at the Petropar refinery at Villa Elisa, near Asuncion[102].

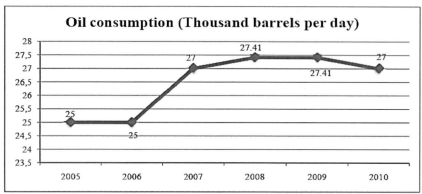

Source: Author compilation from different public sources.

Figure 70. Oil consumption in Mexico during the period 2003-2010.

Oil Refinery

The only oil refinery in Paraguay, located at Villa Elisa, had a capacity of 7 500 barrels per day, very small by Latin American standards. Paraguay's refinery capability was limited in terms of products, forcing the country to import high-priced derivatives such as aviation fuel, premium gasoline, and asphalt. The price of oil was high because of the complex transportation required through Argentina on the Río Paraná and Río Paraguay. Exxon, Paraguay Shell and the Paraguayan company Copetrol marketed all petroleum products to the public with the exception of diesel and fuel oil, which were sold by Petropar.

Oil import and export

In order to satisfy the domestic energy demand, the country imported between 25 100 and 25 900 barrels of oil per day during the period 2008-2010.

Table 36. Oil import during the period 2008-2011

Year	Oil - import	Rank
2008	25 940	100
2009	25 940	102
2010	25 100	105

Source: EIA.

---

[102] Petropar is owned 60% by the government and 40% by the private firm Paraguayan Refinery.

Oil Exploration

Paraguay became increasingly concerned with its oil dependence following the quadrupling of world's oil prices in the autumn of 1973. Although there was enough growth in other sectors of the economy to offset the negative consequences of the energy crisis, nonetheless, it rekindled the interest of policy makers in oil exploration. As a result, the legislature passed sweeping new regulations to promote oil exploration by multinational companies in certain areas of the country. Despite having some of the most liberal petroleum legislation in the world, Paraguay's limited prospects and severe lack of infrastructure in the Chaco region dissuaded most companies from drilling. Indeed, from 1944 to 1986 only forty seven wells had been drilled in Paraguay. Foreign firms conducted petroleum exploration under the supervision of the Ministry of Public Works and Communications. Most oil exploration in the 1980s took place in Carandayty Basin on Paraguay's western border with Bolivia, and in the Curupaity, Pirity, and Pilcomayo Basins bordering Argentina. Active exploration in Bolivia near its border with Paraguay and oil discoveries in Argentina only fifteen kilometers from Paraguay's border, heightened expectations of oil discoveries in the country. Because of Paraguay's complicated geology, however, oil exploration was more difficult than originally anticipated and required sophisticated Brazilian technology. With or without oil discoveries, the government was contemplating the construction of an oil pipeline to Brazilian ports to import oil, or in the case of a large oil discovery, to transport oil exports.

How to increase oil exploration in the country? The first step is to award a concession for exploration in an area of 800 000 hectares, apparently close to the Argentine province of Formosa where the Palmar Largo Basin in under exploitation. "Paraguay has no ways to defend its economy unless it has management over some crude oil. We are totally dependent on imported fuel and the world situation reminds us all the time about it" said Juan Gonzalez Meyer head of Petropar. "In spite of all the biofuels and energy alternatives, it is estimated that the world will continue to depend on crude oil for the next fifty years, so it is imperative that Paraguay begins exploring for oil or gas in our territory and our company's charter allows us to do so". He admitted that besides the exploration block to be awarded a lot of financial support is needed, "drilling a well in the region costs minimum US $5 million plus other expenses and, depending on the basin, the bill soars to US $15 million."

However, it is important to single out that exploration and exploitation of oil has always been in the hands of the big international corporations that are not interested in extracting oil from small countries with low consumption unless they can sell overseas, and this would mean shipping the oil along the river Paraguay and Parana, which is a problem that need to be reduced to the minimum, since it crosses Argentine territory. In other words, Paraguay market it is not an interesting business for major oil companies, even when it is for the country.

According to Quincy Energy S.A, a Paraguayan oil and natural gas exploration company, the Chaco Basin remains one of the world's last minimally explored onshore hydrocarbon areas. Reprocessed seismic data since 2001, recent concepts in seismic stratigraphy and the analysis and interpretation of multiple data bases from several previous operators, allowed for positive revisions to the geological model and hydrocarbon assessment of the Paraguayan Chaco Basin. The recoverable potential in that area of the Paraguayan Chaco Basin located east of the current production has been estimated at more than four billion barrels of oil equivalent.

Several factors render the Paraguayan Chaco Basin attractive for hydrocarbon exploration and development. These include larger and growing markets for hydrocarbon products both domestic and for export to countries such as Brazil, Argentina, Chile, and Uruguay, improved infrastructure in the Chaco region, decades of success exploration and production and a positive change in the political climate. Additionally, new production techniques in the US Permian Basin, the Canadian Montney area in Alberta, and British Columbia, among others, demonstrate that formations having similar properties to those found in the Paraguayan Chaco Basin are commercially viable. Paraguay also has a favorable hydrocarbon law wherein concessions are granted and guaranteed by Congress. Tax laws for investment by foreigners offer benefits conducive to the high risk nature of oil and natural gas exploration and development. The Hydrocarbon Law 779/95 is an excellent Law to attract the substantial amounts of high risk foreign investment required to explore and, if commercial reserves of oil and/or natural gas are discovered, to develop these hydrocarbons and build a vibrant industry.

Finally, it is important to stress that Paraguay's government signed in 2004 twelve hydrocarbon exploration and production concessions, with the purpose of expanding exploration activities in northwestern Paraguay.

Electricity Generation

Paraguay is the only country in Latin American and the Caribbean with almost 100% hydroelectric generation capacity (8 140 MW in 2007 and in 2008). Thermal plants contribute less than 0.1%. All of Paraguay's electricity for domestic consumption comes from a single facility, the bi-national Itaipú hydroelectric dam.

While total electricity generation amounted to 53.73 GWh in 2008, consumption was only 5.70 GWh, which corresponds to around 958 kWh per capita. The electricity export was 43.8 GWh. The electricity production in 2010 was 53.19 GWh; this represents 4% higher than in 2005 (51.17 GWh) but 1% lower than in 2008. Electricity losses was 2 700 MWh, which represent around 5.1% of the electricity produced by the country in 2010. This level of electricity losses is well below regional average and international standards.

The electricity interconnections that allow power exchanges with Brazil and Argentina are shown in Table 39.

In 2008, between 95% of the population in Paraguay had access to electricity; 99% in urban areas and 88% in rural zones, which is just slightly higher than the 94.6% average for the whole region. In 2008, around 300 000 Paraguayan people have no access to electricity.

Table 37. Electricity generation and consumption in 2007 and 2008 (GW)

	Paraguay 2007	Central and South America	World	Rank	Paraguay 2008
Net generation	53.19	1 004	18 795	45	54.91
Net consumption	5.35	843	17 139	105	5.70
Installed capacity (GWe)	8.14	237	4 468	58	8.14

Source: EIA.

Table 38. Installed capacity

Source	Installed capacity (MW)	Installed capacity (% of total)
Itaipú	7 000	86%
Yacyretá	895	11%
Acaray	237	2.9%
Thermal	8	0.1%
Total	8 140	100%

Source: ESMAP and EIA.

Note: Installed capacity shown for Itaipú and Yacyretá refers only to the Paraguayan share in these plants.

Table 39. Electricity interconnections

Entities	Country	Supply point	Voltage (kV)	Power (MW)
Furnas, Electrosul, Electrobras	Brazil	Itaipú	500	7 000
Ebisa	Argentina	Yacyretá	500	1 540
Enersul	Brazil	Pedro Juan Caballero	23	3
Copel	Brazil	Acaray	132	50
Emsa	Argentina	C.A. López	132	30
Transnea/Edefor	Argentina	Guarambaré	220	80

Source: ESMAP.

Looking Forward

A number of external factors have come together to provide many opportunities for growth for the fledging hydrocarbon industry in Paraguay. One of these factors is higher gas prices regionally coupled with increasing demand, particularly in Argentina, Brazil, and Chile, all of which are planning to import LNG at world's prices and at great capital costs.

In order to develop the oil industry many Paraguayan workers will be required. They will need training in various sectors of the oil industry, such as drilling, building and maintaining production facilities, and pipelines. It will also be necessary to educate and train geologists, engineers, technicians, computer programmers, accountants, and many other specialists in the specific needs and skills of the oil industry. This means long-term and well-paid jobs for workers as well as an increase in taxes and royalties for the government. Close cooperation and open dialog between the government and the oil industry can assure that the employment opportunities for those who choose to develop a career in this new frontier will be filled by Paraguayans.

Finally, it is important to stress that the country will continue to be a net exporter of electricity during the coming years, due to excess of electricity production in Itaipú and Yaciretá power plants.

PERU

Energy Reform

Peru's energy policy on hydrocarbons has the initial goal of carrying out a detailed review of current regulations in the sub-sector in order to ensure that they are kept up to date and competitive. Following the drop in crude oil production since 2000, in May 2003 the Peruvian government adopted two methodologies for calculating royalties, and a company can choose which to use after preparing a commercial report. The first is based on different royalty percentages (0-5%, 5-20% and 20%) for different levels of production (0-5 000 barrels per day, 5 000-100 000 barrels per day, and over 100 000 barrels per day). Under the second methodology, the royalty varies from 0% to 20% depending on the income and expenses incurred in the previous year (Deutsche Montan Technologie GmbH, OLADE and CIEMAT, 2005).

The objective of the Peruvian electric sector reform was to establish the basis for a strong sector, able to assure an opportune, reliable, and adequate service to the society, and with prices compatible with the economic costs of operation and expansion of the service. With this objective in mind, the Electric Concessions Law of November 1992 and its Regulation of February 1993 were enacted to provide the legal framework for the reform. According to Hammons (2001), this law and regulation provides the legal framework for the promotion of all the activities related with generation, transmission, distribution, and commercialization of electricity by:

a)   Defining the government role as normative, regulator, and controller;
b)   Redefining and reinforcing the regulation institutions as well as those in charge of the economic operation of the system;
c)   Separating the generation, transmission, and distribution activities in independent companies, establishing free competition in generation, open access to third parties in the transmission systems, and recognition of efficient standard distribution;
d)   Establishing concession contracts as a requirement for the activities that use natural resources, property of the government and/or require the imposition of rights of way, with service obligations;
e)   Establishing a price system that stimulates efficiency, penalizes lack of quality and the lack of security in the supply of service, and also promoting investment in new installations;
f)   Establishing indemnities to customers by inefficiencies in the electric service;
g)   Establishing rules and procedures for developing generation, transmission, and distribution activities, fixing prices and tariffs for electricity, and establishing rights and duties of the electric concessionaires and customers.

Oil Reserves, Production, and Consumption

According to *OGJ*, Peru has proven crude oil reserves of 533 million barrels of oil in January 2011, a decrease of 43% respect to 2007 level (930 million barrels). Peru produced

158 328 barrels per day in 2010, an increase of 8% respect to 2009 (146 450 barrels per day). In 2009, Peru consumed 181 000 barrels per day; this means 14% more than what was produced in that year. Due to the difference between production and consumption, Peru has to import 34 550 barrels per day of crude oil or 19% of its energy needs. The oil refinery capacity of the country in 2009 was 193 000 barrels per day (see Table 40).

The largest oil producer in Peru is Argentina-based Pluspetrol, which controls over one-half of the country's entire crude oil production. Other major oil producers include Occidental Petroleum, Petrobras, and Petrotech. Peru mostly privatized the former State-owned oil company, Petroperu in 1993. However, Petroperu now called "Perupetro,"[103] continues to control the country's only crude oil pipeline, Norperuano, which links the export terminal at Bayovar to oil fields in Peru's interior, most of the refineries, and a majority of the retail oil products market.

Peru's crude oil production is concentrated in the northern part of the country. The largest oil blocks are Block 1-AB operated by Pluspetrol along the border with Ecuador, Block 8 operated by Pluspetrol in the northeastern Amazon region, Block X operated by Petrobras in the northwest, and Block Z-2B operated by Petrotech off the northwest coast. Blocks 1-AB and 8 provide over 65% of Peru's total crude oil production. Most of crude oil produced in Peru is a heavy one known as "Lorento", with 20° API and 1.2% sulfur content.

From Figure 71, the following can be stated: The level of oil production during the period 1989-1993 was close to the level of consumption; sometime above this level and others below. However, after 1993, the level of oil production dropped significantly, and the level of consumption was all the time above the level of production. After 2009, this situation changed and the production of oil started to increase more rapid that the level of consumption.

If this trend continues in the coming years, then the country will produce more oil than what it needs.

Table 40. Peru oil production, consumption, exports, and reserves in 2008 and 2009 (Thousand barrels per day)

	Peru 2008	Central and South America 2008	World 2008	Rank 2008	Peru 2009
Total oil production	121.20	7 411	85 509	48	146.45
Crude oil production	78.56	6 281	73 670	50	71.03
Consumption	172.00	6 091	85 234	61	181.00
Net export/import (-)	-50.80	1 320	-	63	-34.55
Refinery capacity (Million barrels)	193	6 608	85 460	64	193

Source: EIA.

---

[103] Norperuano has two branches, one branch of 306 km starting at San José de Saramuro in the Ucayali Basin, the other of 257 km starting at Andoas in the Maranon Basin. Both branches meet at a central pumping station, where they join into a 35 inch system that carries crude oil 544 km to the Pacific coast. Norperuano pipeline has a maximum capacity of 250 000 barrels per day. Currently, the pipeline transports about 80 000 barrels per day.

Table 41. Oil data from Peru

	2003	2004	2005	2006	2007	2008
Total oil production. Production of crude oil (including lease condensate), natural gas plant liquids, and other liquids, and refinery processing gain (loss). Negative value indicates refinery processing loss.	91.81	93.48	111.50	115.79	114.07	120.23
Crude oil production includes lease condensate.	87.35	79.90	75.45	77.57	77.11	76.58
Consumption of petroleum products and direct combustion of crude oil.	154.22	161.96	157.73	157.60	168.00	172.00
Net exports/imports (-) Net exports = Exports - imports. Negative numbers are net imports. Note: Data range begins with the year 1990.	- 62.41	- 68.48	- 46.23	-41.81	-53.93	- 52
Refinery capacity. Crude oil distillation capacity as of January 1.	191	191	193	193	193	193
Proved reserves As of January 1. (Billion Barrels)	0.323	0.285	0.953	0.930	0.930	0.383

Source: EIA and *OGJ*.

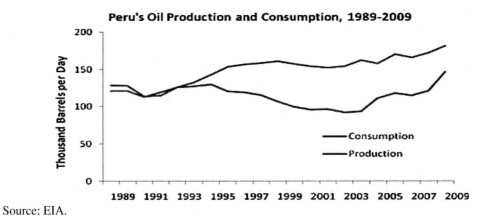

Source: EIA.

Figure 71. Oil production and consumption in Peru during the period 1989-2009.

From Figure 72, the following can be stated: The energy consumption in Peru is mainly fossil fuels (72% of the total) with 50% of oil, 17% of natural gas, and 5% of coal. The use of renewable energy sources is only 28% of the total, being hydro power the main source of energy with 27%. The above structure of the energy mix of the country is not expected to change significantly in the coming years.

Total energy consumption by energy type in 2008 (%)

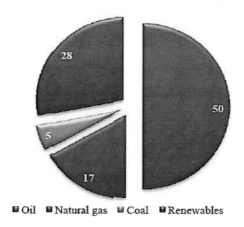

Source: EIA.

Figure 72. Total energy consumption in Peru by type of energy in 2008.

Oil Refineries

According to *OGJ*, Peru has six major oil refineries, with a total capacity of 193 000 barrels per day. Repsol-YPF controls the largest facility in the country, La Pampilla, located in Lima, with a capacity of 102 000 barrels per day. The other privately operated refinery in the country is the 3 250 barrels per day Purcallpa, operated by Maple Gas. Perupetro operates the remaining four refineries and the largest network of retail oil products distribution. The Peruvian government planned to further privatize downstream facilities but the process move slowly due to the opposition presented by labor unions and legislators.

Perupetro will modernize Talara oil refinery to a cost between US $1.3 and US $1.5 billion. The modernization works started in June 2010. Two European companies, France's Axens and Denmark's Haldor Topsoe, will carry out the work of expanding and modernizing the refinery, located some 1 200 km north of Lima. Perupetro allocated around US $400 million to support the modernization work in this refinery.

Oil Pipelines

Peru has only one crude oil pipeline, the 1 000 km Norperuano pipeline, which includes two branches that run, from the Ucayali and Maranon Basins in the northeastern jungle of the country, to the export terminal at Bayovar on the Pacific coast. The pipeline is owned by Perupetro, which has been installing additional loops in order to allow transport of extra heavy crude oil from more distant exploration blocks in the Amazon region. The pipeline has a maximum capacity of 250 000 barrels per day.

Investment in the Oil Sector

During the period 2005-2006, the Peruvian government signed around twenty five new exploration and production contracts. Peru awarded the first exploration and production contract to Petrolera Monterrico. The award is for block XX, located in the north. In October 2005, the Peruvian government awarded contracts to Hunt Oil and China National Petroleum Corporation for blocks 76 and 111, respectively. In March 2005, Global Energy Development signed a new exploration and production contract for block 95 in the Maranon Basin of northeast Peru. The Peruvian government also approved a contract for Burlington Resources in block 104 of the Maranon Basin. Other companies that have recently been awarded exploration contracts in Peru include Petrotech, Petrolifera Petroleum del Peru, and Petrobras.

In June 2005, Petrotech, Peru's third-largest oil producer controlled by Colombia's Ecopetrol SA and Korea National Oil Corp[104], announced Peru's first offshore oil discovery, the San Pedro IX well, which is located in block Z-2B. The well had initial production of 1 200 barrels per day. Petrotech has plans to drill additional wells on block Z-2B in order to increase production to 11 000 barrels per day. The company also plans to expand its offshore exploration at blocks 6, 33, 35, and 36. In 2004, Occidental Petroleum announced that it had discovered at least 100 million barrels of recoverable reserves in block 64, located in the Amazon Basin; the company also announced that it would increase its investments in Blocks 101 and 103 located in the same area (Clough, 2008).

Finally, it is important to single out the following: Petrotech took the decision to invest US $2.5 billion to explore and develop other oil and natural-gas fields in Peru. The aims is to triple its output of crude oil and gas equivalent in the South American nation to 50 000 barrels a day at its offshore fields by 2016, according to a public statement made in October 2009 by Vice President Nelson Castaneda. Ecopetrol plans to spend US $60 billion by 2015 to boost output to one million barrels a day from a current 650 000 barrels, and to more than double its refining capacity. Perupetro and the energy industry is planning to invest US $9 billion in five years in order to explore new oil deposits in the country and to increase oil reserves.

Electricity Generation

According to the EIA, Peru had 7 270 MW of installed generating capacity in 2008, around 52% being thermal and almost 48% hydroelectric, with a negligible share of other renewable sources. The country generated 27.4 billion kWh of electric power in 2008 whilst consuming 24 billion kWh (88% of the total electricity produced in that year). Even though the main installed capacity is evenly divided between two different energy sources, around 72% of Peru's total electricity supply is generated by hydroelectric facilities. Thermal power plants (mostly from diesel fuel, gasoline, and natural gas), provide electricity only during peak hours or when natural conditions reduce hydroelectric output. Around 1% of the energy supply comes from other sources. As result of the privatization process carried out by the

---

[104] The two State-controlled companies, which bought Petrotech for US $900 million from Houston-based Offshore International Group Inc. in February 2009, has the aim to add 100 million barrels of oil reserves in nine areas, equivalent to one-third Peru's total current crude oil potential.

government in the energy sector in the 1990s, in 2007 private companies handled about 69% of generation capacity.

According to the World Bank, in 2010 the total electricity generation in Peru was 29 931 MWh, out of which 1 798 MWh was generated using oil as fuel, representing 6% of the total electricity produced in that year. The electricity consumption per capita was 961 kWh and the electricity losses were 2 540 MWh that represents 8.5% of the total. This percentage of losses is below the acceptable international electricity losses and far below from the average regional losses.

In 2008, Peru's electrification rate was 77%, one of the lowest electrification rates in Latin America (see Table 13). In its 2004 National Rural Electrification Plan, the government of Peru reiterated its commitment to reduce the electrification gap between urban and rural areas, aiming to increase rural coverage from the current 30% to 75% by 2013. The total amount of the Peruvian population without electricity in 2008 reached 6.5 million. According to the International Energy Agency, access to electricity has increased to 85.7% in 2009; this represents an increase of around 8.5% in comparison to 2008, and 40% in the past nineteen years. The government plans to invest around US $2.2 billion during the coming years to connect more than 6 million Peruvians to the electricity grid by 2018.

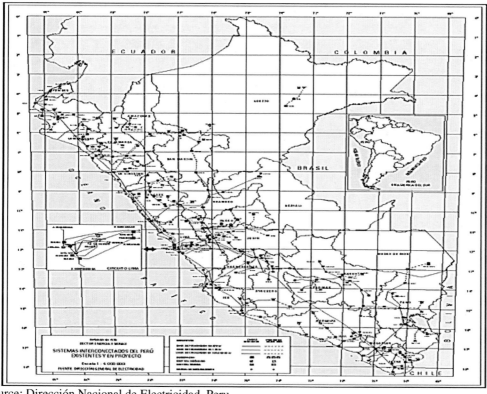

Source: Dirección Nacional de Electricidad, Peru.

Figure 73. National interconnected systems in operation and planned.

The largest electricity distributor in Peru is Edelnor, a subsidiary of Endesa, which supply electricity to the Lima area. The second-largest distributor is Luz del Sur, majority-owned by a consortium consisting of PSEG Global and Sempra Energy; Luz del Sur also operates in the Lima area; smaller distributors owned by the Peruvian government operate in the rest of the country. The government has begun to offer financial incentives to spread electricity service to rural areas, where coverage remains spotty and unreliable.

Peru has two main power transmission grids, one covering the north and center parts of the country, and the other serving the south. An interconnector, owned and operated by Hydro-Quebec International, runs between the two along the Pacific coast.

The largest transmission company in Peru is the Colombia-based ISA Group, which controls over half of the transmission grid in the country through its subsidiaries Red de Energia del Peru and Interconexión Eléctrica ISA Peru. Investment in Peru's transmission grid has outpaced actual demand; therefore there is a considerable surplus of spare capacity. Peruvian law ensures that all generating and distributing companies have fair and non-discriminatory access to the national transmission grid.

Looking Forward

Peru forecasts a liquid hydrocarbons production of half a million barrels per day in five years' time, said Daniel Saba head of Perupetro, the country's company that awards and supervises all oil and gas contracts. In public interview Mr. Saba said "that the industry is planning investments of US $9 billion plus any new deposits that could be discovered in the next five years in order to increase oil production." Peruvian oil production is currently 158 328 barrels per day, and it is expected to double in two years. The last round of licensing opening twenty four potential areas for oil exploration was launched recently.

Finally, in 2011, the Peruvian National Harbor Authority approved the construction, in Punta Arenas in the Piura province, an oil facility for the dispatch and reception of hydrocarbons for the Talara refinery. The construction work will be carried out in thirty seven months increasing the capacity of this important refinery for the country.

TRINIDAD AND TOBAGO

Energy Policy

Trinidad and Tobago's new energy policy seeks to transform a petroleum-based economy, as it was initially, into a natural gas based economy. In recognition of the need to develop its human capital to meet the needs of the expanding energy sector, the government had established National Energy Skills Centers and an Institute of Technology. It is now considered expedient to move towards the tertiary stage in capacity building through the establishment of the University of Trinidad and Tobago. This new university will focus mainly in the study of all available energy technologies, particularly those used for the generation of electricity.

Oil Reserves, Production, and Consumption

Trinidad and Tobago's first barrel of commercial oil was extracted in south west Trinidad in 1908, However, it was only in the decade of the 1960s that the two-island Caribbean State's most important economic sector began to assume a national hue. Since then, petroleum has dominated the economy of the country. The oil production during the period 2000-2010 is shown in Figure 74.

From Figure 74, the following can be stated: The oil production in Trinidad and Tobago declined from 144 670 barrels per day in 2005 to 98 240 barrels per day in 2010; this means a reduction of 32% during the period considered. This trend in the reduction of the oil production level will continue in the coming years.

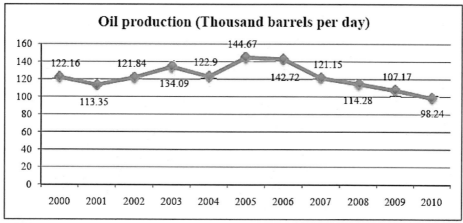

Source: EIA.

Figure 74. Oil production in Trinidad and Tobago during the period 2000-2010.

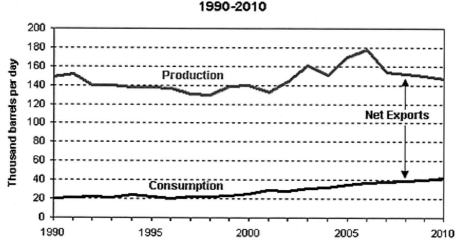

Source: Energy Information Administration.

Figure 75. Oil production and consumption in Trinidad and Tobago during the period 1990-2010.

It is important to know that since 1974 there have been no major oil discoveries in the country, causing a slow decline in the country's ratio of reserves to production. Although proven oil reserves were estimated to last fewer than ten years at the 1987 rate of extraction, decreased production and anticipated new oil finds were expected to allow the country to satisfy its oil needs during the coming years.

It was estimated that over three-quarters of Trinidad and Tobago's crude oil reserves had already been found. The country proven oil reserves were estimated at 728.3 million barrels in 2009. It is important to stress that proved crude oil reserves were 716 million barrels at the beginning of 2003, and 728.3 million of barrels at the end of 2010, showing and increase of 2% during the whole period. Recent findings have suggested that there may be even greater reserves of oil off the shores of Trinidad (up to 2.6 billion barrels). Over 60% of oil reserves were located offshore.

Oil production was historically controlled by large foreign companies, such as Shell, British Petroleum, Texaco, and Amoco. By the late 1980s, however, the government purchased all foreign operations, except Amoco. In 1985, the government completed the purchase of the remaining operations of Texaco as well as the residual 49% share of a small Texan company, Tesoro, from a previous joint venture with the government. Nonetheless, even with the new government purchases, Amoco still produce over 50% of the country's oil and possess most of the newer and more productive oil fields.

In 2010, the average oil consumption in the country was 43 000 barrels per day. Trinidad and Tobago import 92 480 barrels per day in the same year (the total oil import was 24 944 324 barrels), and export 248 300 barrels per day (the total oil export was 16 584 513 barrels).

From Figure 75, the following can be stated: The production of oil was always above the level of consumption during the whole period considered. However, the difference between oil production and consumption started to diminish from 2007, due to a decline in the production of oil and an increase in oil consumption. It is expected that this trend will continue during the coming years.

Oil Refineries

Trinidad and Tobago has two State-owned refineries, one at Pointe-à-Pierre, and the second at Point Fortin. The Pointe-à-Pierre refinery, with a capacity of 220 000 barrels per day, was traditionally the main refinery of the country. Point Fortin's share of refining, however, climbed to 30% in 1985 because of the installation of a pipeline connecting the two refineries to improve efficiency. Total refinery capacity was 310 000 barrels per day.

For decades, crude oil was imported by Trinidad and Tobago from Saudi Arabia, Venezuela, Iran, Indonesia, Nigeria and Ecuador, and then refined and re-exported. Refinery activity, however, was reduced more than 50% in the first half of the 1980s; after 1983 refining of the imported oil ceased altogether as a result of the depressed world's oil market. The percentage of domestically refined crude oil diminished as well.

Electricity Generation

Trinidad and Tobago Electricity Commission is responsible for the design, construction, operation, and maintenance of the country's electrical transmission and distribution network. The utility supplies electric power to customers on both islands via a single interconnected grid. The company purchases the bulk electric power from independent generation companies for resale, and is also responsible for securing fuel supplies for the generation companies. It is State-owned and is by law the sole retailer of electric power in the twin island Republic.

It is important to stress that in Trinidad and Tobago, electricity generation is primarily from natural gas. According to the World Bank, in 2010 the total electricity generation was 7 662 MWh, out of which 18 MWh was produced using oil as fuel (0.2% of the total). It expected that the use of oil for the generation of electricity will continue to be very low in the or even disappear altogether in the future. The total consumption per capita was 5 642 kWh. In 2010, the electricity losses were 168 MWh or 2% of the total; this is the lowest electricity losses in the region and very low from the international standards.

Looking Forward

Regarding the future development of the energy sector in Trinidad and Tobago, it is important to stress the following: The rate of expansion of oil and gas production will be critical to the country's future and depends on both the rate of allocation of acreage and the exploratory effort, as well as on technology and market expansion. The extensive marine acreage was still available and if provided appropriate deep-water technology is utilized, then the prospects for exploration success in that acreage are good.

There are also positive perspectives on the extensive and as yet unexplored deep areas on land, particularly in the light of the recent hydrocarbon finds in Oligocene formations. Further, it is important to be aware that the country's extensive heavy oil deposits had also not been properly evaluated in the past.

For this reason, long-term sustainability through appropriate dynamic asset management was a critical need, and that this could be achieved through creating and focusing on the following three areas: Flexibility, diversity, and the depth and breadth of national involvement.

On the other hand, it is important that the government pay special attention to two additional issues: a) Increasing the number of natural gas suppliers, and b) The need to upgrade the refining business, not simply by the introduction of new capital and technology to produce more environmentally marketable products but also to utilize new and more efficient business processes and practices, as well as developing quality ancillary services. It is also important to emphasize the need to maintain cost competitiveness in the production of petroleum products during the coming years.

Finally, the government should pay special attention to the need for the development of an acceptable set of energy strategies that would treat with the replacement of the ageing first-generation manufacturing plants at Point Lisas in order to increase oil and gas production.

URUGUAY

Energy Policy

It is important to knowledge that the Uruguay's energy policy is very ambitious and is aimed at reducing the country's dependence on imported oil from 60% to 40% in the near future and replaces that 20% with renewable energy sources such as biomass, wind power, solar energy and biofuels in the coming years.

The country is also adopting concrete measures to increase the use of natural gas for electricity generation.

Oil Production, Consumption, and Import

The total oil production in Uruguay in 2009 was 900 barrels per day. The oil consumption in that year was 47 000, which is 10% lower than the level of oil consumption in 2008. Oil imports in 2009 were 46 100 barrels per day.

In 2007, Uruguay's energy supply shows that petroleum accounted for 55% of the total, followed by locally-generated hydro power and by biomass (primarily wood). Uruguay imports all its petroleum needs, which exceeded US $1 billion in 2007, and practically doubled in 2008.

Table 42. Uruguay oil information for 2008 and 2009 (Thousand barrels per day)

	Uruguay World 2008	Central and South America	World	Rank	Uruguay 2009
Total oil production	0.90	7 411	85 509	108	0.90
Crude oil production	0.00	6 281	73 670	94	0.00
Consumption	52.00	6 091	85 234	92	47.00 [1]
Net export/import (-)	-51.10	1 320	--	62	-46.10
Refinery capacity	50	6 608	85 460	85	50
Proved reserves (Billion barrels)	0.00	110	1 330	84	0.00

Note (1): Estimate value.
Sources: EIA.

Oil Refineries

The State's oil company Administración Nacional de Combustibles, Alcohol y Portland (ANCAP) owns Uruguay's only refinery La Teja located in Montevideo, and control the oil sector in the country. In April 2001, Uruguay invested US $160 million at La Teja refinery in order to boost refining capacity from 37 000 barrels per day to 50 000 barrels per day.

Oil Exploration

Uruguay has no known oil resources. For this reason, ANCAP is seeking associations with foreign oil companies in order to help find oil reserves.

In 2009, the government planned to start of offshore exploration for oil in Uruguay raising prospects for energy independence within the national industry. Tens of millions of dollars of investment is expected to flow into Uruguay as a result of YPF Argentina's winning bid for exploration in the maritime zone. YPF has a 40% stake in the exploration and shares the other 40% with Petrobras and Portugal's GALP Energia, which has a 20% share in the consortium.

According to public information, YPF will operate the deep-water exploratory block 3 while Petrobras will operate the shallow-water exploratory block 4, both located along the coast of Punta del Este. Additionally, YPF will act as the lead operator of the exploration project.

The decision to begin oil exploration represents an important advance in the longstanding exploration project and is a positive development, both for Uruguay and its oil industry and for the international oil market as well. There is no information available related to the level of investment in offshore exploration but the high level of participation from major Latin American players and the strategic partnership indicated large-scale cash inflows suggested high level of investment. This is the second Repsol-YPF partnership announced in recent weeks on oil exploration in South America.

On the other hand, Executives at State-owned ANCAP indicated that the company had discovered the first traces of oil in Uruguay, a country that depends on imported crude oil for 60% of its energy. "For the first time in Uruguay's history, free oil has been found in small proportions, emanating from the bedrock," Juan Gomez, member of ANCAP's Board of Directors, said in an interview. He added, however, that only traces of oil were found. "They are not deposits strictly speaking; it is not as though oil is gushing out." ANCAP President Raul Sendic cautioned against undue optimism. "It could be nothing or it could be the tip of the iceberg," he said, referring to the geological finds in the central region of Durazno. He said the rock formations showed great quantities of organic material that likely held the key to substantial hydrocarbon deposits. The find was made in the subsoil of the central province of Durazno following exploratory drilling at a depth of 180 meters by US based Chesapeake Energy Corporation, which was awarded a subcontracting license from the Uruguayan government in 2009. The material was discovered in rock that is from the Upper Devonian epoch, which dates back about 365 million years. Those geological characteristics have sparked optimism because oil has been found in that same type of rock in other countries of the Latin American and the Caribbean region. "It is a very interesting find because it is going to allow Uruguayan authorities to keep working and go deeper in searching the bedrock to see if there are significant quantities of oil. Future work will enable the company to learn with greater precision what amount of organic matter the bedrock contains and what type of crude oil is in the subsoil."

The discovery is the result of oil exploration efforts by Uruguay that date back decades but which have intensified in recent years - both offshore in the so-called "Oceanic Platform"- and onshore. Two years ago, two blocks were awarded in the Oceanic Platform to a consortium made up of Petrobras, Argentina's YPF, and Portugal's GALP Energia. Work will intensify this year in that platform with the awarding of several new blocks. YPF and Shell, meanwhile, have informed ANCAP of their interest in carrying out onshore exploration work in the near future.

Finally, it is important to know the following: Singapore Company Reflect won a US $5 million contract with the purpose of carrying out a survey, which includes the processing of gravimetric and magneto-metric data covering a wide area of Uruguay's Exclusive Economic Zone in water depths ranging from 20 m to 2 500 m. Data acquired by the survey will be made available by ANCAP to companies participating in Uruguay's second licensing round, launched in April 2012. The geophysical data to be obtained by Reflect adds to other contracts that ANCAP signed to improve the knowledge of the Uruguayan basins. ANCAP signed a contract with the international company Fugro for the provision of geophysical services covering a high resolution aero-magnetic survey of Pelotas, Punta del Este, and Oriental del Plata offshore basins.

In addition, ANCAP already holds multi-client agreements with CGG Veritas for near 12 000 km of 2D seismic data (acquired from 2002 to 2008), and has signed an agreement with ION/GXT for the acquisition, processing and interpretation of seismic data offshore, the so-called "Uruguay Span" (seismic data that will link the Uruguayan basins with the neighboring offshore basins in Brazil and Argentina).

All this large amount of data will be useful to enhance the knowledge of the offshore basins, as well as identifying leads and prospects in the Uruguay offshore and, therefore, will be particularly interesting and helpful for the oil companies that are evaluating the exploration opportunities in Uruguay.

Electricity Generation

Hydro power is the main national source for electricity generation in Uruguay, supplemented with oil imports from Argentina and Brazil. Over 60% of installed capacity in the country is hydro, almost all of it produced by four hydroelectric plants. The remainder of the installed generation capacity is mostly covered by expensive small thermal power plants and mobile diesel generators, activated during peak demand. This leaves Uruguay vulnerable to seasonal rainfall patterns, even though, under normal hydrological conditions, Uruguay can supply its off-peak domestic demand.

Table 43. Electricity in Uruguay in 2007 and 2008 (GWh)

	Uruguay 2007	Central and South America	World	Rank	Uruguay 2008	Uruguay 2009
Net generation	9.27	1 004	18 795	92	8.47	9.43
Net consumption	7.14	843	17 139	94	7.68	7.30
Installed capacity (GWe)	2.23	237	4 468	95	2.24	2.24

Source: EIA and Index Mundi (2009).

In 2008, the total electricity generation was 8 470 MWh, out of which 3 432 MWh was generated using oil as fuel; this represents 48% of the total. The total electricity consumption in 2008 was 7 680 MWh, which represent 91% of the total electricity produced by the country in that year. The electricity losses reached 24%, which is very high by the international standards.

It is important to know that the electricity demand increased by 7.5% between 2006 and 2007, and 8% between 2007 and 2008. However, it is foresee that the electricity demand will increase about 3.5% during the next ten years. This estimate if half of the increase produced in the last three years. The current structure of the energy mix is not expected to change in the coming years.

Looking Forward

Uruguay had no domestic oil resources, despite several exploration efforts and, for this reason, one of the main tasks of the government during the coming years is to increase the search for oil offshore deposit, with the assistance of some of the major oil companies in the region. State-owned ANCAP has indicated that the company had discovered the first traces of oil in Uruguay, and the government should provide the necessary resources to confirm the existence of oil in the selected areas.

VENEZUELA

Oil Reserves, Production, and Consumption

In Venezuela, oil production began in 1917, when 120 000 barrels were produced. Until the early 1960s, Venezuela was the world's third-largest producer of oil after the USA and the former USSR.

Output rose to a peak daily volume of 3.7 million barrels a day in 1970 but in 1974 President Carlos Andres Perez began a conservation program, resulting in cutbacks to 2.4 million barrels a day by mid-1975. The 1986 collapse of oil prices eventually forced OPEC's producers to set production quotas, which cut Venezuela's output to 1.5 million barrels per day for the first half of 1987. Venezuela has the world's largest oil reserves estimated in 296 501 million barrels in 2011.

Venezuela's oil production capacity dropped significantly because of 1998-1999 OPEC's production cuts. Wells were abandoned and spending on oil exploration decreased. In the 2000s, plans were adopted calling oil production to be raised from over 3 million barrels per day to more than 5 million barrels per day within the next three years. To achieve this goal, enormous investments in national oil and natural gas sectors were indispensable. Until the first trimester of 2011, the oil production in Venezuela was below 3 million barrels per day.

At the beginning of 2003, oil production in the first nine months of 2002 reached 2.35 million barrels per day. In 2007, the oil production was 2.39 million barrels per day and in 2008 was 2.35 million barrels per day, a little bit lower that in 2007; in 2009, the production reached 2.472 million barrels per day; this represents an increase of 5% with respect 2008. It is important to note that 13% of the total oil production is exported to the Caribbean and South America sub-regions to a preferential price and with a financing of twenty five years.

The production of oil in Venezuela during the period 1995 2008 is shown in Table 44.

Table 44. Total production of oil in Venezuela in 2007 and in 2008

Data	2007	2008	
Petroleum (Thousand barrels per day)	Venezuela	Rank	Venezuela
Total oil production Production of crude oil (including lease condensate), natural gas plant liquids, and other liquids, and refinery processing gain (loss).	2 670.21	9	2 642.90
Crude oil production. Includes lease condensate.	2 432.64	10	2 394.02
Consumption Consumption of petroleum products and direct combustion of crude oil.	713	23	750
Net exports/imports(-) Net exports = Total oil production – consumption. Negative numbers are net imports.	1 957.21	8	1 893
Refinery capacity: Crude oil distillation capacity as of January 1.	1 282	17	1 282

Source: IEA and *OGJ*.

Creation of PdVSA

On 29 August 1975, President Carlos Andres Perez signed into law the Oil Industry Nationalization Act, under which all concessions to private oil companies were rescinded as of 31 December 1975. A State holding company, Petroleum of Venezuela (Petroven), was established in September 1975 with an initial capitalization of US $465 million. Petroven obtained a 50-year renewable monopoly over Venezuelan petroleum production, beginning 1 January 1976. Within a few years, Petroven's sixteen original operating companies were combined into four. In 1986, the State-holding company was reorganized and renamed "PdVSA."

The company has major refinery, pipelines, and service station networks in Europe, the USA, and elsewhere in the Caribbean. PdVSA operates one of the Western Hemisphere's largest refining systems, and is one of the world's largest oil refiners. Domestic refinery capacity stands at about 1.3 million barrels per day, with significant additional holdings in Curaçao, the USA (in Lake Charles, Lemont, Corpus Christi, Paulsboro, Savannah, and Lyondell), and Europe (with Nynas and Ruhr Oel). Venezuela has around 40% of the total oil refinery capacity in the Andean region. In Cuba, PdVSA operates, with the Cuban counterpart, an oil refinery in Cienfuegos province located in the central-south of the country, with a capacity of 60 000 barrels per day, and is implementing plans to increase this capacity up to 150 000 barrels per day during the coming years.

Investment in the Oil Sector

According to a five-year plan released in February 2001, PdVSA planed to spend US $45.3 billion on its oil and gas sector between 2001 and 2006, with the aim of raising crude oil production capacity to 5.5 million barrels per day by 2006. The approved plan also calls for private investors to contribute with US $24 billion. Of its share, PdVSA plans to spend roughly 60% on oil exploration and production, 20% on natural gas development, and around 6% on refinery upgrades. According to the approved plan, the main objective of the investment in refinery upgrades was mostly for improving product quality rather than expanding current capacity of 1.3 million barrels per day. Upgrading the Isla Refinery and the

Paraguaná complex (home to about 70% of Venezuela's refinery capacity) were given top priorities, as well as construction and expansion at the Puerto La Cruz, Amuay, and Cardon refineries.

PdVSA has a reformulated gasoline production capacity of about 200 000 barrels per day. About one-third of Venezuela's refined product are exported to the USA[105], where they are distributed mainly by Tulsa-based Citgo, PdVSA's US refining and marketing subsidiary, and one of the largest US gasoline retailers.

PdVSA's plan for 2005–2010 calls for investing US $6.3 billion from public sources, and an extra US $2.5 billion from private sources in the oil and gas sectors. While no official figures are available, has been estimated that slightly over half the PdVSA target or less than US $3.5 billion was invested. Private investment falls short of the target, due to uncertainty about foreign property rights and investment policy. These estimates indicate that oil output will continue to remain arround current levels of 2.47 million barrels per day reached in 2009. Finally, the objectives of the above mentioned plans were not achieved.

Sedimentary Basins

Venezuela has four major sedimentary basins: Eastern, Western, Barinas-Apure (where most oil production occurs), and the largely unexplored Northern Basin. Due to the maturity of many of these basins, PdVSA spends a good deal of its budget on the application of secondary and enhanced oil recovery techniques to maintain output levels. Proven oil reserves in these fields are estimated at close to two billion barrels of light and medium crude oil. Heavy crude oil with gravities of less than 20° API accounts for about three-quarters of Venezuelan oil reserves. The largest heavy oil reserves are in the Orinoco Heavy Oil Belt in eastern Venezuela.

Regarding heavy crude oil it is important to single out the following: Processing heavy crude oil is a very complex task, requires higher investments and is less profitable. Super-heavy crude oil has a limited market because it is even more costly and difficult to pump. It is often processed into heavy crude oil and then transported to one of a few facilities capable of refining it further. Heavy crude oil has limited value as a policy instrument. An exporting country can cut-off light oil supplies to an importer, and be certain that there will be a market elsewhere. But the same is not true for super-heavy crude oil. The importer has control if it possesses one of the few refineries able to process this type of oil. Cutting off supplies carries the risk of finding no new buyers, causing the exporter as much or more damage as it sought to inflict. This, to a certain extent, is the current relationship between Venezuela and the USA. Venezuela ships heavy crude oil to the USA, a country that has a high number of specialized refineries now operating in the world[106]. This makes it extremely difficult to use these products as an instrument of political pressure. In fact, the power balance may even favor the USA, since refineries capable of handling heavy acidic crude oil are scarcer than the

---

[105] In May 2011, the US government adopted economic sanctions against PdVSA for their closed relationship with the oil industry in Iran.

[106] Venezuela is gradually diversifying exports away from a dependence on the USA. While potential reserves numbers in Venezuela are up due to the inclusion of shale and heavier crude oils, the prices required for developing these findings are also up. In the meantime, real production is dropping in response to problems with exploration and development contracts, union issues, and gradually aging operating fields.

supply of such oil. To reduce this dependency, PdVSA is looking to partner with foreign State-owned or private oil companies to develop and produce heavy crude oil and build refineries at destination. This is one case where a potential conflict is turned into a positive-sum proposition, in which both parties win if the exchange continues, and both stand to lose if it does not (Arriagada, 2006).

Development of extra-heavy crude oil, which the Orinoco Belt region contains in abundance, will account for a growing share of Venezuelan oil investment to be approved in the future. Investment of US $52 billion over the period 2001-2030 will be needed to meet projected production growth, the majority of which will go to projects based on partial or full upgrading of the region's extra heavy crude oil. Cumulative investment in such projects to date has totaled US $13.3 billion, which represent only 26% of the total investment needed.

There are four joint ventures approved for the exploitation of extra-heavy crude oils in the Orinoco Belt in which PdVSA is a minority owner. They are now in different stages of development. The projects could add 600 000 barrels per day of heavy crude oil to international markets, much of which will be destined for the US Gulf Coast. The Orinoco Belt has recoverable reserves estimated at 100 billion barrels or more, although the quality of the oil is poor. All four projects aim to convert the extra heavy crude oil from approximately 9° API crude oil to about 20-23° API, and even as high as 32° API of synthetic crude oil. These projects now represent some of the most successful investments in the Venezuelan upstream but future projects could encounter difficulties in becoming economically viable, as preferential financial terms negotiated under the previous Venezuelan administration are unlikely to be repeated by the new Venezuela's government.

Participation of the Private Sector in the Development of the Oil Sector

Privatization of PdVSA is forbidden under Venezuela's 1999 Constitution. However, since 1996, private oil companies from around the world have participated in rounds of bidding for operating services agreements. The deals, part of Venezuela's reopening to foreign companies, were designed to help PdVSA attain its goal of increasing production capacity. In the third round of bidding in 1997, over 100 foreign companies pre-qualified for bidding on 20 blocks.

Table 45. Orinoco Belt heavy crude oil upgrading projects

Project	Partners (with PDVSA)	Peak capacity (kb/d)	Project life (years)	Start date	Capital investment ($ billion)
Cerro Negro	ExxonMobil	120	35	2001	2.3
Petrozuata	ConocoPhillips	120	35	2001	2.4
Sincor	Total, Statoil	200	35	2002	4.2
Hamaca	ConocoPhillips, ChevronTexaco	190	34	2003	4.0

Source: IEA database.

The sixteen eventual foreign winners included, among others, US Chevron, Phillips, ARCO, Union Texas, Pennzoil, Argentina's Perez Company, Pancanadian, China's CNPC, Repsol, and UK's Lasmo. Reserves and production capacity at these fields proved to be lower than the companies had hoped, and the 1998 oil price collapse further cut investment at the fields. Analysts believe that only three of the eighteen marginal fields awarded in 1997 have proven valuable. In October 2000, Chevron pledged to invest US $4 billion in the Lake Maracaibo region over the next twenty years. Petrobras is considering involvement in new marginal fields, as part of a larger energy cooperation plan being pursued by the governments of Brazil and Venezuela.

Venezuela passed, in 2002, a hydrocarbons law that mandated a 51% share by the national oil company and a higher royalty rate. Operations, such as those under operating service agreements, which may have stretched the legal interpretation of the law when they were begun, were subject to a strict and adverse legal interpretation when they appeared to be poor earners for the government. Taxes once renounced, like the export tax, have been revived so that the government can earn, in essence, a fixed 33.33% royalty. The impact, according to expert analysts like Deutche Bank and Wood Mackenzie, is a massive flight of investment capital from Venezuela's heavy oil sector to Canada's oil sands, effectively freezing development of the Hemisphere's largest oil reserves during one of the greatest oil booms in history.

Venezuela's Hydrocarbon Law, which came into effect at the start of 2002, opened up the country's refining industry and exploration and development of light and medium crude oil to private investment but limits private participation to 49%. It sets royalties between 20% and 30%. The Venezuelan Hydrocarbon Industry Association has claimed that these new fiscal arrangements need to be made more flexible in order to encourage foreign investment in mature and high-risk regions. This would help to compensate for the risk of output being capped by the government, as a result of OPEC production quotas.

Oil Consumption

For Venezuela, oil is the dominant energy source accounting for 40% of 2008 primary energy demand, and the country economy is extremely oil-dependent despite efforts at diversifycation. Oil accounts for roughly three-quarters of total Venezuelan exports, representing about half of government revenues and about one-third of its GDP.

Oil consumption in Venezuela was 713 000 barrels per day in 2007, and 750 000 barrels per day in 2008, an increase of 5.2%. Electricity consumption per capita is expected to rise by 4.7% during the coming years. The electricity consumption reached 83.84 billion of kWh in 2008, and it is expected that in 2013 the electricity consumption will be 119 billion of kWh, an increase of 42%, providing a continuing theoretical surplus based on 3.3% annual average growth in electricity generation. Between 2008 and 2018, it is expected an increase in Venezuelan electricity generation of 45.3%, which is around the middle of the range for the Latin American region. Thermal power generation is forecast to rise by 57% between 2008 and 2018. Venezuela's thermal generation in 2008 was around 32 TWh or 7.08% of the regional total. By 2013, the country is expected to account for 7.71% of regional thermal generation. However, according to Business Monitor International sources, Venezuela thermal generation will account for 10.49% of the regional power generation by 2013.

Despite government effort to increase the electricity generation, Venezuela is suffering shortage of electricity particularly in dry season due to the reduction of electricity generation using hydro power. To eliminate this problem, Venezuelan President announced, in September 2008, "that the government will build twenty one local electricity generating plants to reduce Venezuela's dependence on hydroelectricity, and to satisfy the rapidly growing energy demand nationwide. We are installing twenty one power plants across the country, which were brought from Cuba". They are small units that connect in series for a small town, for a hospital, or food storage facility. The president of the National Electric Corporation said that "the new plants will be able to work autonomously or be connected to the national electricity system". The Vice-Minister of Energy, Maria Gabriela Gonzalez, said that "the new plants are part of a plan to decrease Venezuela's dependence on hydroelectric energy, more than 70% of which comes from the Guri dam in the southeastern State of Bolivar." Amid rising demand, the government estimates the national energy shortage to be between 1 000 MW and 2 000 MW. In the first half of 2011, there were 391 unplanned power outages in the nation's main power lines, and brief power outages continue to be a common occurrence in many cities. In addition to investing in electricity production, the government is importing energy in the short-term and promoting energy conservation in the long-term in order to solve electricity shortage in the future.

The Role of Oil in the Country Foreign Policy

Oil has been a central element in Venezuelan foreign policy since it joined the OPEC in the early 1960s. Though oil has played a role in Venezuelan foreign policy for some time, the current Venezuela's government has wielded its resource wealth to an unprecedented degree. It is difficult to find a similar case of a Latin American and Caribbean country employing its commodity wealth so openly in the international and regional arena with policy objectives.

The use of oil as a regional policy instrument depend on two factors: First, the oil supply must be highly concentrated in a single country to become dominant supplier to a host of nations producing little or no oil, making them dependent on their supplier. In the case of the Latin American and the Caribbean region, such a scenario is valid for Central America and the Caribbean sub-regions. Second, even if clear market dominance exists, the prospects of oil being used as an instrument of power politics depend on the domestic circumstances. Successful petro-politics requires high prices, a robust domestic industry with significant expansion potential, and high levels of efficiency and investment. Absent these factors, it is unlikely that a country can sustain its reliance on commodity revenue as the centerpiece of its foreign policy in the long-term (Arriagada, 2006).

Electricity Generation

According to BMI forecasts, Venezuela will account for 10.49% of the Latin American and the Caribbean regional power generation by 2013. Venezuela's thermal generation in 2008 was around 33 TWh or 7.08% of the regional total, contributing with 31.2% in electricity generation in 2009. It is important to know that fossil fuel-sourced electricity increased its share by 19 TWh during the period 1999-2009. Electricity generation from 1999 was the following: in 1999: 20 TWh; in 2006: 30.7 TWh; in 2007: 31.8%; in 2008: 33 TWh; and in 2009: 39 TWh. The increase in electricity generation in the whole period was 95%.

By 2013, the country is expected to account for 7.71% of thermal generation. Electricity consumption per capita is expected to rise by 4.7% in the coming years. The country's power consumption is expected to increase from an estimated 104 TWh in 2008 to 119 TWh by 2013; this represents an increase of 14.4% providing a continuing theoretical surplus on the basis of 3.3% annual average growth in electricity generation. Between 2008 and 2018, it is expected an increase in Venezuelan electricity generation of 45.3%, which is around the middle of the range for the Latin American and the Caribbean region. This equates to 25.2% in the 2013-2018 period, up from 16.1% in 2008-2013. Thermal power generation is forecast to rise by 57% between 2008 and 2018.

Looking Forward

Since Venezuela has the world's largest heavy oil reserves, development ought to be a crucial component of its energy policy. This includes raising the quality and number of refineries as well as finding partners to purchase super heavy crude oil or the technology to process it.

If Venezuela wants to become less dependent on exports to the USA, it must accept that its current dependence is based on refining capacity. Without US refineries, Venezuelan heavy crude oil would have a negligible market. Refining heavy crude oil requires large investments that PdVSA has yet to provide in order to reduce the dependency from the USA. For this reason, PdVSA is looking to partner with State-owned oil companies from the Southern Cone to explore, develop, and refine heavy crude oil. The best option might be a partnership that begins with production in the Orinoco Oil Belt and combines refining facilities in Venezuela and at the destination, with similar refineries throughout selected partner nations. The aim is of reducing dependency of any particular country for the reprocessing of heavy crude oil. Such an arrangement would promote participation in all process stages and reduce the current dependence in reprocessing capacity to the USA. The fulfillment of these and other projects would encourage more symmetrical relations between Venezuela and its partners.

There are four projects that have been identified by the government to explore and produce oil in the Orinoco Oil Belt. The first project, Conoco's Petrozuata, began commercial production in 2001. Conoco's Petrozuata is producing an estimated of 120 000 barrels per day of heavy crude oil. Conoco's Petrozuata got permission from PdVSA to increase capacity to 150 000 barrels per day in 2003. The company expanded its production to a further 120 000 barrels per day of heavy crude oil in 2006. It initial production of heavy crude oil will be processed at PdVSA refineries and a Conoco plant at Lake Charles, Louisiana. The other three projects include: Exxon-Mobil and VEBA's (Germany) in Cerro Negro, Total-Fina-Elf (France) and Statoil's (Norway) in Sincor, and Phillips and Texaco's Ameriven in Hamaca. Cerro Negro with a capacity of 120 000 barrels per day started producing 105 000 barrels per day of heavy crude oil from mid-2001. Sincor with a capacity of 200 000 barrels per day is producing 160 000 barrels per day of heavy crude oil since 2002; later rising to 180 000 barrels per day. Of the four projects, Sincor is producing the highest quality grade of 32° API for sale on the open market. Limited production of 40 000 barrels per day has already begun. Hamaca refinery has a capacity of 190 000 barrels per day[107].

Finally, it is important to note the following: The Plan for Economic and Social Development of the Nation for the 2007-2013 period includes one main objective related to the energetic strengthens of the country, and the benefits of the combination of the sovereign use of natural resources, particularly oil, with global and regional energy integration for national development, all of which makes Venezuela an energy power. This Plan is intended to promote Venezuela as an energy regional power to strengthen Latin American and Caribbean energy integration, ensuring that both production and consumption of energy contribute to the preservation of the environment, fostering a shift towards the use of alternative energy sources.

---

[107] In 2004, the Hamaca refinery capacity was upgraded to 208 000 barrels per day.

Chapter III

THE CURRENT SITUATION AND FUTURE ROLE OF NATURAL GAS IN THE REGION ELECTRICITY GENERATION

GENERAL OVERVIEW

Worldwide, total natural gas[108] consumption increases by an average of 1.6% per year in the IEO (2009) reference case, and this consumption will increase from 2.91 trillion m^3 in 2006 to 4.59 trillion m^3 in 2030; this represents an increase of 57.7% due, among other things, to the increase of natural gas for the generation of electricity in several countries. The world's total gas reserves in 2010 were estimated in 190.1 trillion m^3. According to EIA sources, worldwide natural gas demand grew by 1.71 billion m^3 per day from 2000 to 2007, nearly 25%. The EIA also projects global natural gas demand to grow over 0.90 billion m^3 per day by the year 2015, and projects a further growth in demand around 1.20 billion m^3 per day by 2025.

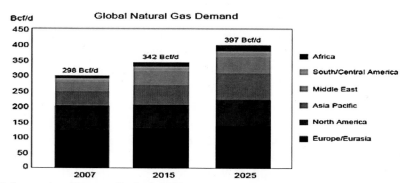

Source: EIA International Energy Outlook 2010.

Figure 76. World's natural gas demand projection.

---

[108] Natural gas is a gas consisting primarily of methane, typically with 0%-20% higher hydrocarbons (primarily ethane). It is found associated with other hydrocarbon fuel in coal beds, as methane clathrate, is an important fuel source, and a major feedstock for fertilizers. Most natural gas is created by two mechanisms: biogenic and thermo genic. Natural gas emits 43% fewer carbon emissions than coal, and 30% fewer emissions than oil for each unit of energy delivered.

From Figure 76, the following can be stated: Asia and the Pacific is the region with the highest increase in the demand of natural gas in the period 2007-2025, followed by South and North America. The demand of natural gas is expected to increase from 7.09 billion m^3 per day in 2007 to 8.13 million m^3 per day in 2015, an increase of 14.6%, and to 11.2 billion m^3 per day in 2025, a further increase of 79.6% respect to 2015, and an increase of 105% respect to 2007.

According to Deutsche Montan Technologie GmbH, OLADE and CIEMAT (2005) future development of natural gas use and trade in the Latin American and the Caribbean region over the next decade will be greatly influenced by Brazil as South America's leading economy. An ambitious plan is currently prepared to increase the country's gas fuelled electricity generation in the next years, with the purpose of reducing the strong dependence on hydro power generation, which is by far the main source of power in this country until now. It seems clearly admitted that hydro power in Brazil will no more be able to meet energy needs during low-rainfall years and, for this reason, gas based power generation has to be urgently developed as well as an increase in the the use of nuclear energy for electricity generation.

In most Latin American and the Caribbean countries the same trend will be followed with Brazil and Chile leading the way, with - as a consequence - a major increase of natural gas in the energy matrix. As in many other regions in the world, the initial development of gas-fuelled power generation will be followed by increased gas consumption for industrial, commercial, and residential use.

Bolivia will clearly remain the main supplier of gas to Brazil, Argentina, and to other countries in South America, considering the pipelines already in operation in the region and recent major gas discoveries in Bolivia.

In 1991, Argentina and Chile concluded the Gas Interconnection Protocol between these two countries. For the implementation of this Protocol several pipeline projects were proposed. The GasAndes Pipeline project was proposed by the consortium of Nova Corporation of Canada, Chilean companies Gasco, Gener, and Argentinean companies Compañía General de Combustibles and Techint (Compañía Técnica Internacional del Perú[109]). The feasibility study of the pipeline was concluded in 1994. The pipeline was commissioned in 1997. The capacity of the pipeline is 3.3 billion m^3. The gas is supplied mainly from the Neuquen gas fields. The total investment of the project was US $1.46 billion.

Central and South America's natural gas production increased by 2.7% per year from 0.15 trillion m^3 in 2005, and it are expected that this production increases to 0.29 trillion m^3 in 2030; this represents an increase of 93.3% respect to 2005. Despite adequate reserves that support healthy prospects for long-term production growth in South America, the region has begun importing LNG to supplement current domestic supplies, which have failed to keep up with demand (especially the so-called "peak seasonal demand").

Argentina became the first country in South America to import LNG, receiving its first cargo in May 2008. Brazil and Chile follow it. In this region, there is currently only one existing liquefaction LNG terminal operating from Trinidad and Tobago. Two regasification LNG terminals are located in the Dominican Republic and in Puerto Rico. The Republic of Bolivia, a landlocked country with a substantial proven natural gas reserve, has entered into a

---

[109] Peru International Technical Company.

proposal with Peru to reach the international gas market with the proposed Pacific LNG facility.

In addition to these facilities, five LNG liquefaction terminal projects have been proposed or are under construction in Colombia, Peru, and Venezuela. Fifteen LNG regasification terminal projects have been proposed or are under construction in Argentina, Bahamas, Brazil, Chile, El Salvador, Honduras, and Uruguay.

In addition, a joint LNG regasification project between Jamaica and Trinidad and Tobago has also been proposed. The two proposed LNG regasification terminal projects in the Bahamas, located on the Grand Bahamas Island and Ocean Cay Island, will be connected with the natural gas network in Florida.

Source: California Energy Commission.

Figure 77. LNG and regasification facilities storage.

In the Andean countries (Bolivia, Colombia, Ecuador, and Peru), regional natural gas consumption was 37% of the region's total energy consumption in 2004 but annual growth was slow. In the Southern Cone, natural gas consumption is expected to rise at a much faster rate, between 3.5% and 13% a year. It is important to stress that the Southern Cone will continue to have the highest consumption of natural gas in the whole region in the coming years. Argentina is the major natural gas producer in the sub-region, exporting to Chile, Uruguay, and Brazil. Bolivia has increased the current production level, with the purpose of satisfying the foresee natural gas demand by the Southern Cone and Brazil in the coming years. Regional forecasts of higher consumption are exhibited in Figure 78.

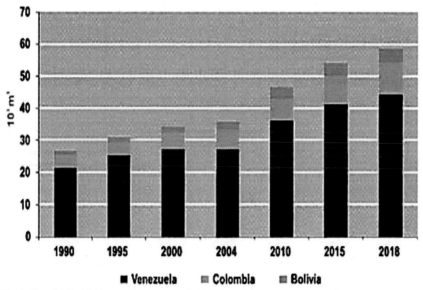

Source: OLADE and World Energy Congress (2008).

Figure 78. Natural gas demand in Venezuela, Colombia, and Bolivia: Forecast from 2010.

From Figure 78, the following can be stated: Venezuela will be the country with the highest increase in the use of natural gas among Colombia and Bolivia, although the majority of this gas will not be used for electricity generation.

Combined-Cycle Gas Power Plant

Whenever natural gas or oil is fired in a power plant, the combined-cycle gas power plant is more economical than the steam-power plant due to its higher efficiency and lower specific price. Modern combined-cycle gas power plants are simpler, less expensive, and operationally more flexible than steam-power plants. For short utilization periods (peaking units), the gas turbine is most economical. Gas turbines can serve as intermediate or base-load units in countries where fuel is abundant at low cost. The lack of water consumption has made this machine popular in dry regions. The short installation time allows a customer to plan a new installation on short notice. If all fuels are readily available at world's market prices, gas-fired combined-cycle power plants are the most economical solution for intermediate and base-load applications. This results in a limited environmental impact (small heat rejection or low water consumption). With clean fuels like natural gas, this technology also achieves lowest emissions (Deutsche Montan Technologie GmbH, OLADE and CIEMAT, 2005).

The Use of Natural Gas for Electricity Generation

Natural gas remains a key energy source for industrial sector uses and electricity generation throughout the projection period 2006 to 2030. Over this period, natural-gas fired electricity generation will increases by 2.75% per year, making gas the fastest-growing power source after renewables in the IEO (2009) reference case. Electricity generation from natural gas worldwide is expected to increases from 3.6 trillion kWh in 2006 to 6.8 trillion kWh in 2030, an increase of 88.9% but the total amount of electricity generated from natural gas continues to be only about one-half the total for coal, even in 2030. Natural-gas-fired combined-cycle capacity is an attractive choice for new power plants because of its fuel efficiency, operating flexibility (it can be brought online in minutes rather than the hours it takes for coal-fired power plants and some other generating capacity), relatively short planning and construction times (months instead of the years that nuclear power plants typically require), and capital costs lower than those for other technologies.

The industrial sector currently consumes more natural gas than any other end-use sector, and is expected to continue that trend through 2030, when 40% of world's natural gas consumption is projected to be used for industrial purposes. In particular, new petrochemical plants are expected to rely increasingly on natural gas as a feedstock, particularly in the Middle East, where major oil producers are working to maximize revenues from oil exports and, for this reason, turn to natural gas for domestic uses. In the electric sector, natural gas is an attractive choice for new generating plants because of its relative fuel efficiency and low carbon dioxide intensity. Electricity generation will accounts for 35% of the world's total natural gas consumption in 2030 (IEO, 2008).

Production, Consumption and Reserves of Natural Gas

The Latin American and the Caribbean region is the world's smallest consumer of natural gas. Trinidad and Tobago is Latin America's top gas exporter and, at the same time, the only major LNG exporter in the region. Venezuela and Brazil are the region's largest natural gas producers, Brazil being a net importer and Venezuela producing all of its natural gas for domestic use except for the generation of electricity. Several countries are investing in LNG import capacity, including Brazil, Argentina, and Chile. The EIA notes that despite adequate natural gas reserves that support healthy prospects for long-term production growth in South America, the region has begun importing LNG to supplement current domestic supplies, which have failed to keep up with demand. LNG is the fastest-growing component of the global natural gas market, increasing at a 7% annual rate over the last decade. For countries that lack indigenous natural gas resources and delivery infrastructure, LNG represents a rapid and cost-effective means of introducing natural gas into their local fuel mix.

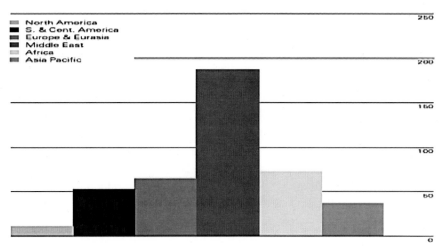

Source: BP Statistic Review of World Energy (2010).

Figure 79. World's natural gas reserve by region in 2009.

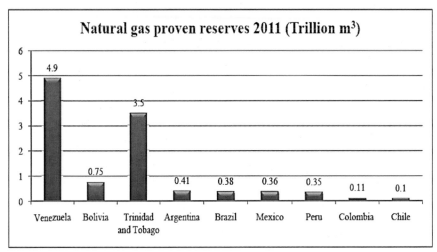

Source: *OGJ*.

Figure 80. Largest natural gas proven reserves in Latin America and the Caribbean in 2011.

Currently, there are twenty five LNG importing countries in Europe, Asia, South America, Central America, North America, and the Middle East, up from seventeen importing countries in 2007, an increase of 47%. Numerous developing countries, including Jamaica, Colombia, Panama, El Salvador, and Costa Rica, among others, are considering plans to build new LNG terminals and enter the global LNG trade.

Despite the fact that the Latin American and the Caribbean region is the world's smallest consumer of natural gas, this fossil fuel is one the main energy sources for power production in the region, and its role will even be strengthened in the future. To this aim the distribution and access to natural gas will be enforced by strengthening the pipeline network system in the region.

In 2003, Latin American and the Caribbean's proven natural gas reserves amounted to 7.5 trillion m^3 representing 5% of the world's total reserves. In 2004, natural gas reserves registered a slight descent of 0.02% reaching the amount of 4.98% of the world's total. In 2005, the natural gas reserves were estimate in around 4.4% of the world's total reserves; this represents a further decrease of 0.6% with respect previous year. The country with the largest natural gas reserves in the region is Venezuela (4.97 trillion m³) very far from the second country with the largest reserves (Bolivia). According to EIA, Latin American and the Caribbean's natural gas production in 2009 was 6,720 billion m³. In 2008, the level of consumption in the whole region (except Mexico) was 4,706 billion m³, an increase of 2.75% in comparison to 2007. The level of consumption in Central and South America represent 4.27% of the world's total.

From Table 46 and Figure 80, the following can be stated: During the period 2010-2011, almost all countries in the region increased their natural gas reserves: The country with the major increase was Trinidad and Tobago from 436,100 million m³ in 2010 to 3.5 trillion m³ in 2011, an increase of more than eightfold.

Figures 82 and 83 describe the flow chart for natural gas production and consumption. In Figure 83 two ways of extract natural gas is included: The extraction of natural gas associated to the extraction of crude oil, and the extraction of non-associated gas. Figure 83 include the different uses of the natural gas.

It is important to stress that there is a large not quantified natural gas reserves concentrated in the sub-regional bloc of the Andean zone, especially in Peru, Bolivia, and Venezuela. In the case of Mexico and Brazil, their proven natural gas reserves will allow these countries to meet much of their massive domestic energy demand in the coming years.

Table 46. Countries by natural gas proven reserves in Latin America and the Caribbean

Rank	Country/Region	Natural gas proven reserves (Million m³)	% of total	Date of information
—	World	190 163 119. 46	100%	1.1. 2010
9	Venezuela	4 983 000	2.62%	1.1. 2010
29	Bolivia	750 400	0.39%	1.1. 2010
32	Trinidad and Tobago	436 100	0.23%	1.1. 2010
33	Argentina	398 400	0.21%	1.1. 2010
35	Brazil	364 200	0.19%	1.1. 2010
36	Mexico	359 700	0.19%	1.1. 2010
38	Peru	334 100	0.18%	1.1. 2010
50	Colombia	112 000	0.06%	1.1. 2010
52	Chile	97 970	0.05%	1.1. 2010
56	Cuba	70 790	0.04%	1.1. 2010
81	Ecuador	7 985	0.00%	1.1. 2010
92	Guatemala	2 960	0.00%	1.1. 2010
100	Barbados	113. 3	0.00%	1.1. 2010

Source: World Fact book.

Table 47. Natural gas production by country

Rank	Country/Region	Annual natural gas production (Million m³)	Date of information (Estimate)
—	World	3 127 000	2008
14	Mexico	60 350	2009
19	Argentina	41 360	2009
20	Trinidad and Tobago	39 300	2008
28	Venezuela	23 060	2009
34	Bolivia	14 200	2008
40	Brazil	10 280	2009
41	Colombia	10 000	2011
50	Peru	3 390	2008
58	Chile	1 650	2008
67	Cuba	400	2008
71	Ecuador	283.2	2009
85	Barbados	29.170	2008

Source: World Fact book.

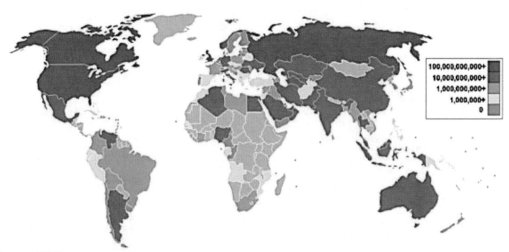

Source. US Department of Energy.

Figure 81. Map of the world's natural gas reserves.

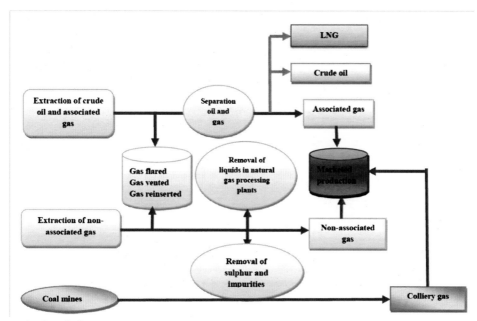

Source: Author design.

Figure 82. Simplified flow chart for natural gas production.

Countries with the highest level of natural gas consumption are Mexico, Argentina, Venezuela, Trinidad and Tobago, Brazil, Bolivia, Colombia, Peru, Chile, and Ecuador. Trinidad and Tobago and Bolivia are currently the largest exporters of natural gas in the Latin American and the Caribbean region. In Brazil and Chile, natural gas is a small component in the energy mix. In Argentina natural gas consumption makes up 47% of the primary energy mix.

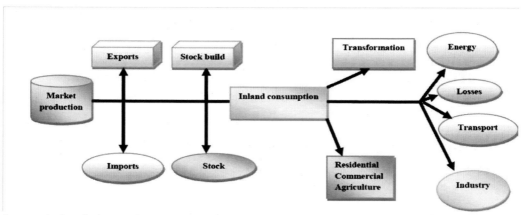

Source: Author design.

Figure 83. Simplified flow chart for natural gas consumption.

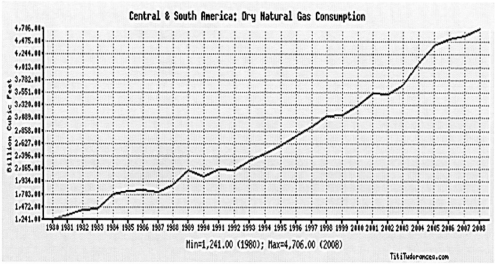

Source: Titi Tudorancea.

Figure 84. Natural gas consumption in Central and South America during the period 1980-2008.

In Central and South America, natural gas is the second-fastest-growing energy source after nuclear power (although nuclear generation is growing from a very small base and remains only a minor part of the region's total energy consumption). In Central America, natural gas is not used for electricity generation because the sub-region does not have natural gas but it may be introduced in the future due to the growing demand for electricity.

From figure 84, the following can be stated: Natural gas consumption shows a clear increase trends since 1980 moving from 35.14 billion m^3 (1,241 billion cubic feet) in 1980 up to 133.26 billion m^3 (4,706 billion cubic feet) in 2008, this represents an increase of 279%. There will be no change in this trend in the coming years.

Global demand for natural gas is expected to expand significantly as more nations adopt environmentally cleaner fuels to meet future economic growth and prioritize alternatives to minimize the impact of increasing oil based energy costs. The environmental benefits of natural gas are clear. Natural gas emits 43% fewer carbon emissions than coal, and 30% fewer emissions than oil, for each unit of energy delivered. Many of the most rapidly growing gas markets are in emerging economies in Asia, particularly India and China, the Middle East, and South America, economies which battle the balance between air quality and living standards on a daily basis.

From Table 48, the following can be stated: All Central American countries will increase the consumption of electricity during the period 2010-2020 above 4%. The country with the lower increase is El Salvador with 4%. The country with the highest increase is Costa Rica with 5.3%.

The inherent cleanliness of natural gas, when compared with other fossil fuels used for the electricity generation, means that using gas for this specific purpose can help to reduce the emission of the air pollutants that produce smog and acid rain, and that could exacerbate the greenhouse effect.

Table 48. Electricity demand forecast – Central America (GWh)

Year	GU	ES	HO	NI	CR	PA	Total
2006	7 185	4 866	6 321	2 896	8 594	5 752	35 614
2010	8 825	5 693	7 575	3 460	10 506	6 907	42 966
2013	10 174	6 404	8 662	3 896	12 234	7 920	49 290
2015	11 135	6 926	9 438	4 217	13 575	8 692	53 983
2018	12 676	7 791	10 669	4 765	15 882	10 006	61 789
2020	13 775	8 427	11 505	5 204	17 643	11 003	67 557
% growth	4.8%	4%	4.4%	4.3%	5.3%	4.7%	4.7%

Source: World Energy Council (2008).

Finally, it is important to stress the following: The natural gas system is extremely efficient as are most types of appliances and equipment that operate on natural gas. The higher the energy efficiency is, the greater the conservation of energy and the lower environmental impacts. When the entire cycle of producing, processing, transporting, and using energy is considered, natural gas is delivered to the consumer with a total energy efficiency of about 90%, compared with about 27% for electricity. Moreover, gas appliances and equipment are extremely efficient as evidenced by the fact that the residential use of gas per customer is about 16% less today than it was in 1980.

Furthermore, natural gas is a reliable source of fuel because the pipeline delivery system is underground and protected from weather-related disruptions. This reliability is one of the reasons businesses that cannot afford power disruptions find gas-fired distributed electricity generation so attractive.

Without doubt, natural gas will become the bridge fuel toward the clean and cheap energies of the future, and will call for major investments, especially in gas pipelines. The share of natural gas in the basket of primary sources for power generation in many countries will increase in the coming years, reducing the relative share of oil byproducts and hydro power for electricity generation.

Trade in natural gas will grow at a substantially faster pace to cover demand in several countries of the region.

LIMITING FACTORS FOR NATURAL GAS INTEGRATION

It is important to single out that natural gas integration in the region could face some serious constraints linked with the resistance to the liberalization process in leading countries, and to the increase participation of private actors in various parts of the gas sector from exploration to distribution.

In Argentina, where transmission and distribution markets were fully opened to private capital, a serious debate has been seen between Energas, the national regulator, transmission companies, distributors, traders, and consumers. Companies believe that changes imposed by the national regulator will affect their profitability, and hinder future investments. Similar problems appear in Venezuela, where the current government gives to market analysts the impression that it does not favor the liberalization process. However, it remains clear that 4,147 billion of m^3 of proven natural gas reserves (even including associated natural gas) is a strong incentive to attract industry partners. A push for natural gas development is part of the government's plan to diversify the economy from oil dependence.

Brazil also raises some questions as to the real signs the government is giving for opening its natural gas markets. Some industry analysts believe that the strong role of States and federal authorities, coupled with the duties of the National Petroleum Agency and the power of Petrobras, will complicate and delay the full implementation of the energy's market reform. This could slow down the full development of natural gas penetration in the energy market.

Increased natural gas market integration will be based not only on new interregional pipeline links but also LNG supplies from Venezuela, and possibly Trinidad and Tobago. Cristobal Colon LNG project in Venezuela has recently revived on a smaller scale, including PdVSA and partners such as Shell, Exxon-Mobil, and Mitsubishi. In Trinidad and Tobago, a project is under way to triple the current LNG production to 9 million tons by adding two additional trains and export mainly to USA and Spain (Deutsche Montan Technologie GmbH, OLADE and CIEMAT, 2005).

An analysis performed by OLADE in 2000s highlights the following prospects on the natural gas market in the region: Serious gas supply problems in the Southern Cone will arise around 2010. The two main supplier countries in the area -Argentina and Bolivia- cannot meet the demand to follow growing needs in deficit countries such as Chile and Brazil. LNG from Venezuela is then required to supply northeast Brazil from 2010, and in 2015 LNG supply should be extended to southeast Brazil, Argentina, and Chile. If production in Argentina follows a conservative profile (i.e., low production) difficulties are enhanced, and LNG supply from Venezuela or Africa would be also required after 2010 to meet demand for both Chile and Argentina. If natural gas production in Argentina is on the high side, it displaces the most part of LNG needs until 2015 leaving only a terminal to supply northeast Brazil. Argentina is not supplying the level of natural gas contracted by Chile during the past years, due to an increase in the national demand of natural gas and the reduction of the production of this type of energy source.

Whatever scenario is considered there is in the short-term a competition between Argentina and Bolivia to meet the promising Brazilian market. In the medium-term this competition is extended to Venezuela as a third potential supplier. This competition is reflected in the four routes to supply the south-southeast Brazilian market (excluding the existing Bolivia–Brazil pipeline):

a) The old Mercosur route, open to both Argentina and Bolivian gas;
b) The pipeline project from Uruguaiana to Porto Alegre, open only to natural gas from Argentina;
c) The pipeline project from Montevideo to Porto Alegre, open only to natural gas from Argentina;
d) A direct line from Bolivia to Porto Alegre through Paraguay, open preferably to natural gas from Bolivia.

According to different experts' opinions, the Uruguaiana route seems to be the most advanced solution, which gives an advantage to natural gas from Argentina in the short-term. However, on the basis of distance and flow optimization perhaps the preference would be to a link along the Mercosur route, with gas shipped from both Bolivia and Argentina and possibility of swaps. According to first estimations, gas from Camisea would not be competitive to displace LNG from Venezuela to northeast Brazil. However, it could displace LNG supplies to Argentina and Chile. An alternate scenario involving a lower gas demand (20% reduction in 2010 and 25% reduction in 2015) allows eliminating LNG imports until 2015. It would correspond to a situation of "suppressed demand" where LNG price would be too high to compete with local natural gas and competing fuels.

In addition of the above, it is important to single out the following: Central American countries have regulations for the exploration and production of hydrocarbons, as well as for hydrocarbon trade and supply but in view of the lack of a natural gas market, there are no specific regulations for the services corresponding to this sub-sector. In some cases, the hydrocarbon laws refer to natural gas but always in relation to general exploration and production activities. Only El Salvador (which has a project for the construction of an LNG regasification plant) has a natural gas bill for regulation, reception, storage, regasification, transport, distribution, and marketing of natural gas.

In all Andean countries, except for Venezuela, major reforms have taken place since the 1990s, with the objective of changing the institutional structure and the regulatory framework of the natural gas sector. In general, these reforms led to a reformulation of the State's role and allowed the private sector to act as entrepreneurs keeping the State as policymaker and regulator. In the upstream, the natural gas prospecting and extraction regulations were altered mainly to attract foreign risk capital, thereby increasing available reserves. To achieve this objective, most countries in the sub-region adopt the following group of incentives to attract foreign investment:

a) Reduction of taxes and of royalty percentages;
b) Extension of the concession terms;
c) A greater participation in production and freedom to export by eliminating the domestic market supply obligation (World Energy Council, 2008).

The First Meeting of the Council of Andean Community Ministers of Energy, Electricity, Hydrocarbons and Mines, held in Quito in January 2004, defined the bases for the Andean Energy Alliance, to be established through efforts in five areas:
1. Construction of energy (electricity and gas) markets integrated through harmonized physical systems and regulatory frameworks;
2. Positioning in international hydrocarbon markets in a strategic context of energy security;
3. Promotion in the Andean countries of entrepreneurial development of "energy clusters";
4. Framework for the negotiation and classification of energy services in the WTO and other international organizations;
5. Development of the renewable energy sources theme, its tie-in with the environmental theme and with the Integral Plan for Social Development.

The Action Plan of the Andean Council of Ministers of Energy, Electricity, Hydrocarbons and Mines gave special priority to develop the natural gas theme in the sub-region. The Chairman of that Council of Ministers, in coordination with the Secretariat of the Andean Community, accordingly called the First Meeting of the Ad Hoc Group for Gas Matters, which took place in Lima on November 13 and 14, 2003. International organizations directly concerned with natural gas, like OLADE, ECLAC, IDB and CAF, took special part in that meeting. As a result of the meeting, it was decided to advance the execution of a working plan drawn from the document especially prepared by ECLAC for the meeting, which contains the following recommendations:

a) With bi-national integration processes as a starting point, move ahead with criteria that are not only economic but also have a strong social component and that are aimed at long-term integral development. It is advisable to gradually build up an infrastructure system that will progressively improve the people's quality of life and contribute to that development. Therefore, these strategies should emphasize mechanisms that facilitate the access of poor sectors to clean and efficient energy sources like gas and electricity, in that way coinciding with the basic principles of sustainable development;

b) Respect the natural role of regional and international organizations with broad experience on the subject by reinforcing that role;

c) Work on the orderly definition of an agenda of tentative efforts to induce member countries to participate creatively in coordinating this long-term vision and its key objectives.

It was agreed at the First Meeting of the Council of Andean Community Ministers of Energy, Electricity, Hydrocarbons and Mines to create the Permanent Group of National Experts on Gas, whose main responsibilities are:

a) Conduct studies of the potential demand for natural gas up to the year 2030, with realistic hypotheses and contrasting scenarios. Integral methodologies would be employed to consider demand within each country by regions and by homogeneous consumption or user groups, in order to determine foreseeable penetrations and the relative price conditions that would tend to ensure forecast fulfillment. Emphasis would be placed on the access of the poor, and a territorial and industrial vision of development would be used to facilitate the global integration of markets and centers of population in order to stem the spread of poverty in major cities;

b) Based on the findings of these studies, analyze the range of feasible, necessary and advisable interconnections, determining the entry dates and the investments required;

c) Make audits of each country's reserves, establishing the foreseeable supply and demand balances, and estimating the reserves each country needs to discover, in order to evaluate the cost/benefits and balances among them and the supply security vis-a-vis the advantages of integration;

d) Outline and move ahead with agreements on financing mechanisms, price policies, and trust fund management, in order to ensure upstream and downstream investments. State-owned corporations can contribute to this objective by using oil revenues rationally;

e) Establish administrative mechanisms and the responsibilities of the future regional supranational regulating agency or equivalent body;

f) Analyze methodologies for rate-setting and rules for the open access, supply security, competition, and protection of investments of users, in order to establish in the mid-term the initial drafts of the common regulatory frameworks to be studied in depth, and negotiated by the different countries and actors in the system.

Table 49 includes a synthesis of the legal framework of the natural gas industry in a group of countries within the Andean zone, including Venezuela, which is not currently a member of the Andean Community of Nations.

Table 49. Synthesis of the legal framework of the natural gas industry

Country	Prospecting and Production	Transport	Distribution
Bolivia	The state retains the ownership of the hydrocarbons. YPFB drafts the concession contracts and associates with companies where it has majority holding and control of operations.	YPFB monopoly	YPFB and temporary concessions divided in geographic areas with exclusivity. Prices regulated by the Government.
Colombia	Through contracts. Ecopetrol enters into partnership with private companies with a minority stake (30%)	Controlled by two companies (Ecogas and Prolmgas)	Concessions divided in geographic areas with exclusivity. Government regulated prices.
Ecuador	The state retains total control of the upstream plants, but activities are carried-out by private companies.	Controlled by Petroecuador.	Concessions divided in geographic areas with exclusivity
Peru	The state retains the ownership of the hydrocarbons. This right is licensed to the private sector by contracts negotiated by Petroperu.	Licence and service contracts.	License and service contracts divided in geographic areas with exclusivity
Venezuela	Private companies may participate mainly in non-associated natural gas, always associated with PDVSA, which has majority holding and control of operations.	Monopoly of PDVSA Gas or of its subsidiaries.	PDVSA Gas and concessions divided in geographic areas with exclusivity. Government regulated prices.

Source: World Energy Council.

NATURAL GAS PRICES

Natural gas price issues have created, in recent years, some tension among some Southern Cone countries. Bolivia had been a traditional supplier of cheap natural gas to both Brazil and Argentina but, in July of 2006, the Bolivian government announced it was raising its border price for Argentina's customers from US $3.2 to US $5 per million Btus; this represents a 56% increase in the traditional natural gas price. The final price of natural gas was about US $6 per million Btus after transportation.

On the other hand, talks between Bolivia and Brazil regarding the increase in the traditional natural gas price and the nationalization of Petrobras' facilities in Bolivia have been very tense between these two countries. The dispute was solved after the personal involvement of the presidents of both countries.

Chile was paying to Argentina from US $2.8 to US $3.4 per million Btus as an added benefit from Argentina's price controls, even in case when the country did not receive the full supply of natural gas accorded. The natural gas price imported from Bolivia rose to about US $5 per million Btus.

Finally, it is important to know that, according to some expert opinions, the price of natural gas wills growth in the future due to an increase in the demand of this important fossil fuel and the reduction in the use of oil for electricity generation in many countries.

The situation of the gas sector in a group of selected countries are briefly presented in the following paragraphs

ARGENTINA

Argentina is the largest producer and consumer of natural gas in South America, and has a globally significant unconventional resource base.

Argentina produces more natural gas than any other country in South America but its output has declined over 10% from peak levels reached in 2006. From Figure 85 can be easily seem that the decline continue in the following three years. Argentina is also the continent's largest natural gas consumer.

From a net exporter of natural gas to neighboring countries before 2008, the country became a net importer of natural gas from that year. Recent assessments suggest that Argentina possesses one of the world's largest endowments of shale gas, which has become a focus of efforts to reverse the sector's recent decline.

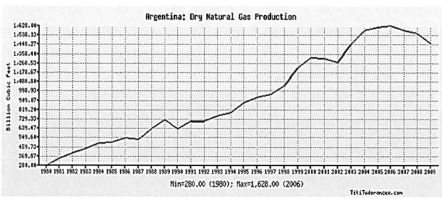

Source: Titi Tudorancea.

Figure 85. Natural gas production.

From Figure 85, the following can be stated: The production of natural gas increased from 7.93 billion m^3 (280 billion cubic feet) in 1980, to a little less than 38.46 billion m^3

(1,358 billion cubic feet) in 2000. The production declined during the period 2000-2002 and increased again up to 2006. After 2006, the production of natural gas declined again from 46.10 billion m^3 (1,628 billion cubic feet) in 2006, to 41.01 billion m^3 (1,448 billion cubic feet) in 2009.

Roughly one-third of natural gas consumed in Argentina is used to generate electricity, while industry and the residential sector each account for close to 20% of the demand. Natural gas is also used in the transportation sector, as roughly 1.9 million of Argentina's vehicles operate on compressed natural gas.

Argentina has suffered in past years severe wintertime shortages of natural gas – reportedly of up to 40% of demand at prevailing prices – that have adversely impacted industrial users whose supplies were interrupted or diverted to satisfy basic residential needs. Seasonal shortages of natural gas also plague some summer months, as electricity demand soars with high temperatures. To avert similar problems in the future, the State energy company has taken steps to import greater volumes of LNG from Bolivia.

Energy Reform

Up to 1989, Argentina's electric power sector, regulated by Law 14.772 of 1958, was considered a public service provided by the State or State-owned companies. The main State-owned utilities at that time were: AYEE, a State company created in 1957, Hidronor created in 1957, and SEGBA created in 1962. Each of these companies provided bundled generation, transmission, and distribution services as integrated utilities. There were also nineteen provincial utilities, primarily distributors, and several electricity cooperatives. The main source of generation was hydroelectric. The industry was regulated by the federal government through the Secretary of Energy.

The electric power sector, which suffered from poor management practices and insufficient investment in the past, was also suffering other financial and operational difficulties. The absence of clear objectives, the political motives of the State-owned companies, and an economic environment of hyperinflation (that reached 200% per month in 1989) affected the performance of the electricity industry. Blackouts, which worsened during dry seasons due to the heavy reliance on hydroelectric generation and electricity theft, were very common problems in the country in the past. Overall, federal utilities were losing more than 20% of their power to non-paying customers. Electricity prices averaged about US $60 MWh in the 1980s.

Argentina began deregulating natural gas production in 1989, as part of its privatization of YPF. In 1990, the government passed a law removing the government from direct operation in the electricity industry and introducing basic principles of competition. The Electricity Act of 1992 established the legal framework for further restructuring and privatization with the ultimate intention to stimulate competition and to benefit consumers both in terms of price and quality of service. As with the oil industry, YPF (Repsol-YPF)[110] retains a dominant position in the upstream sector. The second-largest natural gas producer in Argentina is the French company Total.

The natural gas industry was privatized in June of 1992. The Gas Law split State monopoly "Gas del Estado" (State Gas) into eight distributors (Metrogas, Gas Natural, Pampeana, Litoral, Sur, Centro, Cuyana, and Noroeste) and two pipeline companies

---

[110] In April 2012, Repsol-YPF was nationalized by the current Argentinean government.

(Transportadora de Gas del Sur SA (TGS) and Transportadora de Gas del Norte SA (TGN)); TGN and most of the distribution operations were sold in December 1992.

TGS delivers two-thirds of the country's natural gas, serving southern Argentina and Buenos Aires. Enron and Perez Company own 70% of the company. TGS and TGN are not permitted to sell gas and must provide open access to their pipelines. Argentina's largest gas distributor is Metrogas. Prices for natural gas are set in line with that of petroleum but tariffs on natural gas are adjusted every six months in relation to a US index and seasonal fluctuations. Privatization has resulted in lower prices, which are among the lowest in the region.

However, and despite Argentina having the region's most deregulated oil and gas industry, there is a lack of competition with Repsol-YPF, which is controlling close to 60% of the gas supply (though this will fall to 44% as the government will not renew third party gas supply contracts it made with YPF before the Repsol-YPF merger in 1999). Based on this situation, Repsol-YPF has the power to dictate prices and terms and exert influence over competing fuels. However, this situation changed in April 2012 due to the nationalization of Repsol-YPF by the government.

Under the umbrella set by the Emergency Act passed in early 2002, the government made several decisions regarding the energy sector. It aimed to:

a) Minimize the devaluation effects on end users' prices. In practice, this meant frozen tariffs in the case of natural gas and electricity and the implementation of withholding taxes on exports, which reduced the market reference price for oil and natural gas exporters in order to avoid increasing domestic prices and, at the same time, increase government income;

b) Guarantee end users' supply, ensuring the coverage of operational costs to existing producers but not fixed costs recovery and promoting new expansions, most of them still in project status.

Frozen tariffs of regulated activities were implemented subject to future renegotiation of concession contracts. Consequently, the devaluation increased the relative competitiveness of the Argentina's economy with respect to the rest of the world. Local industry benefited from the frozen tariffs of natural gas and electricity and the distorted oil-derivatives prices.

An agreement between natural gas producers and the government was signed in 2004. The latter committed to increase regulated tariffs to industrial customers in order to allow a gradual recovery of natural gas prices.

The energy sector faced, and still faces today, an economic long-run mismatch between what the economy needs from the energy industry and what this industry can offer to the economy under the current relative prices scenario. In practice, this meant a lack of investments in all energy sub-sectors since the end of 2001. Consequently, domestic demand growth was gradually absorbing installed capacity, including those investments originally committed to exportations, because the horizon of hydrocarbons reserves was significantly reduced, particularly on natural gas. These facts were evidenced in April 2004, when the government announced reductions on natural gas exports to Chile in order to avoid curtailments on domestic demand.

Frozen tariffs and distorted prices blocked most of the investment recovery for those companies existing at the time the crisis started. In the power market, the measures adopted led to a significant imbalance between what the demand paid and what generators had to receive, which resulted in a significant credit requested from generators. The government proposed to swap such credits with shares of a new company to be created for building and operating a new power plant. A new State-owned company promoted by the government, Energía Argentina Sociedad Anónima (ENARSA), was created in October 2004. The primary initial assets of ENARSA were full exploration and exploitation rights of most oil in offshore areas but its business scope covers all energy-related activities. It is argued in Argentina that the withdrawal of the government from the energy sector during the 1990s was excessive and, consequently, a more significant presence is now required something that the government is doing step by step.

The government said that ENARSA will allow them to follow what happens in the energy sector "from inside" and, consequently, evaluate whether the private energy companies' behavior is adequate or not. On the other side, many private companies see ENARSA as a tool by which the government may press them to agree to conditions which otherwise would not be accepted.

Natural Gas Production, Consumption, and Reserves

Natural gas is Argentina's most important energy source. Argentina has the fourth-largest proved reserves of natural gas in the Latin American and the Caribbean region. According to EIA, in 2009 the reserves was 0.48 trillion m^3. The proven reserves of 2009 will satisfy the level of consumption reached in that year for the next 10.5 years. Based on projected economic growth, internal consumption is expected to double over the next twelve years, growing at a rate of 4.2% or 4.5% per year (growth has averaged 5.1% per year for the past decade).

On the other hand, *OGJ* estimates that Argentina had proved natural gas reserves of 0.41 trillion m^3 as of January 1, 2011, a decline of approximately 50% from reserve levels of a decade ago.

According to recent analysis made by EIA and Advanced Resources International, Argentina has 21.9 trillion m^3 of technically recoverable shale gas resources – the world's third largest assessed endowment, behind only China and the United States.

Table 50. Production, consumption and reserves of natural gas in Argentina (Billion m^3)

	Argentina 2008	Central and South America	World	Rank	Argentina 2009
Production	46.68	156.12	3 297.63	20	43.83
Consumption	47.04	139.53	3 327.45	17	45.69
Net export/import (-)	-0.36	16.62	--	56	-1.89
Proved reserves (Trillion m^3)	0.48	7.86	5.60	29	0.48

Source: EIA.

The Neuquen Basin located in western Argentina, contains more than half of the country's technically recoverable shale gas resources. YPF recently discovered a large formation of commercially promising tight gas and shale gas – thought to total 0.13 trillion m^3 – in the vicinity of Neuquen's Loma La Lata field, which for decades has been a leading source of conventional production.

According to Table 50, in 2008 Argentina produced 46.68 billion m^3 of natural gas, and 43.83 billion m^3 in 2009; this represents a decrease of 6.2% respect to 2008. The consumption was 47.04 billion m^3 in 2008, and 45.69 billion m^3 in 2009; this represents a decrease of 2.9%.

The distribution of final energy consumption by sector is the following: The industry including non-energy uses consume around 40% of the electricity produced in the country, while the other 60% is consumed by the residential, services, agriculture, and the transport sectors, among others.

It is important to know the following: Natural gas production in Argentina has been sustained falling since 2003 reaching, in 2009, the equivalent to 43.83 billion m^3, down 10% in the period. During the 2000s, 484 exploration wells were drilled, less than half those averaged during the 1990s, and 47% less if we compare the exploration wells drilled in the 1980s.

Natural gas consumption is increasing to the detriment of oil. The market share of gas grew from 40% in 1990 to 51% in 2009 (an increase of 11% during the period), while the share of oil fell from 46% to 36%; this represents a decrease of 10%. Biomass and coal play a relatively small role (4% and 2%, respectively) in the energy balance of the country; the rest of the energy consumption is supplied by nuclear power and hydroelectricity (7%). The rate of connection to the natural gas network is relatively high (approximately 60%).

Four regions, Neuguina, Salta, Tierra del Fuego, and Santa Cruz, contain most of Argentina's natural gas production, with the Neuquen region accounting for over half of the country's total production. As is the case in the oil sector, Argentina has begun to look towards its offshore basins as its traditional production centers have matured. Over 10% of Argentina's 2010 natural gas production was from offshore resources, which mostly entailed the Cuenca Marina Austral 1 concession that is operated by Total. All offshore natural gas production derives from the Austral-Magallanes Basin in the country's extreme south, which includes federal waters off of the provinces of Tierra del Fuego and Santa Cruz.

Dozens of projects to exploit Argentina's unconventional tight sand and shale gas resources – most of them in the Neuquen province – are under review or development. Many firms, including Exxon-Mobil, Apache, Pluspetrol, Total, and YPF, are attempting to take advantage of the more attractive fiscal terms offered by the government for energy unconventional projects. According to some sources, Argentina already produces over 6.51 million m^3 of unconventional natural gas per day or about 5% of total production.

Upon the creation of ENARSA in 2005, the Argentina government transferred all unallocated offshore exploration blocks to the new company and authorized it to seek partnerships with foreign companies. In January 2005, ENARSA signed an agreement with a consortium led by Petrobras to explore three offshore blocks in the Colorado Marina Basin.

Export and Import of Natural Gas

Argentina is a net exporter of natural gas, principally to Chile. However, this relationship was strained in 2004, when Argentina repeatedly reduced natural gas exports to Chile in order to make up for domestic shortages. Since then, Argentina has regularly cut exports to Chile in order to meet domestic demand. The recent level of supply of natural gas to Chile only cover 10% of the level agreed. In July 2006, Argentina doubled a tax on natural gas exports to Chile, a move seen by many as a means to offset higher costs for natural gas imports from Bolivia. Argentina is Chile's sole source of natural gas imports, and the continuing supply disruptions have forced Chile to pursue alternatives for its future import needs, and to use fossil fuels for electricity generation, increasing the energy bill and the emission of CO_2.

Natural Gas Pipelines

TGS operates the 3 408 km San Martin pipeline, with a capacity of 30.60 million m^3 per day connecting the southern part of the country with Buenos Aires. TGS also operates the Neuba I and II pipelines. Another company, TGN, operates two main pipelines. The first of them, the 1 440 km, 24 million m^3 Norte pipeline, runs from Campo Duran to the main compressor plant in San Jeronimo, eventually reaching Buenos Aires. The second pipeline, the 1 120 km, 35.40 million m^3 Centro Oeste pipeline, runs from the Loma la Lata field, in the Neuquen province to San Jeronimo. In order to meet rising demand, TGS is currently increasing capacity on the San Martin pipeline, while TGN is expanding the Norte pipeline.

Argentina has extensive pipeline linkages with its neighbors, including several pipelines connecting Argentina to Chile. There are three pipelines in the south: Tierra del Fuego, El Condor-Posesion, and Patagonia, which supply methanol plants in Chile. In the north, the 928 km, 9 million m^3 per day GasAtacama pipeline runs from Cornejo in Argentina to Mejillones in Chile. Also in the north, the 7.50 million m^3 per day NorAndino, operated by Belgium's Tractebel, runs parallel to GasAtacama. In the central region, the 464 km, 9.30 million m^3 per day GasAndes pipeline, connects the Neuquen Basin in Argentina to the city of Santiago in Chile. Also in the central region, the 528 km, 10.20 million m^3 per day Gasoducto del Pacífico, connects the Neuquen province to central Chile.

The 448 km, 3 million m^3 per day Parana-Uruguayana pipeline connects Argentina and Brazil. The pipeline provides natural gas to AES Brazil Energia's 600 MW power plant in Uruguayana. There are plans to construct a 614 km pipeline extension from Uruguayana to Porte Alegre, to supply natural gas to thermal power plants operating in the city.

In January 2003, Argentina natural gas began to flow to Montevideo, Uruguay, through the 400 km, 5.70 million m^3 per day Gasoducto Cruz del Sur (GCDS, Southern Cross pipeline). The GCDS project also includes a concession covering a possible extension from Uruguay to Porto Alegre in southern Brazil. Construction of the pipeline started in March 2001. The pipeline was completed in November 2002 and it was inaugurated by the presidents of Uruguay and Argentina, on 29 November 2002 in Montevideo. The pipeline is 215 km long and it has capacity of 1.8 billion m^3 of natural gas per year. According to South American Business Information, it cost US $150 millions. The pipeline transports the gas from the fields located in the Neuquen Basin. There is a proposal to prolong the pipeline to southern Brazil. The spur line would start in Colonia, Uruguay, and end in Porto Alegre, Brazil. A total of 415 km would be laid in Uruguay and 505 km in Brazil. According to Business News Americas, in Rio Grande do Sul it would be linked with the Gasbol pipeline.

While Argentina is a net exporter of natural gas, it also imports natural gas from Bolivia through the 432 km, 6.90 million m^3 per day Yacimientos-Bolivian Gulf (Yabog) pipeline. This pipeline serves Argentina's northern regions, which are not well supplied by the domestic natural gas transmission network.

Argentina began importing natural gas from Bolivia in 2004, to cover a domestic shortfall, which it had not done since 1999. Argentina continued to import gas from Bolivia following the end of the energy crisis of 2004. In October 2006, the two countries signed a deal for Argentina to import natural gas for an additional twenty years. Under the terms of the deal, Argentina imports from Bolivia will eventually approach 0.03 billion m^3 per day, a fourfold increase from current levels. The price that Argentina pays for the natural gas will also increase to US $5 per million Btu and eventually become linked to market rates. To facilitate this increase in volume, Argentina and Bolivia announced, in August 2006, that they would launch a tender for a new US $1 billion pipeline system connecting the two countries; the system will have a maximum capacity of 2.10 million m^3 per day and include an integrated LNG plant.

Liquefied Natural Gas Facilities

Argentina imported approximately two dozen cargoes of LNG or almost 1.4 million tons in 2010 in order to satisfy its energy needs. Trinidad and Tobago accounted for nearly 90% of those imports, with the remainder arriving from Qatar. Argentina government tenders suggest that LNG import volumes likely will double in 2011.

ENARSA has contracted with YPF to develop and execute a LNG strategy. Argentina began importing LNG in 2008, with the installation of the Bahía Blanca GasPort, a dockside receiving terminal and regasification vessel that uses proprietary technology from Excelerate Energy. In June 2011, a second and larger Excelerate Energy floating storage and regasification vessel, also financed by YPF and ENARSA, was inaugurated in Escobar (LNG Escobar) with base load and peak throughput capacities of 14.16 million m^3 and 16.99 million m^3 per day, respectively.

Argentina is pursuing bilateral arrangements to secure greater and more predictable supplies of LNG. For example, Argentina and Uruguay plan to jointly issue a tender for construction of a floating LNG terminal to be located near Montevideo, the supplies from which the two countries would share equally. ENARSA is also developing a regasification project through a partnership with PdVSA. Finally, Argentina and Qatar have signed an agreement to study the desirability of constructing a third LNG terminal that would be supplied with 5.4 million tons of Qatari LNG per year.

Investment in the Natural Gas Sector

The government approved several investment projects in order to increase the production or the supply of natural gas and LNG in the coming years. Two new combined cycle gas thermal power plants, the José de San Martín and Manuel Belgrano, each with a capacity of 830 MW, are under construction and expected to start full operations before the end of 2011. Endesa, Total, AES Corporation, Petrobras, EdF, and Duke Energy, are the main shareholders in the investment in these plants. Both facilities, which have been financed through the FONINVEMEM with a total investment amounts up to US $1,097 million. In addition, the Planning Ministry announced, in July 2007, the commissioning of five new thermal power plants with a total capacity of 1.6 GW and an overall investment of US $3,250 million. These dual-generation turbine (gas or fuel oil) plants started operations in 2008. The plants are the following: Ensenada with a capacity of 540 MW, Necochea with a capacity of 270 MW, Campana with a capacity of 540 MW, Santa Fe with a capacity of 125 MW, and Cordoba with a capacity of 125 MW. Finally, ENARSA has recently launched bidding for eleven small and transportable generation units (15 MW MW-100 MW) to be installed on barges. These new units will add between 400 MW and 500 MW of new generation capacity.

In 1999, Repsol-YPF began generating electricity from plants served from its gas fields in Argentina. Repsol-YPF will focus on improving its network of gas stations as well as invest in transport and distribution infrastructure, storage of natural gas, regasification plants, and electricity generation. Much of the increased production will come from Repsol-YPF's operations in Bolivia and Trinidad and Tobago.

In 2008, Argentina and Brazil both completed construction of their first LNG plant. Brazil is now building its third plant, aiming to have it ready by 2013. A terminal jointly managed by Argentina and Uruguay could be operational in Uruguay by 2012.

Electricity Generation

In 2010, the total electricity generated in the country was 115 081 MWh, out of which 62 528 MWh was generated using natural gas as fuel; this amount represents 54.3% of the total electricity produced by the country in that year. Since 2002, electricity generation using fossil fuels, particularly natural gas, has been increasing significantly.

Looking Forward

For Argentina, natural gas was in 2008 the dominant fuel, accounting for 53.6% of primary energy demand, followed by oil at 32.4%, hydro at 11.3%, nuclear at 2.2%, and coal at 0.5%. Argentina's 2008 market share of 11.78% is set to fall to 11.25% by the end of the forecast period. Natural gas – used widely in the electricity, industrial, and residential sectors, and increasingly in transportation – comprises approximately one-half of Argentina's total energy consumption, and this trend is expected to continue in the coming years.

It is important to stress that Argentina is the largest producer and consumer of natural gas in South America, and has a globally significant unconventional resource base. The country produces more natural gas than any other country in South America but its output has declined over 10% from peak levels in 2006. After being a net exporter of natural gas to neighboring countries, the country became a net importer in 2008 but started to import some natural gas from Bolivia in 2004, as result of the reduction of domestic natural gas supply to national costumers and to Chile.

Recent assessments suggest that Argentina possesses one of the world's largest endowments of shale gas, which has become a focus of efforts to reverse the sector's recent decline.

Roughly one-third of natural gas consumed in Argentina is used to generate electricity, while industry and the residential sector each account for close to 20% of Argentina's natural gas demand.

Argentina has suffered severe wintertime shortages of natural gas – reportedly of up to 40% of demand at prevailing prices – that have adversely impacted industrial users whose supplies were interrupted or diverted to satisfy basic residential needs. To avoid similar problems in the future, the government has taken steps to import greater volumes of liquefied natural gas with the purpose of improving the energy mix. Actions have been taken recently to begin as soon as possible the exploitation of a large formation of commercially promising tight gas and shale gas – thought to total 0.125 trillion m^3 (4.5 trillion cubic feet) – in the vicinity of Neuquén's Loma La Lata field, which for decades has been a leading source of conventional production. The future exploitation of this new large natural gas deposit will increase the participation of this type of energy source in the country energy balance in the coming years.

BOLIVIA

The Energy Reform

In May 2005, Bolivia's Congress approved a new Hydrocarbons Law that codified the results of the 2004 referendum. The law levies an additional 32% tax on oil and natural gas production at the wellhead, on top of the existing 18% royalty. The Law calls for the compulsory conversion of existing contracts to the terms of the new Law. The new Hydrocarbons Law likely will not affect current natural gas production but could have serious repercussions on the future expansion of the sector.

In May 2006, President Evo Morales signed a decree re-nationalizing the entire natural gas sector. Under the terms of the decree, foreign companies would not be allowed to own natural gas reserves and Yacimientos Petrolíferos Fiscales Bolivianos (YPFB) would take a majority stake in all natural gas projects. The government established a November 1, 2006 deadline for private oil companies to negotiate new agreements with YPFB. The decree gave foreign companies 180 days to sign new contracts ceding control to Bolivia. The two foreign companies hardest hit by the adoption of the decree were Repsol–YPF and Petrobras[111].

In addition, private companies would assume a new role under an operating service agreement structure, whereby they would produce natural gas on behalf of YPFB for a fee.

---

[111] Brazil buys 70% of Bolivian gas, is the single largest investor in both energy exploration and in the agricultural industry around Santa Cruz de la Sierra, and is its largest industrial goods supplier.

The re-nationalization of Bolivia's natural gas resources could have a profound impact upon the long-term development of the energy sector in the Southern Cone. Bolivia's ability to expand its natural gas exports will depend upon its ability to harness its sizable proven natural gas reserves before competing gas sources (LNG, increasing domestic production in Brazil and Argentina, pipelines from Venezuela, among others) entrench themselves in the region. Major natural gas consumers in the region will look towards and invest in these alternatives, if Bolivia is unable to maintain and expand its existing market share.

Royalty payments to the Bolivian government at the largest gas fields, including San Alberto and San Antonio, will now increase from 50% to 82%. All producers are obliged to sell at least 51% of their holdings to the Bolivian government, with the value of that share to be assessed by audit and negotiation. The State will take between 40% and 60% of production from other fields. Bolivia has left itself an open door through which it can compromise or retreat (Goldwyn, 2006).

Foreign companies extracting and exporting Bolivia's natural gas have invested about US $3.5 billion over the past decade. But new investments largely have been frozen since last year over concerns about what the government nationalization plan would mean for producers.

Proven Natural Gas Reserves

According to EIA sources, Bolivia had proven natural gas reserves of 810 billion m^3 in 2010, which represent 11% of the regional natural gas reserve, and 0.4% of the world's total reserves.

However, Bolivian officials indicated, in May 2011, that the country's total natural gas reserves is around 300 billion m^3, far lower than estimates natural gas reserves reported in 2010. Due to the new information provided by the Bolivian authorities, the country has fallen from the second-largest to the sixth-largest holder of natural gas reserves in South America, following Venezuela, Peru, Argentina, Brazil, and Colombia.

Tarija department contains over 85% of the country's total natural gas reserves, followed by Santa Cruz department (10.6%), and Cochabamba department (2.5%). In the mid-1990s, Bolivia privatized its natural gas sector, leading to an influx in foreign investment. The resulting increase in exploration led to a 600% increase in proven natural gas reserves from 1997-2005.

There have been several important discoveries in recent years, the most important of them include Margarita (probable with a reserve of 0.40 trillion m^3), Ipati (probable with a reserve of 0.36 trillion m^3), San Alberto (probable with a reserve of 0.35 trillion m^3), and Sabalo (probable with a reserve of 0.32 trillion m^3). However, since 2003, probable and proven natural gas reserves have declined slightly, as exploration has not kept pace with depletion from production.

Natural Gas Production and Consumption

According to EIA sources, Bolivia produced 15.54 billion m^3 of natural gas in 2008, which represent 10% of the regional total production, and 0.005% of the world total production.

In 2009, the total production was 13.38 billion m^3 of natural gas; this represents a decrease of 14% in comparison to 2008. In 2008, the consumption of natural gas was 3.03 billion m^3, which represent 0.02% of the regional total consumption, and 0.001% of the world total consumption. In 2009, the consumption was three billion m^3; this represents a decrease of 1% in comparison to 2008.

Production has risen sharply since 1999, corresponding with the start of natural gas exports to Brazil. Before the nationalization of the gas industry, Petrobras operated two fields, San Alberto and Sabalo, representing one-half of Bolivia's total natural gas production. Approximately three-fifths of Bolivian natural gas production comes from the Sabalo (34% of the total production in 2010) and San Alberto (26%) fields. They both lie in the Tarija department, which accounts for over 70% of Bolivian natural gas production. Santa Cruz ranks second at just below 20%. Government has announced that La Paz, Beni, and Pando will soon join Chuquisaca, Cochabamba, Santa Cruz, and Tarija as natural gas producing departments.

Roughly, one-fifth of Bolivian natural gas production is slated for the domestic market, which is dominated by electricity demand (over 50% of Bolivian natural gas consumption), industry (roughly 25%), and transportation (just below 20%).

Import and Export of Natural Gas

In 2008, Bolivia exported 12.48 billion m^3 of natural gas, which represents 75.2% of the regional total export.

Table 51. Natural gas in Bolivia

Natural Gas (Billion m^3)	Bolivia 2008	Central and South America	World	Rank	Bolivia 2009
Production Dry natural gas.	15.54	156.12	3 297.63	33	13.38
Consumption Dry natural gas.	3.03	139.53	3 327.45	74	3.00
Net exports/imports(-) Net Exports = Exports - imports. Negative numbers are net imports. Note: Data range begins with the year 1990.	12.48	16.62	--	71	10.38
Proved reserves[1] as of January 1.	810	7 680	186 570	26	810

Note: In 2011, the government declared that the natural gas reserves were 300 billion m^3.
Source: EIA and Short Term Energy Outlook.

The nationalization of Petrobras' assets in Bolivia had a ripple effect since Brazil buys 70% of Bolivian gas (85% of the total natural gas export of the country), is the single largest investor in both energy exploration and in the agricultural industry around Santa Cruz de la Sierra, and is its largest industrial goods supplier. A political solution was founded after a meeting of the presidents of both countries during which a just compensation for the nationalization of Petrobras' assets in Bolivia was discussed and agreed.

However, according to Arriagada (2006), the Brazilian government took a decision to become independent of Bolivian supplies as soon as practicable. To prove it was serious, Brazil adopted the following four measures:

1. It called off expansion of the Bolivia–Brazil gas pipeline as a signal that it intends no further increases in gas purchases from Bolivia;
2. It announced construction of multiple large LNG plants to be supplied by Trinidad and Tobago, Nigeria, Angola or Indonesia;
3. It tripled investment in natural gas exploration and production;
4. It cancelled Petrobras' commitment to invest US $5 billion in Bolivia from 2007 through 2011.

Despite their differences, however, Brazil and Bolivia complement each other and are likely to continue cooperating in the framework of a regional integration process involving these two countries.

Natural Gas Pipelines

Transredes operates Bolivia's domestic natural gas transport network of around 3 000 km. The 1 264 km northern section of the system connects the cities of La Paz, Oruro, Cochabamba, and Santa Cruz with natural gas fields in the Chapare region. The 1 760 km southern section of the system connects the cities of Sucre, Potosi, and Tarija with the natural gas resources of the Gan Chaco region; the southern system also connects domestic natural gas resources with export pipeline to Brazil and Argentina.

In 1999, Bolivia began exporting to Brazil under a twenty year take-or-pay contract through the Gasbol pipeline. The 3 200 km Gasbol connects Santa Cruz, Bolivia to Porto Alegre, Brazil, via Sao Paulo. The system has a maximum capacity of 0.03 billion m^3 per day. Gasbol also has a 272 km extension that connects to a gas-fired power plant in Cuibana in Brazil.

Gasbol has been a recurring source of contention between Brazil and Bolivia. The agreement between the two countries is a take-or-pay contract, meaning that Brazil often must pay for natural gas that it does not actually use. There have been times in the past when, due to dampened economic growth, Brazil has not been able to use the entire volume. In addition, Bolivia has objected to the low price that Brazil pays for natural gas from the Gasbol system, which was well below international level. There is also a pipeline to Cuiaba, in the Mato Grosso State of Brazil, which has an installed capacity to transport 3.9 million m^3 per day of natural gas.

The Yabog pipeline, which runs from Río Grande in Bolivia to Salta in Argentina, was completed in 1972 with a capacity of 5.9 million m^3 per day. In that year Bolivia started the export of natural gas to Argentina, accounting for 15% of the total Bolivia's export of natural gas. A contract between YPFB and ENARSA extends through 2026 stipulates grow in the current supply of natural gas up to nearly 27.7 million m^3 per day by 2017. Argentina paid an average of US $7.27 per million Btu for Bolivian natural gas in 2010.

Argentina and Bolivia are building another small cross border pipeline, known as "Juana Azurduy" pipeline, which is due to be completed before 2012. The Argentina's government has proposed a Gasoducto del Noreste Argentino to serve its remote northeastern provinces with the larger volumes of natural gas that Bolivia has promised for future years.

Electricity Generation

Electricity has been broadly governed by the Electricity Law of 1994 and other regulations, which privatized and unbundled the electricity sector. However, the sector has changed dramatically in recent years through a new constitution, new institutions, and President Morales's renationalization campaign. In 2009, the Autoridad de Fiscalización y Control Social de Electricidad (AE) replaced the Superintendencia de Electricidad as the regulatory and planning body with oversight of the electricity sector. AE's stated objectives are to promote universal access to electricity, equitable and affordable rates, and efficient, sustainable, and secure system operations.

The National Committee for Load Dispatch (CNDC) is Bolivia's equivalent to a Regional Transmission Organization or Independent System Operator. CNDC is responsible for the operation of the national interconnected system and the administration of and planning for the Ministry of Energy and Mines (MEM). The national electricity company, ENDE, was essentially re-founded in 2008 after its assets had been privatized in the 1990s. In May 2010, four electricity firms, which accounted for more than half of the electricity market, were expropriated by the government after failed contract renegotiations: Corani (had been 50% owned by France's GDF Suez), Guaracachi (had been 50% owned by the United Kingdom's Rurelec), Valle Hermoso, and the Empresa de Luz y Fuerza Eléctrica Cochabamba. The nationalizations returned the firms' assets to the recently reconstituted ENDE. Following the announcement, the government claimed control over 80% of Bolivia's electricity generation and expressed a desire to achieve complete government control over the sector in the future.

In Bolivia, the national interconnected system connects major population centers and represents 83% of the installed capacity. The national interconnected system provides electricity to the largest cities and operates in the departments of Cochabamba, Santa Cruz, Oruro, Potosi, and Chuquisaca. Its grid extends over 1 920 km and covers the central and southern parts of the country. The population in the northern and western parts of Bolivia remains largely unconnected to the national grid, either served by the off-grid system or having no access to electricity at all. The off-grid system consists of numerous self-producers and independent power plants in rural or isolated areas.

In 2008, Bolivia generated six billion kWh of electricity from nearly 1.5 GW of installed capacity. Thermoelectric power plants, which are the largest source of generation, primarily burn natural gas and a small amount of oil, and account for 60% of the total productions; 38% of the total is produced by hydroelectric. The contribution of other renewables to electricity generation is almost negligible (2%). In 2009, electricity generation using natural gas was 2 423 MWh, which represents 42.3% of the total of the electricity produced by the country in that year, an increase of 4.3% from previous production.

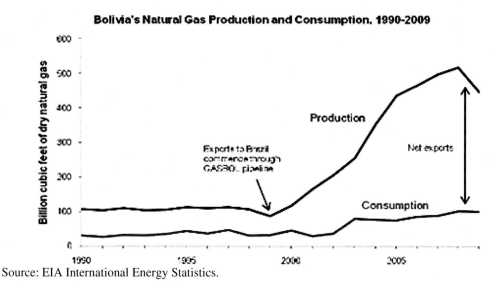

Source: EIA International Energy Statistics.

Figure 86. Bolivia's natural gas production and consumption during the period 1990-2009.

From Figure 86, the following can be stated: Production of natural gas during the whole period exceeded the consumption and the gap between the production and consumption are widening each year since 2003 but the gap started to narrow from 2008, and it is expected that this trend will continue in the coming years. This favorable situation allows the government in the past years to increase exports of natural gas to Brazil and Argentina.

Finally, it is important to single out the following: In February 2011, a consortium that includes Total, Petrobras, and YPFB Chaco announced the beginning of commercial production in the Itau field (near San Alberto field), which will produce over 1.41 million m^3 of natural gas per day. According to some plans, future phases of development could more than triple those volumes.

Looking Forward

The Bolivian government plans to invest in nearly 1 GW of new capacity, mostly gas and hydroelectric, by 2015. The reason is the government desire to increase its reserve margin or the cushion between available capacity and peak load from around 10% in order to enhance system reliability and minimize disruptions.

Finally, it is important to stress that YPFB has announced that it and foreign partners plan to invest over US $4 billion in the natural gas sector by 2015. Bolivia's government goals include a near-doubling of natural gas production by 2015.

BRAZIL

Energy Reform

Historically, Brazil's oil and natural gas industry was controlled by the State-owned Petrobras. In 1995, the Brazilian Federal Constitution was amended to allow privately or publicly-owned companies to be engaged in the exploration and production of oil and natural gas, subject to conditions set forth in specific legislation governing the sector. In 1997, the Petroleum Law, enacted pursuant to the constitutional amendment, created the National Petroleum Agency (ANP) to promote a transparent regulatory framework, to organize bidding rounds for new concession areas, and to regulate and oversee the Brazilian oil and natural gas sector.

Petrobras plays a dominant role in Brazil's entire natural gas supply chain. In addition to controlling the vast majority of the country's natural gas reserves, the company is responsible for most domestic Brazilian natural gas production and for gas imports from Bolivia. Further, Petrobras controls the national transmission network and it holds a stake in eighteen of Brazil's twenty seven State-owned natural gas distribution companies. However, Brazil passed a new Natural Gas Law in 2009, which created a separate regulatory framework for natural gas. This Law is expected to facilitate private investment in the sector.

Taking into account the recently discovered offshore natural gas resources in São Paulo, combined with gas imports and gas consumption incentive policies, it is expected an increase of emissions of global and local pollutants. This problem could intensify air pollution in populated areas, forcing the adoption of stronger enforcement policies and actions.

Natural Gas Production, Consumption, and Reserves

Natural gas production in Central and South America will doubles between 2007 and 2035. The fastest growth is projected for Brazil, averaging 7.4% per year. The majority of Brazil's current natural gas production comes from fields located offshore of the Rio de Janeiro[112] and Espirito Santo States in the Campos and Espirito Santo Basins, respectively. In addition, numerous recent discoveries of oil and natural gas in the sub-salt Santos Basin to the southwest of the Campos Basin are expected to increase the country's natural gas production potential.

Oil and Gas Journal reported that Brazil had around 0.36 trillion m^3 of proven natural gas reserves in 2008. This reserve was almost the same in 2011. According to the BP Statistical Review of World Energy 2009, Brazil's oil and natural gas reserves are among the fastest growing in the world. The Campos, Santos and Espirito Santos Basins hold the majority of reserves (88%) but there are also sizable reserves in the interior stretches of the country. Despite Brazil's sizable natural gas reserves, natural gas production has grown slowly in

---

[112] The State of Rio de Janeiro is the largest supplier of natural gas in Brazil, accounting for 49.7% of the country's output, followed by Amazonas State, with 17.9%. Between 2000 and 2009, Brazilian production of natural gas grew by an average of 5.3% a year, reaching around 11 billion m^3, in 2009. That year, Brazil ranked 33th globally among natural gas producers. With the discovery of sub-salt reserves this potential will increase. The supply of natural gas in Brazil increased in 2009 after operations began in Niteroi, Rio de Janeiro State, Camarupim, Espirito Santo State, and Lagosta, in the Santos Basin in the Sao Paulo State.

recent years, after a deep decrease between 2006 and 2007 of 39%, mainly due to a lack of domestic transportation capacity and low domestic prices. The production of natural gas from 2006 to 2010 decreased 35% or 5.51 billion m^3. Of the proven domestic oil and natural gas reserves, approximately 90% are located offshore. It is expected that, in 2016, Brazil produce at least 100 million m^3 per day of natural gas, guaranteeing self-sufficiency and exportable surplus.

It is important to stress that in Brazil natural gas power generation is complementary to hydroelectricity facilities. They operate as when dispatched to the national grid authority helping to regulate reservoir storage capacity and making the electric power system less dependent on variation in rainfall.

By November 2007, public announcements regarding discoveries between five to eight billion boe at the Tupi field in the Santos Basin led many industry observers to increase their estimates of Brazil's oil and natural gas reserves. In light of the vast and still untapped estimated potential oil and natural gas resources of the entire pre-salt area, Brazil potentially has between 70 million of boe and 100 billion boe in oil and natural gas reserves, according to industry experts, which if confirmed, would place Brazilian reserves among the five largest in the world (ahead of Venezuela and Nigeria).

Along with their potential to significantly increase oil production in the country, the pre-salt areas is estimated to contain sizable natural gas reserves as well. According to Petrobras, Tupi alone could contain between 0.14 trillion m^3 and 0.20 trillion m^3 of recoverable natural gas, which if proven, could increase Brazil's total natural gas reserves by 50% (see Figure 87).

From Figure 88, the following can be stated: Natural gas production in Brazil was lower than the natural gas consumption during the period 1996-2006. Since 2000, Brazil started to import natural gas from Argentina and Bolivia. However, the level of natural gas production and consumption increased systematically since 2001 but demand has declined since 2008.

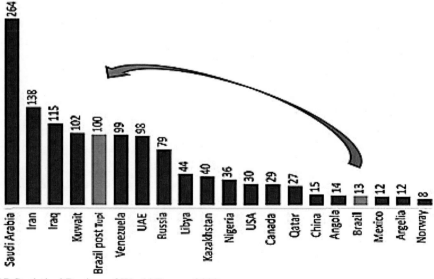

Source: BP Statistical Review of World Energy 2009.

Figure 87. Countries with the highest natural gas reserves (Billion boe).

Table 52. Natural gas production and consumption in Brazil in 2008 and 2009
(Billion m³)

	Brazil 2008	Central and South America	World	Rank	Brazil 2009
Production	13.38	156.12	3 297.63	36	10.89
Consumption	25.05	19.53	3 327.45	29	19.83
Net export/imports(-)	-11.70	16.62	--	17	-8.94
Proved reserves (Trillion m³)	0.36	7.86	186.57	33	0.36

Source: EIA.

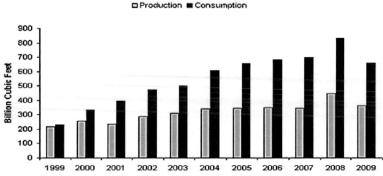

Source: EIA International Energy Statistics Database.

Figure 88. Natural gas production and consumption in Brazil during the period 1996-2009.

Only in two years the consumption dropped from 25.05 billion m³ in 2008 to 19.83 billion m³ in 2009; this represents a decrease of 21% or 5.22 billion m³. However, according to expert's opinions, it is expected that gas demand growth of about 4.3% per year over the next twenty years[113]. Demand growth will be met by increasing domestic production as well as by increased natural gas imports, both in the form of pipeline gas (primarily from Bolivia) and liquefied natural gas (LNG). In order to meet rising demand and decrease reliance on imports, Petrobras plans to bring several new natural gas projects online over the coming years. The largest is the Mexilhao project, which contains estimated total reserves of 0.23 trillion m³. Current plans call for production to come online in 2011 at 4.36 billion m³ per year, with a possibility to raise the production to up to 5.47 billion m³ per year (an increase of 25%).

Thermoelectric power accounted for 35% of that natural gas demand in 2007, compared to 19% in 2002; this represents an increase of 16%. Natural gas currently accounts for only 3% of Brazil's energy consumption and, for this reason, it is questionable now whether the forecast for natural gas to grow to about 25% of Brazil's energy matrix by 2010-2011, thanks to thermal power generation, will bear out. Another proposed option to increase the use of natural gas for the electricity production is to produce and liquefy Brazil's natural gas at sea

---

[113] Global natural gas growth is forecast to be about 1.3% per year over the same period.

on floating platforms, from which the LNG could then be loaded onto ships for transport to existing LNG regasification terminals on the country's coast.

The opening of the Brazilian oil and natural gas industry attracted the attention of private companies. As of December 2007, a total of sixty companies were active in Brazil in the exploration and production of oil and natural gas, thirty two from Brazil and the remainder twenty eight from the following countries: Argentina, Canada, Denmark, France, Italy, Japan, Norway, Portugal, Spain, The Netherlands, Republic of Korea, United Kingdom, and the United States.

Natural Gas Fields

Brazil has three main producing regions. According to Ellsworth and Gibbs (2004), these are:

a) *Southeast:* The Campos Basin, located off the coast of Rio de Janeiro, is the largest producing basin in Brazil supplying natural gas to Rio de Janeiro and Sao Paulo States. The offshore Espirito Santo Basin, located north of the Campos Basin, supplies natural gas to markets in the State of Espirito Santo,

b) *Northeast:* The Reconcavo Basin is the largest basin in northeastern Brazil, with proved and probable natural gas reserves of almost 0.05 trillion m^3. Next in size is the Potiguar Basin, with natural gas reserves of 0.02 trillion m^3, followed by the Alagoas Basin, with onshore and offshore natural gas reserves of just over 14.16 billion m^3.

c) *Amazon:* The Amazon is isolated from the major producing and consuming areas of northeastern and southeastern Brazil and encompasses a 'closed' natural gas system. Two fields, the Campos and Santos Basins, hold the largest reserves of natural gas in Brazil. Other sizable natural gas reserves are located in the country side.

The Campos Basin offshore field is located in the State of Rio de Janeiro. Most onshore fields are located in the Amazonas and Bahia States. The production from these fields is primarily for domestic consumption. However, due to a lack of transportation infrastructure Petrobras plans to bring several new natural gas projects online over the coming years. The largest is the Mexilhao project, expected to come online before 2012. Recently oil discoveries were made in Brazil's offshore sub-salt that has generated considerable excitement. There are plans to build a natural gas pipeline from Tupi (the newly discovered field) to Mexilhao, where the natural gas could then flow into the national grid.

Natural Gas Pipelines

Petrobras operates Brazil's domestic natural gas transport system. The total length of the pipeline network is around 6 430 km primarily located in the northeast and southeastern parts of the country. The system is not completely integrated. Separate systems were located in the southeast and northeastern parts of the country and the State of Espirito Santo.

For years these systems were not interconnected, which has hindered the development of domestic production and consumption. However, in March 2010, the southeast-northeast interconnection gas pipeline (Gasene) linked these two markets for the first time. This 1 392 km pipeline, which runs from Rio de Janeiro to Bahia, is the longest ever built in Brazil. Gasene is intended to offset supply shortfalls in the northeast caused by declining local production with southeastern offshore supply. The other major natural gas market in Brazil is the Amazon region. In 2009, Petrobras completed construction of the Urucu pipeline linking Urucu to Manaus, the capital of the Amazonas State. This project is expected to facilitate the development of the Amazon region considerable and largely untapped, natural gas reserves. In 2005, construction began on the Gas Unificacao or Gasun. The 2 240 km Gasun will link Mato Grosso dul Sul, in southwest Brazil, to Maranhao in the northeast. Two natural gas import terminals have been completed and the gas pipeline network has been expanded to 7 659 km. Seven new gas pipelines have been integrated into the national gas structure.

In order to exploit the gas potential of the offshore sub-salt reserves, Brazil will need to construct additional pipeline infrastructure in the area. In 2008, Petrobras announced that it would construct a 240 km natural gas pipeline linking the Tupi field to its Mexilhao development. From there, a pipeline would link Mexilhao to shore, allowing any natural gas production from Tupi to flow to the domestic market. The Merluza and Lagosta fields, a pair of smaller natural gas and condensate fields in the Santos Basin, currently are producing and sending natural gas and liquids to shore via a pipeline that is more than 160 km long.

Other large Brazilian fields in the Santos Basin lie even farther from shore, and because of a lack of current infrastructure to bridge the distances, much of the initial natural gas production associated with oil extraction at the field is likely to be reinserted. The Tambau gas field and the Urugua and Tupi oil fields have significant natural gas resources.

Brazil imports natural gas from Bolivia via the Gasbol pipeline linking Santa Cruz, Bolivia to Porto Alegre, Brazil, via Sao Paulo. The 3 200 km Gasbol has a maximum capacity of 0.03 billion m^3 per day. Gasbol also has a 272 km extension that connects to a natural gas-fired power plant in Cuibana, supplying 0.03 million m^3 per day. According to ANP, Brazil imported about 10.80 billion m^3 of natural gas from Bolivia in 2007. Brazil also receives natural gas from Argentina via the Parana-Uruguayana 443 km pipeline.

Declining natural gas output in Bolivia and the increase cost of Bolivian gas have also led Brazil to construct their own LNG terminals. Brazil has two LNG regasification terminals, both installed in the past two years: One is the Pecem terminal in the northeast, and the second is the Guanabara Bay terminal in the southeast. Both facilities are floating regasification and storage units operated by Golar LNG, with a combined send out capacity of 20.95 million m^3 per day. The Pecem received its first LNG cargo from Trinidad and Tobago in July 2008, while the Guanabara Bay terminal came online in May 2009. According to ANP, Brazil received 0.4 billion m^3 of natural gas in the form of LNG in 2009, mostly from Trinidad and Tobago. Brazil is now building its third LNG terminal, aiming to have it ready by 2013.

Import of Natural Gas

Brazil imported 8.94 billion m^3 of natural gas in 2009, a 24% drop from 2008, year during which Brazil imported 47% of the total natural gas consumed in the country. The decline in Brazilian overall natural gas demand, coupled with policy choices aimed at reducing imports, led to this decline.

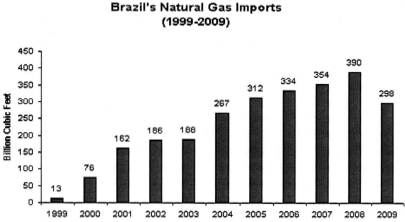

Source: EIA International Energy Statistics Database.

Figure 89. Brazil's natural gas import during the period 1999-2009.

The country currently receives imports by pipeline from Bolivia and LNG imports from Trinidad and Tobago and Nigeria. Import growth in the future is expected to be met more with LNG than with conventional pipeline imports.

From Figure 89, the following can be stated: The import of natural gas increased significantly between 1999 and 2008. From that year, the import of natural gas started to decline, due to an increase in domestic natural gas production, and this trend is expect to continue in the coming years.

Electricity Generation

The total electricity produced in the country using natural gas as fuel in 2009 was 154 970 MWh, representing 35% of the total (445 142 MWh).

To avoid another energy crisis in the future, the government is adopting measures to increase the participation of natural gas, nuclear energy, and different renewable energy sources in electricity generation and, at the same, to reduce the participation of hydro in the energy balance, which is now very high.

In the past, the Brazilian government has tried relatively unsuccessfully to attract substantial investment in natural-gas-fired power plants. Its lack of success has been due mostly to the higher costs of natural-gas-fired generation relative to hydroelectric power, and to concerns about the security of natural gas supplies. Brazil has relied on imported Bolivian natural gas for much of its supply but concerns about the impact of Bolivia's nationalization of its energy sector on foreign investment in the country's natural gas production has led

Brazil to look toward LNG imports for secure supplies. Brazil has invested strongly in its LNG infrastructure. With Brazil diversifying its natural gas supplies, substantially increasing domestic production, and resolving to reduce the hydroelectric share of generation, natural gas is projected to be its fastest-growing source of electricity, increasing by 7.2% per year on average from 2007 to 2035.

Looking Forward

The government of Brazil has adopted a number of actions with the purpose of increasing natural gas supply for electricity generation in recent years. This has been done to diversify Brazil's energy matrix in order to reduce the nation's excessive dependence on only two primary energy sources: hydro power to generate electricity and oil for the fuels sector. A major focus of this effort has been on increasing natural gas imports through the adoption of policies focused on gas pipeline capacity expansion and South American energy integration. Brazil's gas pipeline length increased up to 6 430 km from 3 954 km existent in 1996.

The restructuring of Brazil's electricity sector at the end of the 1990s, specially the deregulation of Brazil's electricity market through the introduction of eligible consumers and independent power producers having open access to the transmission grid, boosted the use of natural gas for power generation to some degree. The amount of electricity generated from natural gas increased from none in 1995 to 19.3 TWh as of 2004 (Ministry of Mines and Energy, 2005). As of September 2005, natural gas fired thermal power plant capacity had reached 9 157 MW, with around 1 868 MW under construction (ANEEL, 2005).

There have been, however, a number of problems related to expanding natural gas supply and demand that need to be solved in the future, with the purpose of increasing the participation of natural gas in the energy mix of the country. These problems are the following:

a) First, there is still considerable uncertainty regarding relative energy prices;
b) Second, the Brazilian natural gas distribution network remains incipient, meaning that development in the market is still heavily dependent on the expansion of thermal power generation fuelled by natural gas;
c) Third, the pricing of natural gas supplies from Bolivia in dollar terms has made this fuel very expensive since the devaluation of the Brazilian real in recent years, and the increase of international oil prices to which the price of the imported natural gas is related;
d) Fourth, some potential natural gas users have found it difficult to deal with, or have refused to accept, the take-or-pay clause in natural gas contracts. Thus, it is worth considering revised or additional policies to expand the use of natural gas in ways that are economical, energy efficient, and environmentally beneficial.

Brazil has learned about the costs and benefits of energy mix diversification efforts from its experiences over the past few decades. Natural gas is a growing energy option, and several policies foster its use in the coming years, especially for transport and for the replacement of industrial fuel oil. New natural gas-fired-thermal power plants are being proposed, raising concerns in urban areas about air pollution (especially ground level ozone) resulting from fuel combustion and fugitive emissions, and their impact on the environment. Several actions have been proposed in order to overcome these problems with the purpose of increasing the role of natural gas in electricity generation in the coming years.

COLOMBIA

The 2001 Law designed to promote renewable energy sources, lacks certain key provisions to achieve this objective, such as feed-in tariffs, and has had for this reason, little impact so far in the use of this type of energy for electricity generation in the country. As result, large hydro power and thermal power plants dominate the current development plans adopted by the government for the expansion of the electricity sector in the coming years.

Natural Gas Production, Consumption, and Reserves

According to *OGJ*, Colombia had proven natural gas reserves of 0.12 trillion m^3 in 2010, almost the same of the natural gas reserves reported in 2006. The country produced 9.54 billion m^3 of natural gas in 2008, an increase of 3 billion m^3 from the total produced in 2004, while consuming 7.95 billion m^3. In 2009, the country produced 11.10 billion m^3, an increase of 16% respect to 2008, and consumed 9.21 billion m^3, an increase of 16% respect the year before. A large portion of the country's gross natural gas production (43% in 2008) is re-injected to aid in enhanced oil recovery.

Table 53. Production and consumption of natural gas in Colombia in 2008 and 2009 (Billion m^3)

	Colombia 2008	Central and South America	World	Rank	Colombia 2009
Production	9.54	156.12	3 297.63	43	11.10
Consumption	7.95	139.53	3 327.45	50	9.21
Net export/import (-)	1.59	16.62	--	62	1.92
Proved reserves (Trillion m^3)	0.12	7.86	186.57	46	0.12

Source: EIA.

The Chuchupa and Ballena gas fields produce about 80% of the output, averaging 15 million m^3 per day. Colombia has natural gas reserves spread across eighteen basins, seven of which have active production. The bulk of Colombia's natural gas reserves are located in the Llanos Basin, although the Guajira Basin accounts for the majority of current production. According to Colombia's Ministry of Energy and Mines, BP and Chevron-Texaco are the two largest natural gas producers in the country (Chevron-Texaco is the largest natural gas producer). Chevron-Texaco exploits three fields in the Guajira Basin, Chuchupa, Ricohacha and Ballena. BP operates the Cupiagua and Cusiana natural gas fields in the Casenare department, which are the two largest natural gas fields in the country. Ecopetrol is the third natural gas producer in Colombia.

The Colombian government is forecasting 3.1% annual growth in natural gas consumption through the end of the next decade. The government has also been promoting the use of natural gas to its citizens as a low-cost alternative energy source (the cost of natural gas as an energy source is only one-fifth of that of electricity in Colombia).

However, it is important to stress that if no additional natural gas reserves are found, current reserves will be depleted by 2015 and the country should increase the import of natural gas after that year. Depending on reservoir behavior, there may be domestic market deficits by the start of the current decade. Export possibilities depend on exploration success in increasing reserves (Deutsche Montan Technologie GmbH, OLADE and CIEMAT, 2005). The country imported 1.92 billion m^3 of gas in 2009, almost 0.33 billion m^3 more than in 2008 and this trend is expected to increase in the coming years, especially after 2012.

Natural Gas Pipelines

The Colombian natural gas pipeline system consists of 378 km of propane pipelines for the transportation of LPG, 1 001 km of pipelines for natural gas, and 561 km that are being converted for natural gas service. The major natural gas pipelines are the 340 km Mariquita to Cali (TransGas Occidente), the 575 km Ballena to Barrancabermeja (Centragas), and the 780 km Barrancabermeja to Neiva to Bogotá (Centro Oriente).

Two companies operate the natural gas transmission pipelines in Colombia. These are the State-owned Ecogas and the privately-owned joint stock company Promigas. Even though Promigas' transmission network is smaller in overall length than of Ecogas, it moves about 60% of the natural gas transmitted throughout Colombia, mostly from production sites in La Guajira department to the Jobo terminal in Sucre department.

Ecogas operates three main pipelines: The Ballena-Barrancabermeja, linking Ballena field on the northeast coast to Barrancabermeja in central Colombia; the Barrancabermeja-Nevia-Bogotá line, which integrates the Colombian capital into the transmission network, and the Mariquita-Cali line through the western Andean foothills. There are other small stretches of pipeline operated by private firms.

In April 2003, Colombia and Venezuela agreed to build a US $320 million, 0.60 billion m^3 natural gas pipeline linking Colombia's Guajira Basin to Venezuela's Maracaibo region. Colombia has held also discussions with Panama and Ecuador about extending the pipeline into those countries.

Plans are in development to build a US $250 million natural gas pipeline parallel to the Ballena-Barrancabermeja pipeline to improve the supply to central Colombia, which would transport output from the Chuchupa, Ballena, and Rioacha fields. In early 2008, the Antonio Ricaurte pipeline came online, linking northeastern Colombia with Venezuela. Initially, the pipeline will allow Colombia to export natural gas from the Punta Ballenas area to western Venezuela. Current plans call for the flow of the pipeline to then be reversed in 2012, with Venezuela exporting 4.20 million m^3 per day of natural gas to Colombia. While initial contracted volumes for export from Colombia to Venezuela ranged between 2.40 million m^3 per day and 4.50 million m^3 per day, actual exports have often exceeded these levels.

According to media reports, natural gas exports to Venezuela peaked near 9 million m^3 per day in late 2009, partly due to rising demand in Venezuela for natural gas for power generation and re-injection. Media reports indicated that export flows had fallen to near contracted volumes by the end of 2009.

In late 1999, Colombian officials announced support for a Colombian-driven regional natural gas grid that would extend into Ecuador and Panama, and then eventually to other Central American countries. The Colombia-to-Panama pipeline is a planned 18 inch diameter line that would be 592 km long and run from the Colombian port of Cartagena to Colón, Panama. This US $300 million pipeline would initially transport 2.10 million m^3 per day, with expansion to 4.20 million m^3 per day possible a few years later. The natural gas would initially come from Texaco's fields in the Guajira region, where it is currently being reinserted to boost crude oil output, and instead be used to generate power in Enron's Bahia Las Minas thermoelectric power plant in Panama. This pipeline would serve to further spur investment in developing Colombia's natural gas resources.

Exploration and Investment in the Natural Gas Sector

Similar to the oil sector, natural gas production has risen substantially in the last few years, owning to greater investment at existing fields, rising domestic consumption, and new export opportunities.

Recent increases in natural gas prices have attracted investors to Colombia's Caribbean coast in search of natural gas. In particular, the offshore Chuchupa and Ballena oil and gas fields are believed to hold reserves of 190 billion m^3 and 26.10 billion m^3 respectively; a thorough exploration of these fields for natural gas resources began in 2001. In 2000, Canadian hydrocarbons companies Millennium Energy Inc. and Mera Petroleum Inc., signed an agreement with Ecopetrol to explore for natural gas in the onshore Salinas block in La Guajira department. The concession area for these two companies may contain as much as 0.06 trillion m^3 of natural gas. The seismic work has been completed; cost of the initial drilling phase is expected to be around US $2 million. Plans were approved to construct a facility at the Cusiana-Cupiagua oil fields for processing associated natural gas. BP Amoco and Ecopetrol are agreeing to invest between US $120 and US $130 million in the plant.

In October 2004, US based Drummond, one of the largest coal producers in Colombia, announced that it would begin drilling for coal bed methane at its properties in the country. While most of the natural gas will fuel power generation at its facilities, Drummond also planned to sell any surpluses on the open market.

In May 2004, a consortium of Petrobras (40%), Exxon-Mobil (40%), and Ecopetrol (20%) signed an agreement to explore for natural gas in the Tayrona block in the offshore Caribbean See. Petrobras will operate the exploration phase, while Exxon-Mobil will operate any production stemming from the exploration activities. The agreement marked the first upstream investment by Exxon-Mobil in Colombia since 1996. In June 2004, BP was awarded a natural gas production license for the Cuisiana/Cupiagua complex, which the company hopes will compensate for the reduction in oil production at the site. To better utilize the natural gas resources at the field, BP plans the construction of a gas-to-liquids plant at the field. The plant will have an initial capacity to produce 84 000 barrels per day of high-quality diesel fuel.

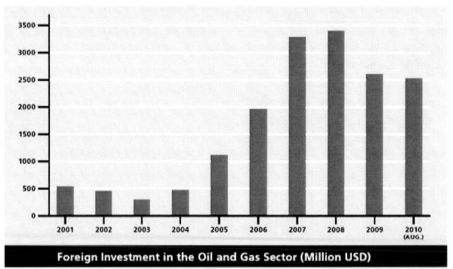

Source: Bank of the Republic of Colombia (Banco de la República de Colombia).

Figure 90. Foreign investment in the oil and natural gas sector of Colombia.

From Figure 90, the following can be stated: In the last decade; the investments in the oil and gas sector increased significantly from around US $500 million in 2004 to almost US $3,500 million in 2008, year when the investment peak was reached. After this peak, the investment in the sector started to decline reaching around US $2,500 million in August 2010; this represents a decrease of 29% in the last two and a half years.

Finally, it is important to single out that the government has released a series of incentives for promoting development of natural gas in the Cusiana-Cupiagua fields. Among other things, the new plan eliminates the US $0.10 per million Btu pipeline transport charge previously levied; instead, gas producers will now pay a separate transportation fee for shipping natural gas through Colombia's gas pipelines. The government also will now allow partners to enter export agreements for projects where the reserves will last six years or more. Another improvement outlined in the plan will allow gas producers to jointly sell their natural gas, whereas each company now has to sell its natural gas individually.

Electricity Generation

An interesting characteristic of the Colombian electricity sector is a system of cross-subsidies from users living in areas considered as being relatively affluent, and from users consuming higher amounts of electricity, to those living in areas considered as being poor and to those who use less electricity.

The electricity sector has been unbundled into generation, transmission, distribution, and commercialization since sector reforms carried out in 1994. About half the generation capacity is privately owned. Private participation in electricity distribution is much lower.

Electricity supply in Colombia relies on the national interconnected system and several isolated local systems in the non-interconnected zones. Thirty thermal power plants feed electricity into the national interconnected system. On the other hand, the non-interconnected zones are mostly served by small diesel generators. In 2010, the country produced 55 314 MWh of electricity, out of which 6 591 MWh was produced using natural gas as fuel (11.9% of the total). The current level of participation of natural gas in the generation of electricity in the energy mix of the country is not expected to change significantly in the coming years.

The installed electricity capacity using natural gas as fuel was around 3 500 MW in 2009, from a total of 13 456 MW electricity capacity installed in that year (26% of the total).

Electricity Imports and Exports

Colombia is a net power exporter. In 2008, the country exported 1.59 TWh of electricity to Ecuador and in 2009 the level of electricity export reached 1.92 TWh, an increase of 21%. Colombia imported only very small volumes of electricity from Venezuela and Ecuador (0.02 TWh each).

The level of electricity import shows decreasing trends since 1998 and it is expected that this trends will not change in the near future. According to the Ministry of Mines and Energy, exports are estimated to increase at 5% annually for the coming years.

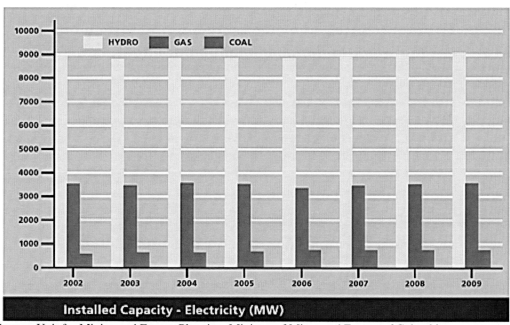

Source: Unit for Mining and Energy Planning, Ministry of Mines and Energy of Colombia.

Figure 91. Electricity installed capacity in Colombia.

Puebla-Panama Plan

The Puebla-Panama Plan includes a project of electric interconnection between Colombia and Panama that will allow the integration of Colombia with Central America. This project, carried out by Interconexión Electrica S.A. in Colombia, and Empresa de Transmisión Electrica S.A. (ETESA) in Panama, entails the construction of a transmission line with 300 MW of capacity (3% of installed capacity) from Colombia to Panama and 200 MW of capacity in the reverse way. The line is expected to become operational before 2012.

Favorable investment conditions have helped electricity generation keep up with demand and avoid any major blackouts since 1991. Electricity generation has risen from 47 000 MWh in 2003 to 55 314 MWh in 2009; this represents an increase of 17.7%. It is expects that power demand to grow by an average between 3.7% to 4% annually between 2010 and 2020, while total installed power generation capacity is expected to expand to 17 800 MW by 2017 up from 13 456 MW today; this represents an increase of 32,3% (Viscidi, 2010).

Looking Forward

Colombia should continue to provide regulatory and contractual stability to ensure investor confidence in the energy sector of the country. The process of energy integration has stalled largely due to inconsistencies in the regulatory frameworks between Colombia and its neighbors, as well as political differences.

With Ecuador, Colombia must create a stable formula for the price of electricity exports. Similarly, Colombia and Panama must smooth out differences over regulations and environmental issues within the framework of the implementation of the Puebla-Panama Plan. For example, if negotiations resume, the Colombia-Panama Free Trade Agreement could include a clause establishing the terms of electricity trade. Colombia would also have to establish a framework for exporting natural gas to Central America and the Caribbean. If bilateral relations improve further, Colombia could also expand energy integration with Venezuela, by resuming electricity exports through two existing cross-border transmission lines. Regulations should clarify third-party access and tariffs for all pipelines, and tariffs should be appropriate to attract investment in building new pipelines. Ecopetrol should take the lead in expanding the pipeline network and building storage capacity for oil and natural gas.

On the other hand, the government should continue to enforce environmental regulations to protect the country's fragile ecosystems. The process for granting environmental licenses has become more efficient in recent years but some companies still face difficulty to obtain the necessary permits to work in the country within a reasonable period. The government should also continue to plan a long-term strategy for meeting the country's electricity demand in the coming years. In addition, Colombia should develop more long-term contracts for power generation and rely less on the spot market. Long-term contracts would guarantee markets at a reliable rate for producers of natural gas and other electricity feedstock. Given the more limited transportation options for natural gas - compared to more fungible crude oil and the importance of natural gas in the energy matrix, the government should provide incentives for the production of natural gas, which is currently under the same regulatory regime as oil (Viscidi, 2010).

CUBA

Natural Gas Production, Consumption, and Reserves

In 2010, Cuba has estimate reserves of 70.8 billion m^3 of natural gas, which represents 0.04% of the world's total natural gas reserves. Cuba is one of the three Caribbean States with natural gas reserves[114]. The country produced, in 2008, a total of 420 million m^3 of associated natural gas. In 2009, the production reached 1 515 million m^3, an increase of 260.7%. However, in 2011, this production dropped to one million m^3 of natural gas, a decrease of 34%. The consumption of natural gas represents only 2.7% of total primary energy consumption of the country (Alhajji, and Maris, 2003).

It is important to know that Cuba's natural gas production is all associated natural gas found within the crude oil reservoirs. The island's geology to date has not proven to be a major source of dry non-associated natural gas reservoirs. Associated natural gas production is being used as fuel for onsite power generating plants owned and operated by Energas, a joint venture between Canada's Sherritt, Cuba's CUPET, and Electric Union.

Natural Gas Exploration

The island's geology to date has not proved to be a major source of reservoirs rich in dry non-associated natural gas, which could have made Cuba a net exporter of piped gas or a LNG exporter such as Trinidad and Tobago. For this reason, the future of Cuba's oil and gas exploration and production sector could very well be in the deep offshore Gulf of Mexico waters, along the western approaches to the Florida Straits and the eastern extension of Mexico's Yucatán Peninsula. In industry circles this area has been christened as the "Donut Hole."

Table 54. Natural gas production in Cuba during the period 2000-2008 (Billion m^3)

Year	Cuba	Change (%)	(% of Central and South America)	(% of world)
2000	595	16.7	0.6	0.024
2001	311	-47.6	0.3	0.012
2002	340	9.1	0.3	0.013
2003	368	8.3	0.3	0.014
2004	368	0	0.3	0.013
2005	396	7.7	0.3	0.014
2006	396	0	0.3	0.014
2007	595	50	0.4	0.020
2008	396	-33.3	0.3	0.013

N/A: No available data.
Source: Titi Turodancea Bulletin.

---

[114] The other Caribbean States with important natural gas reserves are Barbados and Trinidad and Tobago.

Locally produced associated natural gas from the Varadero, Jaruco, and Puerto Escondido fields is now being used as fuel for onsite power generating plants, after years of burning the associated gas produced in the Varadero field with a negative impact in the environment.

The power plants and related sour gas processing units supplies natural gas at no cost to the joint venture and to Electric Union, which buys all the power from the plants. Each has a one-third interest in Energas. The US $250 million dollar project is being financed by Sherritt International. Depending on the natural gas reserves of the recently discovered Puerto Escondido field, additional electricity generating capacity could be built in the future. Several international companies are exploring different areas in the deep offshore Gulf of Mexico waters, along the western approaches to the Florida Straits, and the eastern extension of the Yucatán Peninsula.

Natural Gas Pipelines

CUPET is in the process of building a system of pipelines that will move natural gas and crude oil production from Puerto Escondido, Santa Cruz del Norte to Boca de Jaruco and then on to La Habana, and crude oil to the oil super port in Matanzas.

There are today approximately 240 000 households in metropolitan La Habana city that are connected and use natural gas as a cooking and water heating fuel. This fuel is mostly associated natural gas from the Puerto Escondido/Boca de Jaruco fields, but it also includes some naphtha manufactured gas.

The inevitable rationalization of the oil refining industry in Cuba and its environmentally sensitive tourist industry, will force Cuba to consider, and probably develop, an energy policy that should rely heavily on clean burning natural gas as its fuel of choice, as well as in the use of other renewables sources such as hydro, wind, and solar energy. Today the use of oil for the electricity generation in Cuba is still very high.

Cuba's future natural gas needs could be sourced as LNG from Trinidad and Tobago, as Puerto Rico and the Dominican Republic are currently doing or by piped natural gas from Mexico through undersea natural gas pipelines that could be built from the Yucatán Peninsula. These pipeline options are technologically feasible today, just as the various 152 km, US $650 million natural gas underwater pipeline projects between the Bahamas and Florida have demonstrated.

According to the US Geological Survey (2005), in the North of Cuba there is an estimate of 0.29 trillion m^3 of natural gas (0.26 trillion m^3 of associated-dissolved gas and 0.3 trillion m^3 of non-associated gas), and a total of 0.9 billion barrels of natural gas liquids.

Investment in the Natural Gas Sector

A LNG re-gasification facility to receive Venezuelan-sourced LNG is currently being planned for the southern coast port city of Cienfuegos by Cuvenpetrol, a joint venture between PdVSA (51%) and CUPET (49%). The one million ton re-gasification trains are planned for 2012 at a cost of over US $400 million. The natural gas is destined as fuel for that city's thermoelectric power plant, and as a feedstock (hydrogen) for the Cienfuegos refinery and future petrochemical/fertilizer plants to be built in the area.

Once the tanker arrives at the regasification terminal, the LNG is offloaded into large storage tanks, built with full-containment walls and systems to keep the LNG cold until it is turned back into a gaseous state and moved into pipelines, which will deliver the natural gas to the various end-users.

Finally, Sherritt Company announced on March 2011, that it wills investments in its power assets in Cuba a total of US $158 million in 2011 up from US $20 million in 2010, an increase of 690%. All of the investment will go into the 150 MW Boca de Jaruco combined-cycle power plant.

Electricity Generation

Cuba generated, in 2009, a total of 17 621 MWh using all energy sources available in the country. Around 8% of the total electricity generated by the country was produced using natural gas as fuel. The participation of natural gas in the electricity generation should increase during the coming years with the possible construction of new gas-fired power plants or the expansion of the current plants in operation.

Looking Forward

The main actions that need to be implemented by the Cuban government during the coming years for improving the results of energy policies already adopted are, among others, the following:

a)   Enhance offshore hydrocarbons exploration. In the event that offshore oil and natural gas were to be found, current energy policies would be changed. Power generation could be based on natural gas-fired combined cycle units; light crude oil could be refined to supply all of the oil products needed in Cuba;

b)   Expand pilot projects for the use of LPG in buses and taxis. An assessment should be made of the possibilities of producing bio-methane from organic wastes and bio-diesel from oleaginous plantations, in order to use these energy sources in the transport sector;

c)   Expand the use of LPG in the country;

d)   Use the developed capacities and experience in the use of different renewable energy sources for electricity generation. It is important for the government to find appropriate financing mechanisms for their rapid introduction (on a large scale) in the energy sector, particularly for electricity generation, and for implementing the government's goal of electrification for 100% of the population in the coming years, using proper systems;

e)   Enhance energy efficiency.

The policy measures adopted by the government during the 1990s crisis and included in the National Energy Sources Development Program had an important contribution to the economic recovery after the crisis, and in the enhancement of different social programs implemented in recent years. The implementation of the above-mentioned energy policy measures could contribute substantially to sustainable energy development, and to reduce the environmental impact of energy use in the country.

CHILE

The employment of natural gas as an energy source started in Chile during the 1970s when ENAP initiated the distribution of natural gas in the southern region of Magallanes. Chile imports 90% of the natural gas that the country consumes. During the last twenty years the production of natural gas has declined while consumption has quadrupled in the same period.

The reduction of import of natural gas from Argentina in the last years forced the government to adopt a group of measures to reduce the impact in the supply of electricity to the industry and the population. The measures adopted were the following:

a) Stabilization of fuel prices through the injection of US $1.26 billion into Fuel Price Stabilization Fund;
b) Temporary reduction of specific tax on gasoline;
c) Electricity subsidy for the most vulnerable 40% of the population;
d) 2009 National Light Bulb Replacement Program;
e) Subsidies for poor families;
f) The month of April was included in peak hour measurement;
g) Rationing decree;
h) Energy saving campaigns;
i) Extension of daylight savings time;
j) Flexibilization of water use for power generation;
k) Installation of back-up turbines and engines;
l) Conversion of combined cycles gas turbine to permit their operation with diesel;
m) Investment in diesel logistics;
n) Financial offers from generators;
o) Law to insure supply in case of bankruptcy and law to permit recovery of taxes on power companies.

Natural Gas Production, Consumption, and Reserves

The *OGJ* reported that Chile had 110 billion m^3 of proven natural gas reserves in January 2006. In 2010, the proven natural gas reserves were estimate to be 97.97 billion m^3; this represents a decrease of 12% of the proven reserves announced in 2010.

From Figure 92, the following can be stated: The production of natural gas decreased from 2004 to 2007 from 1,200 billion m^3 in 2004 to 1,090 billion m^3 in 2007. From 2007 to

2008, the production of natural gas increased from 1,090 billion m³ to a peak of 1,800 billion m³ in 2008. After 2009, the production of natural gas decreased again from 1,800 billion m³ reached in 2009 to 1,650 billion m³ in 2010.

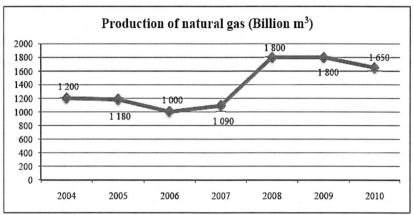

Source: Index Mundi.

Figure 92. Natural gas production in Chile during the period 2004-2010.

Chile has vigorously explored the country for natural gas reserves but has so far not met with any significant success. Despite its lack of domestic reserves, Chile's natural gas consumption has ballooned in recent years. Historically, low domestic production constrained consumption, with natural gas only constituting 8% of total energy consumption in 1996 and 26% in 2004. A combination of increasing energy demand, environmental concerns, and the unreliability of hydro power prompted the Chilean government to reconsider its energy policy and encourage the use of natural gas. To that end, Chile began large-scale imports of natural gas for the first time in 1997; since then, the country's natural gas consumption has increased by an average of 21.7% a year, reaching 8.78 billion m³ in 2005. After that year the consumption of natural gas started to decline and reached 2.30 billion m³ in 2008; this represents a decrease of 74% in comparison to the peak reached in 2005 (see Figure 93).

Source: Titi Tudorancea.

Figure 93. Natural gas consumption in Chile during the period 1980-2008.

The natural gas consumption in 2008 represented 30% above total natural gas production of the country in that year. For this reason, Chile had to import 690 million m^3 of natural gas to satisfy the demand of that year. Chile's share of gas consumption in 2008 was around 2.61% of the Latin American and the Caribbean region, while it had no significant share of production. By 2013, Chile's share of gas consumption is forecast to be 2.65%; this represents 0.04% higher than in 2008.

Natural Gas Pipelines

Seven pipelines, all built in the late 1990s, link Chile with Argentina. Three in the south, Tierra del Fuego, El Condor-Posesion, and Patagonia, supply methanol plants operated by Methanex, the world's largest methanol producer. Methanex exports most of the methanol produced here to North America and Asia. The productions of the plants have been impacted by the disruption of natural gas imports from Argentina, forcing some plants to shut down or reduce runs. In the north, the GasAtacama pipeline runs from Cornejo in Argentina to Mejillones in Chile. Owned by Endesa and US based CMS, the 928 km GasAtacama pipeline supplies 9 million m^3 per day to the companies' Nopel power plant. Also in the north, the 7.50 million m^3 per day NorAndino, operated by Tractebel, runs parallel to GasAtacama.

In the central region, the 464 km, 9.30 million m^3 per day GasAndes pipeline, majority owned by Total, went into operation in 1997 and connects the Neuquen Basin in Argentina to Santiago in Chile. Also in the central region, the 528 km, 10.20 million m^3 per day Gasoducto del Pacífico connects Neuquen Basin to central Chile. Majority owned by Transcanada, El Paso, and Gasco, Gasoducto del Pacífico supplies municipal distributors and gas-fired power plants. In April 2006, the Gasoducto del Pacífico consortium submitted an environmental impact study for a proposed extension of the system to connect the main trunk line with the Campanario power plant in Cabrero.

In light of the disruption of supplies from Argentina in 2004, Chile has pursued alternative sources of natural gas imports. In June 2005, Suez Energy International, a subsidiary of Tractebel, began a formal feasibility study for a pipeline linking Peru's Camisea natural gas project with northern Chile. The project would feature a 1 488 km pipeline system between Pisco in Peru, and Tocopilla in Chile, with installed capacity of 24.30 million m^3 per day. In addition, the pipeline would have connects to the GasAtacama and NorAndio, allowing potential exports to Argentina, if future conditions permitted. This pipeline is part of the natural gas ring proposed by Peru, Chile, Argentina, Uruguay, and Brazil. The ring would utilize new and existing pipelines to link natural gas reserves in those countries, facilitating greater energy integration in the Southern Cone. The ring would also reduce the dependence of some countries, notably Brazil, upon Bolivian natural gas production.

Investment in Liquefied Natural Gas

There are numerous large-scale power projects in the development pipeline for Chile. Colbun is currently building the 250 MW Candelaria combined-cycle gas-fired turbines in the country in order to increase the gas installed capacity. Endesa completed a 370 MW combined-cycle gas-fired turbine at its existing San Isidro plant, near Santiago in 2007. Southern Cross, a private equity fund, began construction, in April 2006, on the 120 MW Campanario project, a gas-fired power plant in central Chile that will also have the ability to run on diesel. AES Gener, a subsidiary of US-based AES Corporation, sought regulatory approval in early 2005 for its 740 MW Totihue combined-cycle gas-fired turbine plant south of Santiago. However, a combination of local opposition to the plant and uncertainty about future natural gas supplies has caused the company to delay the project for the foreseeable future. Many of the proposed gas-fired power projects will also have the ability to run on fuel oil or diesel.

In the longer term, LNG could provide another potential fuel source for electricity generation in Chile. For this reason, the government is currently making substantial investments in building LNG terminals designed to increase its energy independence. This movement originates from the cuts in natural gas supplied by Argentina in 2004. These cuts resulted in Chilean generators being forced to rely on much more expensive fuel sources and highlighted Chile's reliance on foreign supplies.

Chile has two LNG regasification terminals. One is currently in operation since September 2009. It is located in Quintero Bay, close to the capital city of Santiago. The US $1.1 billion project is designed to satisfy all the natural gas demand for residential, commercial, industrial, and electric generation purposes in the central part of Chile. This amounts to about 40% of the nation's demand. The owners and primary natural gas off-takers are ENAP (20%), Metrogas (20%), BG Group (40%) and Endesa Chile (20%). Quintero LNG terminal has three storage tanks allow the discharge of LNG with a total capacity of 334 000 m^3. The first LNG tank has a capacity of 14 000 m^3 and is operational since June 2009. The second and third tanks have a capacity of 160 000 m^3 each and are operational since the winter of 2010. A regasification plant with three vaporizers that can process 2.5 million tons per year of LNG, producing about 10 million m^3 per day on base and 15 million m^3 per day at peak, is connected into the pipeline network.

The second LNG terminal was inaugurated in July 2010. It is located in Mejillones Bay, in northern Chile. Mejillones LNG project involves an investment of nearly US $500 million and is designed to deliver up to 5.5 million m^3 per day of natural gas, which will generate up to 1 100 MW. This project involves the construction of a dock that can receive ships with LNG producers from different countries such as Trinidad and Tobago, Yemen and Qatar.

The production and domestic supply of natural gas is limited only to oil fields in the Magallanes Basin (Delaveau, Zavala 2010). The production of this field is used to provide natural gas for electric generation, primarily in support of the massive mining industry in that part of the nation. The owners are GDF Suez and Codelco.

The main attraction of the first LNG terminal is that it will be able to use the existing Chilean infrastructure of combined-cycle power plants that were designed for gas rather than needing once again to radically change the nation's generation technology. The intention is that LNG will act as a direct substitution for Argentinean natural gas, and as the LNG will be bought mainly on the free market, this will reduce Chile's energy dependence.

Thermal generators are traditionally supplied with natural gas from Argentina. ENAP plans to develop a natural gas-fired power plant alongside its Aconcague refinery and also stated that it would supply its San Isidro project from a potential LNG import terminal, this partly due to a Chilean law guaranteeing supply precedence to domestic users. A second LNG reception port in Quintero at a cost of $1.2 billion has been approved in order to face an important reduction of natural gas from Argentina.

In June 2007, the Ministry of Mining announced an international bid to attract natural gas and oil exploration and production investments in ten geographic blocks located in the Magallanes Basin. On October 2007, a total of seven companies and/or consortiums presented offers for nine of the ten blocks under bidding. On November 2007, the government granted nine blocks to six international companies. ENAP participates with 50% of the rights in three of these blocks. On April 2008 the awarded officially entered into the agreements with the Chilean government (Delaveau and Zavala, 2010).

In the natural gas distribution sector, there are currently six gas distribution network companies, three trading firms and eight transportation companies.

Without question, LNG has several potential upsides for Chile including adding security to their sources of supply as well as plugging the country into the international natural gas market. Experts in Chile also point to the flexibility of fuel benefit for increased natural gas-fired power projects, those predicated upon LNG imports. Yet, many of the "pros" have been similarly pointed to as "cons" for LNG in Chile as the global LNG market tightens, supply becomes scarcer and LNG and natural gas prices on the international market continue to trend upwards.

Electricity Generation

In 2009, the total production of electricity in Chile was 58 509 MWh from 56 300 MWh produced in 2008, an increase of 4%. The electricity produced using natural gas as fuel was 4 630 MWh, with represents only 8% of the total electricity produced in the country in that year.

It is expected that electricity demand will increase at 5% per year in the period up to 2030. In that same period, the share of natural gas in the generation mix is expected to increase to 46%; this represents around four times the current level of participation of natural gas in the energy mix of the country. The installed capacity of natural-gas fired electricity generation is expected to reach 14 GW in 2030. This will be achieved by the construction of ten new combined-cycle gas-fired power plants in the coming years.

Looking Forward

According to Mr. Marcelo Tokman, former Minister of Energy, the current challenges that Chile has to face in the power sector in the future can be summarized as follows:

1. Having sufficient energy available to meet the requirements of a country with a growing economy;
2. Limiting the demand of electricity to what is strictly necessary;
3. Diversifying the energy mix to avoid supply and price risks;
4. Maintaining competitiveness in the face of energy price increases;

5. Making energy development compatible with local development and environmental conservation;
6. Minimizing the risks and impacts of climate change;
7. Taking advantage of international opportunities (technological advances, public policies, integration, among others.);
8. Ensuring an equitable supply for the entire population, particularly in rural area;
9. Being prepared to deal with critical supply and price situations;
10. Putting the necessary institutions and regulatory framework in place to respond to new challenges.

Finally, it is important to stress the following: Given its limited fossil fuel resources and increasing energy demand, Chile will continue to rely on natural gas and oil imports from Argentina in the short to medium-term. LNG imports from other suppliers located in Asia, the Middle East, and Russia could help to reduce the dependence from Argentina. But as demand for LNG continues to rise, higher prices could reduce the fuel's comparative advantage over diesel, a heavy polluter and historically more expensive fuel option.

Conventional thermal sources, especially natural gas-fired power plants, have become increasingly important to Chile's electricity supply as a way to reduce susceptibility to hydroelectricity's seasonal fluctuations. In recent years, the government has been promoting the country energy independence by implementing an energy security policy that diversifies its primary energy matrix. One of the measures adopted is the construction of LNG terminals in order to reduce the dependency of Argentinean natural gas. Another measure is the international bidding process called by the country for the blocks of oil and natural gas located in the southern part of the country. The initiative was considered a big success and it attracted foreign interest to the country. The exploitation of new deposit of natural gas in this area will represent an important element in the decision of the government to diversify the energy mix and to reduce the energy dependency of the country of foreign suppliers.

ECUADOR

Natural Gas Law

According to the 1978 Hydrocarbon Law, even if private oil companies would like to try to commercialize (for example for export) the side produced natural gas, national legislation makes this almost impossible. Art. 34 of the Law states that "the gas which is a side product to the oil extraction is the possession of the State and does not belong to the private oil company exploiting the oil well.

The natural gas can only be used by the contractors or associates in those quantities necessary for operational needs (power generation or transportation) or for re-injection in the oil well (to increase flow rates of oil). Excess natural gas has to be handed over, if desired, to Petroecuador without any other compensation for the oil company than just transport and additional production costs (Art. 36)". Art. 35, however, do say that "the State of Ecuador via Petroecuador may enter into additional contracts with any party to use the side produced gas."

Even more important is Art. 39. The Article says that "without authorization of the Ministry, gas venting or flaring is prohibited, in theory the State of Ecuador could ban all venting and flaring of side produced gas."

Natural Gas Production, Consumption, and Reserves

The Ecuadorian energy system is based on fossil fuel sources and renewable energies, with the balance between these two being some 89% and 10%, respectively. Ecuador has small proven natural gas reserves.

According to *OGJ*, Ecuador had 10.35 billion m^3 of proven natural gas reserves as of January 2006. In 2010, Ecuador reserves went down to 8.46 billion m^3; this represents a reduction of 1.89 billion of m^3 in comparison with 2006 or 18%.

In 2008, Ecuador produced a total of 1.34 billion m^3 of natural gas, almost all was associated gas from oil production, with the exception of the Amistad field. The consumption of natural gas was 0.27 billion m^3, which represents 20% of the total production of natural gas of that year. Of the 1.34 billion m^3 of natural gas produced, 0.81 billion of m^3 was vented or flared, 0.24 billion m^3 was reinserted to enhance oil recovery, and only 0.27 billion m^3 was marketed. In 2009, the natural gas consumption was 0.30 billion m^3; this represents an increase of 11% in comparison to 2008.

The low natural gas utilization rates are due mainly to the lack of infrastructure to capture and market natural gas. The only large-scale natural gas project in Ecuador is the Amistad field, located in the Gulf of Guayaquil, which produced an estimated 0.66 million m^3 per day in 2010. All of Amistad's natural gas production flows to Noble Machala facility, a 130 MW onshore gas-fired power plant that supplies electricity to the Guayaquil region. Other efforts to develop natural gas reserves in the Gulf of Guayaquil include plans by Chile's ENAP and Venezuela's PdVSA to work with Petroecuador to explore additional blocks in the area.

Ecuador's domestic energy mix is largely dependent on oil. Natural gas consumption is small, particularly for the electricity generation. However, natural gas could provide an alternative for imported LPG, which is mainly used for residential heating and cooking. In addition, increased natural gas production could supply more gas-fired power plants, replacing expensive diesel generators in the future.

According to Huiskamp (2007), the reasons for application of the natural gas for electricity generation are the following:

a) The production of LPG, which Ecuador at this moment is still importing for nearly 8 million barrels per year or nearly 6 million barrels of oil equivalent, and going up and also the resources to purchase this amount of energy;

b) Electricity production, since the natural gas is often produced in remote areas, the transportation of electricity is easier and cheaper than the construction and operation of the necessary infrastructure for LPG;

c) Rural electrification is one of the priorities of various international development programs and a priority of the current Ecuadorian government's electrification program and the use of natural gas for the electricity generation could be an alternative to be considered by the government.

**Table 53. Production and consumption of natural gas in Ecuador
in 2008 and 2009 (Billion m^3)**

	Ecuador 2008	Central and South America	World	Rank	Ecuador 2009
Production	0.27	156.12	3 297.63	71	0.30
Consumption	0.27	46.51	3 327.45	99	0.30
Net export/imports (-)	0	16.62	--	61	--

Source: EIA.

There are two main reasons for the flared natural gas reduction opportunities not being applied yet: Low natural gas prices, and national ownership of the excess side produced gas. The domestic natural gas price is heavily subsidized. The price paid by the end consumers (US $1.60 per 15 kg bottle or US $107 per ton) does not even cover the costs for transport, storage, bottling, and wholesale. Ecuador has the lowest natural gas prices of the whole Latin American and the Caribbean region. The low price makes that there exists virtually no incentive of private producers to commercialize the gas flared. The subsidies (as well as for domestically produced natural gas as for imported natural gas) use vast amounts of public resources and create an unsustainable financial structure, which is also seen within the electricity sector. It is completely uneconomic that after so much usable energy is thrown away, the country import the same energy for three times the price received for it in domestic sales.

Petroecuador informed on June 2011 that natural gas production from block 3 located in the Amistad gas field will reach 2.40 million m^3 per day at the end of next year. The field was formerly operated by a local unit of Noble Energy Inc., but Petroecuador took it over after the US company refused to change its production-sharing contract to a new service agreement. Petroecuador said in a statement that the drilling of two wells and the rehabilitation of another three wells will increase natural gas output from 1.05 million m^3 per day to 1.50 million m^3 per day in the short-term, and to 2.40 million m^3 per day at the end of 2012.

Petroecuador will invest about US $18 million for the rehabilitation process. According to the company, with the increase of natural gas production from the block 3, Ecuador will save about US $500 million per year for imports of diesel and LPG.

Electricity Generation

In 2009, Ecuador generated 17 335 MWh of electricity and consumed 10 515 MWh, which represents 61% of the total electricity produced in that year. The production of electricity using natural gas as fuel was, in 2009, 1 183 MWh, which represents 6.8% of the total electricity produced in that year. This percentage is very low compare with other Latin American and Caribbean countries, and show that natural gas can be used more in electricity generation in the energy mix during the coming years, substituting oil for this specific purpose.

Looking Forward

In the future, national natural gas production could provide an alternative for imported LPG, which is mainly used for residential heating and cooking. In addition, increased natural gas production could supply more gas-fired power plants, replacing expensive diesel generators in electricity production. According to experts' opinion, the country had natural gas reserves in the Oriente and offshore in the Gulf of Guayaquil totaling 400 billion m^3. Reserves in the Oriente were collocated with petroleum deposits. Reserves in the Gulf of Guayaquil, thought to be among the largest in Latin America, remained unexploited because of an uncertain domestic market for natural gas. For this reason, one of the main actions that the government should consider to enhance the energy sector in the coming years is to explore these areas in order to confirm the existence of natural gas deposit economically exploitable.

Finally, it is important to stress the following: There is a certain possibility of taking advantage of the natural gas that exists at the north western part of Peru and, through a bi-national project Ecuador-Peru, export-import natural gas to use it in electricity generation as well as in industries.

With the natural gas that would arrive to Ecuador from Peru it would be possible to assure a stable, clean, and low cost energy generation, which, beyond of diversifying the energetic matrix, it would lower the cost of kWh that currently is one of the most expensive of South America (Brito Castillo, 2007).

MEXICO

Energy Policy

According to Lynch (2003b), Mexico's energy policy stresses expanding the natural gas market and reducing reliance on fuel oil; it is now its intention to change over to natural gas as its primary fuel in the future. The Secretary of Energy has initiated an integral fuel policy, which seeks to significantly reduce the use of fuel oil within ten years. The policy has four main components:

a) The construction of new natural gas-fired combined-cycle power plants;
b) The conversion of several power plants from fuel oil to natural gas operation;
c) An increase in the industrial use of natural gas to meet resulting new environmental standards implemented in 1998;
d) The promotion of industrial and domestic use of natural gas.

Legislation enacted during 1995 opened natural gas transportation, storage, and distribution to private (including foreign) investment and allows private companies to import and export natural gas[115]. According to approve regulations, exploration, production, processing, and first-hand sales of natural gas, as well as production of basic petrochemicals

---

[115] It is important to know that as Mexico becomes a natural gas importer, de facto liberalization is taking place without a constitutional sanction. One notable example is the multiple services contracts mechanism used by Mexico's Energy Regulation Commission to grant distribution and natural gas development licenses.

should be carried out exclusively by PEMEX; however, private investment is allowed in natural gas transportation, natural gas storage (including LNG liquefaction and regasification plants, as well as salt caverns and marginal fields), natural gas local distribution, natural gas marketing, natural gas stations and providing services to PEMEX, including oil field services.

Natural gas transportation, storage, and distribution include coal-bed methane, and are regulated through permits issued by CRE. PEMEX and private companies compete in the provision of transportation and marketing services but the company does not participate in the local distribution business. Marketing by private parties is not a regulated activity while first-hand sales by PEMEX are indeed a regulated activity.

Foreign investment is permitted up to 100%, except in distribution (retail) and public transportation, where private investment may participate through "neutral investment" granting the foreign investor economic rights but limited corporate rights. PEMEX, which prior to 1995 controlled all of the country's natural gas industry, maintains control over the gas upstream sector under the current regulations in force, provided the companies are not involved in more than one function. Companies are awarded thirty year licenses through competitive bids. The regulations also loosened import and export controls on companies and established regulations for distribution infrastructure.

The natural gas industry in Mexico is now the least regulated of its energy sub-sectors. CRE oversees the natural gas industry, and under the 1995 Law, is mandated to achieve a competitive, efficient, safe, and sustainable natural gas industry as part of Mexico's efforts at increasing use of natural gas for environmental, economic, and other reasons. CRE's powers include enforcement of regulations, inspections of facilities, issuance of permits, regulation of prices, and overall supervision of the industry.

Until recently, Mexico had not given high priority to the development and use of its natural gas reserves. A major constraint has been the lack of investment in pipeline infrastructure for transporting natural gas over long distances.

Natural Gas Production, Consumption, and Reserves

Despite Mexico abundant reserves of petroleum and natural gas, strong economic growth is causing energy demand to outpace the country's ability to generate additional supply. A lack of infrastructure forced Mexico to flare significant amounts of natural gas while, until recently, inadequate investment in exploration and production has hampered production of this important clean energy source for electricity generation with the aim of replacing the use of oil for this specific purpose. Budgetary constraints on major infrastructure projects like natural gas pipelines, transmission lines, and power plants prevent electricity generating capacity from keeping up with electricity consumption. The country is a net natural gas importer from the United States and will be through 2015, given that most of Mexico's natural gas production is in the south, where inadequate infrastructure hinders transport of the gas to northern growth centers.

According to *OGJ*, Mexico had 0.4 trillion m^3 of proven natural gas reserves as of January 2010. The southern region of the country contains the largest share of proven reserves. However, the northern region will likely be the center of future reserves growth, as it contains almost ten times as much probable and possible natural gas reserves as the southern region. In 2008, according to EIA sources, Mexico produced 0.06 trillion m³ of natural gas, while consuming 0.07 trillion m³, with imports coming both via pipeline from the United States and LNG.

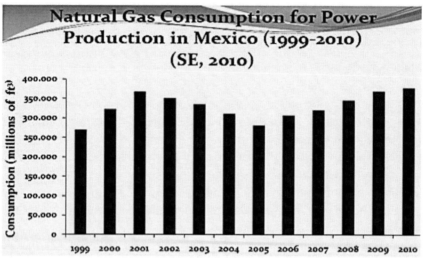

Source; UDLAP.

Figure 94. Natural gas consumption for power production in Mexico during the period 1999-2010.

From Figure 94, the following can be stated: The period under consideration can be divided in two: The first one covering 2001-2005. During this period the consumption of natural gas for the production of electricity decreased from around 100 524 m³ in 2001 to around 82 119 m³ in 2005; this represents a decrease of 18%. The second one covering 2006-2010, the consumption of natural gas for the production of electricity increased from around 84 950 m³ in 2006 to around 135 920 m³ in 2010; this represents an increase of 60%.

From Figure 95, the following can be stated: The level of consumption of natural gas during the period 2000-2009 was higher than the level of production and the gap between these two indicators tend to increase in the coming years, forcing the government to increase the import of natural gas and to use of foreign currency to purchase it.

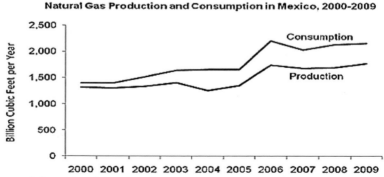

Source: U. S. Energy Information Administration.
Note: One cubic feet = 0.283168466 cubic meter.

Figure 95. Natural gas production and consumption in Mexico during the period 2000-2009.

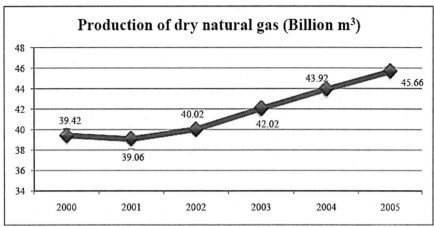

Source: EIA.

Figure 96. Dry natural gas production in Mexico from 2000 to 2005.

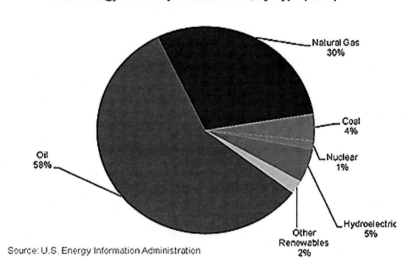

Figure 97. Total energy consumption in Mexico by type.

Mexico's natural gas production has grown in recent years, following steady declines during the late 1990s. During that time, natural gas consumption has grown steadily, driven mostly by the electricity sector, whose share of total natural gas consumption increased from 18% in 1997 to 31% in 2008. PEMEX itself is the single largest consumer of natural gas, with around 40% of domestic consumption.

The domestic market development plan for natural gas in Mexico shows that domestic demand will grow by over 100% in the next ten years. Imports will rise dramatically by 590% from 4.2% of the demand in 1999 to 20% of the demand in 2010-2011. The Mexican government foresees that for 2011, the import of natural gas will cover between 19% and 20% of the domestic demand.

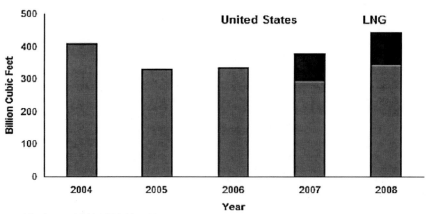

Note: One cubic feet = 0283168466 cubic meter.

Figure 98. Natural gas imports by source by Mexico during the period 2004-2008.

It is important to know that if no additional natural gas reserves are brought on line, current reserves will be depleted by 2020 and imports will grow substantially after that year. Forecasts for Mexico do not contemplate exporting to Central America but only minor exchanges with the United States (Deutsche Montan Technologie GmbH, OLADE and CIEMAT, 2005).

Most of Mexico's natural gas is produced in the southeastern part of the country, far from the major consuming areas in the north and northeast. Associated gas is produced both onshore (primarily in the southern Chiapas and Tabasco regions) and offshore. Natural gas also is produced in the northeastern part of the country at the largest non-associated gas Burgos field. The Burgos Basin has been in production since 1945, with maximum production of more than 18 million m^3 per day reached in 1970. PEMEX hopes to increase Burgos production through 3-D seismic technology combined with new drilling techniques and hydraulic fracturing; the first major contract (US $110 million) for this work went to Schlumberger. PEMEX plans to spend US $5.5 billion by 2015 on these and other efforts at Burgos fields. According to a study performed by the Gas Technology Institute, these investments are expected to yield significant increases in production of non-associated gas over the next twenty years. With increased trans-border shipment of natural gas between the United States and Mexico expected in the future, the substantial additional output from Burgos field could have a sizable impact on the US natural gas market.

Natural gas demand is climbing rapidly in Mexico, due to greater reliance on gas-fired power generation and privatization of natural gas distribution systems in the largest cities. PEMEX is forecasting a doubling of natural gas demand to over 0.07 trillion m^3 by 2011 and the company is expected to become a much larger consumer of natural gas in the coming years as new combined-cycle-power plants are built and existing ones are converted to natural gas. Industrial development along the Pacific Coast from Puerto Vallerta to Acapulco will also create more demand for natural gas.

While demand is forecast to achieve rapid growth over the next decade production, on the other hand, is failing to keep pace. Even with an ambitious development program and the expectation that natural gas production will increase by an average of about 9% annually through 2010-2011, Mexico will still only be able to supply about 80% of its growing domestic needs in this period.

Another problem relates to the high consumption of natural gas across all sectors of the economy but especially in the power sector. Although the production of natural gas increased at the rate of 4.7% a year and reached 0.06 trillion m^3 in 2008, this has not been enough to cope with the rise in domestic demand, which has been growing at an annual rate of 5.9% (Vargas, 2007).

Natural Gas Pipelines

Mexico has about 13 253 km of natural gas pipelines, which are centralized in two main belt systems: One in the north running from Chihuahua State to Matamoros on the Gulf of Mexico at the US border, and the other in the south extending from Guadalajara to Tabasco.

There are ten natural gas pipelines that cross the USA-Mexico border with more on the way: About 30% of US gas exports pass through the Samalayuca pipeline (completed in 1997) which crosses the USA-Mexican border east of El Paso, Texas, and supplies natural gas from West Texas to the Samalayuca I and II power plants near Ciudad Juarez, Mexico, as well as other markets in northern of the country.

According to Lynch (2003b), the pipelines that run from the United States into Mexico include the Mexicali (connected with California), Naco (connected with Arizona), Coral Mexico, Piedras Negras, Reynosa, Samalayuca, Ciudad Juarez, and Arguelles pipelines; the latter six are connected with Texas.

One-third of US natural gas bound for Mexico travels through the Coral Mexico pipeline, which crosses the border near McAllen, Texas. The 8.49 million m^3 per day line, completed in October 2000, supplies a PEMEX facility near Reynosa in Mexico with gas from south Texas. The cost of the 166 km pipeline was US $50 million.

The North Baja pipeline, operational since 2003, is the biggest transporter of gas imports from the USA into Mexico. The US $230 million, 339 km pipeline provide 14.16 million m^3 per day of natural gas to supply southern California and northern Mexico from sources in Arizona.

A Sempra Energy pipeline supplies a power plant in Rosarito in Baja California. The 37 km pipeline has a capacity of 8.5 million m^3 per day and began operating in April 2000. The pipeline, which runs from Naco in Arizona, has a capacity of 3.68 million m^3 per day. The pipeline supplies natural gas to power plants in Hermosillo and Agua Prieta in Mexico.

Tidelands Oil and Gas Corporation constructed a multi-use pipeline from Eagle Pass, Texas, to Piedras Negras in Coahuila State in Mexico. The 9.6 km bi-directional pipeline carries natural gas, propane, and butane. The mentioned company is also considering constructing a 14.16 million m^3 per day natural gas pipeline from El Paso in the USA into northern Mexico.

Within Mexico, the 203 km Gasoducto del Bajio gas pipeline was completed in 2001. This US $55 million project is supplying natural gas to industrial and residential consumers in the States of Guanajuato and Aguascalientes, where the transported natural gas ends up in a distribution system run by Gas Natural de Mexico, a unit of Spain's Gas Natural.

In October 1997, the CRE granted a thirty year permit for a consortium of private companies to transport natural gas to the Yucatán Peninsula. The consortium invested US $276 million to build the 720 km pipeline, which transport gas from the petrochemical complex at Ciudad Pemex in Tabasco State, to the Merida III power plant (and other plants slated for conversion to natural gas) in the Yucatán Peninsula. In February 1998, the CRE approved permits for two other gas pipelines, both of which are to run from Palmillas to Toluca, but over different routes.

A gas pipeline from Ciudad Pemex in southern Mexico to Escuintla in Guatemala has been built with private money. The 555 km, US $450 million pipeline was completed in 2004 and carry 2.83 million m^3 per day of natural gas to utility and industrial customers. The pipeline run parallel to an existing oil pipeline and could be extended as far as Panama, while also supplying gas to Costa Rica, El Salvador, Nicaragua, and Honduras. Cost of running the pipeline to Panama is estimated to be US $850 million.

The Use of Liquefied Natural Gas for Electricity Generation

Rapidly growing demand from the electricity sub-sector for natural gas has spurred greater interest in LNG. Mexico is expected to aggressively develop LNG facilities to meet demand but large costs involved have so far kept any projects from breaking ground; if Mexico does go ahead with LNG, it is unknown how many projects will advance. Commercial interests want to place the regasification infrastructure near Altamira on the Gulf of Mexico or Ensenada in Baja California, both of which having the advantage of being close to large Mexican markets and the southwestern United States where there is already pipeline infrastructure in place. The Mexican government is also interested in sites for LNG import terminals along the Pacific Coast of central Mexico, with potential sites including Topolobamba, Manzanillo, and Lazaro Cardenas, which could all serve as access points for Guadalajara and the surrounding industrial areas. Manzanillo and Lazaro Cardenas also have the advantage of relative proximity to Mexico City while Lazaro Cardenas is already connected to a pipeline.

A joint venture of Sempra and CMS Energy is pursuing plans to construct from 2005 a LNG terminal 24 km north of Ensenada, in Baja California State. The companies proposed the construction of a 64 km pipeline connecting the regasification plant to the North Baja pipeline.

The list of companies that are interested in Mexico's LNG market and are supporting different projects includes Shell, Marathon, a joint venture between El Paso and Phillips, Chevron-Texaco, and a joint venture between BP and Williams. Shell, Marathon, Chevron-Texaco, and the El Paso-Phillips joint ventures could import LNG from Australia and Indonesia, while Sempra-CMS wants to bring in gas from Bolivia. Shell is presently considering an investment of US $500 million for a LNG regasification terminal in Baja California, which would have a capacity of 0.04 billion m^3 natural gas per day.

The project would include a distribution pipeline; the natural gas would be sold to local industries and power plants and any surplus natural gas would be exported to the United States. Shell has reportedly already contracted for 7.5 million metric tons per year of LNG from sources in the southern Pacific region.

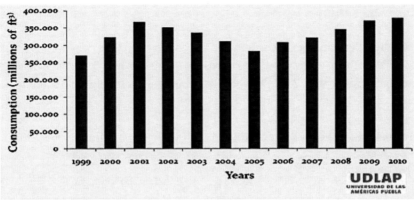

Note: One cubic feet = 0.028316 m³.

Figure 99. Gas consumption in Mexico during the period 1999-2010.

From Figure 99, the following can be stated: Since 2006, has been a systematic increase in the consumption of natural gas in the production of electricity in Mexico, with the purpose of replacing the use of oil with this specific purpose. It is expected that this trend continue in the future.

Import of Natural Gas

Mexico has historically relied on imports of natural gas from the United States. In 2001, 10% of Mexico's demand was met through US gas imports. The gas comes from Texas and the Gulf of Mexico, both largely mature markets that are struggling to accommodate demand growth in the US market. The Mexican Energy Ministry forecasts that by 2010-2011, imports will cover between 19% and 20% of national requirements, with domestic supply falling short of demand by 0.06 billion m^3 per day. Mexico is expected to be a net natural gas importer through 2015. Opponents of a more open energy sector believe government estimates of future demand are inflated as a means of justifying the need for private sector foreign involvement in hydrocarbon exploration and production.

Exploration in Natural Gas

PEMEX has been investing heavily in exploration and is drilling for more non-associated gas. The extra drilling has been able to shore up natural gas production but what is needed is a significant increase in output. Recent discoveries of non-associated gas hold promise for improving Mexico's supply outlook, namely a major discovery in the Lankahuasa gas field in Veracruz State, the offshore Playuela field, and the Hap field in the Sound of Campeche. Potential reserves from these three fields equates to a quarter of Mexico's proven reserves of natural gas.

Electricity Generation

The total installed electricity capacity in the country in 2008 was 58 GW. Of the total installed capacity, 75% is thermal, 19% hydro, 2.4% nuclear and 3.3% renewable other than hydro. Gross generation was 234 TWh in that year (not including co-generation and auto-generation).

Table 56. Effective energy generation in Mexicox during the period 2008-2010

Years	Hydro electric	Thermal [1]	IPP's [2]	Dual [3]	Coal fired	Nuclear	Geothermal	Wind driven	Total
2010 [P]	11 503	21 742	11 907	2 778	2 600	1 365	965	85	52 945
2009	11 383	21 731	11 457	2 100	2 600	1 365	965	85	51 686
2008	11 343	21 191	11 457	2 100	2 600	1 365	965	85	51 105

Source: Secretaría de Energía with data from Comisión Federal de Electricidad and Luz y Fuerza del Centro.

[1] Thermoelectric power plants (residual fuel oil, natural gas, and diesel).
[2] Installed capacity of independent power producers.
[3] Dual power plants can operate with coal or fuel oil.
[P] Preliminary.

From Table 56, the following can be stated: Thermal power plants generated 21 742 MW in 2010, representing 45% of the total electricity generated in that year, followed by hydro with 21.7%. The contribution of coal, nuclear energy, geothermal, and wind energy are very small (see Table 56).

Looking Forward

According to government sources, Mexico will need to bring additional generating capacity online over the next several years in order to meet projected increases in electricity demand. Natural gas-fired turbines will likely supply most of this capacity.

The most important element of Mexico's power sector development in the near future is the considerable rearrangement of the fuel mix expected by 2014, which indicates a doubling in natural gas use for electricity generation. By 2020, the EIA expects Mexico to increase natural gas use in the power sector fivefold or 44% of all generation.

PERU

Energy Reform

In the 1990s, Peru privatized part of the electric sector. Following the electricity concessions law of 1992, reformed in 2005, the Peruvian government reduced its participation in the commercial power sector by privatizing some of its commercial assets, and allowing the participation of private investors. Most of the distribution is privately owned. There is spare capacity of transmission grids, except in rural areas, where the government is stimulating investment.

The government still holds the 1 008 MW Mantaro project, 30% of most of the privatized generation and distribution companies, and 100% of the transmission companies in the center north and the south (Etecen and Etesur). Around 65% of the generation capacity, almost all the transmission capacity, and two distribution companies that serve the capital of Peru have been privatized. The government still owns one hydroelectric plant that represents 30% of the total generation capacity, and several regional distribution companies. Off-grid systems are operated by the government. It should be noted that the 2005 Law of Electricity Concessions authorizes national and foreign individuals or corporations to be involved in, develop, generation, transmission, and distribution activities.

Natural Gas Production, Consumption, and Reserves

According to *OGJ*, Peru had proven natural gas reserves of 0.37 trillion m^3 in 2011, the seventh largest reserves in South America. The country produced 7.67 billion m^3 of natural gas in 2010, most of which was exported. In June 2010, Peru began exporting natural gas from its LNG plant at Pampa Melchorita, which is capable of processing 6.45 billion m^3 per year. This was South America's first plant in operation in the whole region.

Peru's demand for natural gas has risen rapidly in recent years from 1.68 billion m^3 in 2005 to 3.69 billion m^3 in 2009, an increase of 11%, driven by government incentives, economic growth, and new natural gas supplies. Construction of new natural gas-fired power plants also spurred demand; natural gas-fired power plants account for two-thirds of total gas consumption in Peru. According to official sources, Peru could increase its natural gas reserves up to 0.48 trillion of m^3 due to new reserves found in blocks 56, 57 and 88 in the Camisea region, and in the north of the country. It is expected that in the coming years, Peru could become a net exporter of natural gas as the Camisea project comes fully on-stream.

From Figure 100, the following can be stated: Natural gas production increased significantly since 2006 with the major increase produced during 2009 and 2010. In 2009, the production of natural gas was around 3.96 billion m^3, and in 2010 was close to 6.80 billion m^3; the increase was of 71% approximately.

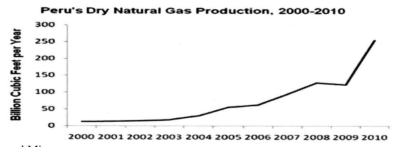

Source: EIA and Minem.

Figure 100. Natural gas production in Peru during the period 2000-2010.

To help mitigate Peru's high oil import bill, the Peruvian government is looking to implement a plan that will stimulate natural gas consumption in the country. The plan targets public and private transportation by converting vehicles to run on natural gas.

Natural Gas Exploration

a) The Camisea Project and the Development of the Natural Gas Sector

The Camisea project consists of several natural gas fields located in the Ucayali Basin of southeastern Peru, principally in block 88 along the Camisea River. Analysts estimated that block 88 contains 0.33 trillion m^3 of proven plus probable natural gas reserves, and 482 million barrels of associated LNG. An international consortium led by Hunt Oil has developed the upstream portion of Camisea, with production beginning in August 2004. The initial production capacity at Camisea was 13.50 million m^3 per day of natural gas, and 34 000 barrels liquid per day of LNG. However, output capacity is expected to increase on Camisea's block 56, adjacent to block 88. Transportadora de Gas del Peru (TGP), a consortium led by Techint, constructed and now operates parallel natural gas and LNG pipelines that carry Camisea production to Lima and to a fractionation plant in Paracas.

The Camisea project provides natural gas for domestic consumption; however, natural gas production from the Camisea project eventually exceeds domestic demand and, for this reason, project sponsors agree to export any excess production. In January 2006, a LNG export terminal at Pampa Melchorita, 168 km south of Lima, started its construction. The Peru's LNG facility will have an operating capacity of 4.2 million tons per year, with most of the production destined for the western United States and Mexico. Peru's LNG plans to build a pipeline to feed natural gas from existing natural gas pipelines to the LNG export terminal. Peru's LNG has also held discussions with ENAP, Chile's State-owned oil company, about exporting LNG to that country. Even though the countries share a land border, trading natural gas via LNG could be more cost-effective than the construction of a natural gas pipeline. Both countries already have plans to build the necessary LNG infrastructure.

With the start of natural gas production from the Camisea project, the Peruvian government has encouraged greater investment in gas-fired power plants as a way to reduce reliance upon hydroelectricity. In July 2006, BPZ Energy plans to bring online its 140 MW, gas-fired power plant in Caleta Cruz. Panamanian-owned Empresa de Generación Eléctrica de Chilcha, plans to build a 520 MW combined cycle power plant south of Lima. The plant will use natural gas supplied from Camisea. In September 2004, Etevensa, the Peruvian subsidiary of Spain-based Endesa, began a construction upgrade of a combined cycle gas-fired turbine at its existing Ventanilla plant, the largest thermal power plant in Peru. The upgrade project increased the capacity of the facility to 380 MW. Many industrial users and independent power producers have also begun transitioning to natural gas.

The Camisea project involves two different stages. The first stage includes the construction of the facilities required to produce gas in block 88, to separate the natural gas from the associated natural gas liquids, to transport the natural gas to Lima, where it is consumed, and to transport the natural gas liquids to a processing plant on the Peruvian coast in order to produce propane, butane, natural gasoline, and diesel. The next stage involves the development of a second field (block 56) near Camisea, the expansion of the natural gas transportation system, and the construction of a liquefaction plant. The two stages of the project have an approximate cost of US $5 billion. Most of the project's development cost will be borne by international consortiums of private sector companies in charge of the project, which consists of natural gas production and gas processing (upstream component), pipeline transportation (downstream component), and natural gas distribution in Lima and the surrounding metropolitan area (distribution component).

The upstream component includes four well pads to extract natural gas from two natural gas reservoirs (located in the Camisea fields at the Ucayali Basin) and an initial processing plant to separate natural gas and LNG. This component also includes a fractionation plant and marine terminal on the coast for processing and exportation of the LNG.

The downstream component consists of two pipelines (one for natural gas and one for LNG) that will transport the natural gas across the Andes. Both pipelines run in parallel from the Camisea field (in the Amazon Basin), 431 km east of Lima, to the city of Pisco. The natural gas pipeline then continues northward along the coast up to Lima.

Development of Camisea fields is a central component of the Peruvian government's energy strategy, with the potential of producing US $5.2 billion in energy cost savings in present value terms over a thirty year period. By developing a stable and low-cost source of energy, it is expected that Camisea fields will provide direct benefits to the Peruvian population and increase the competitiveness of Peruvian industry. Marginal costs of power generation will be reduced by 30% on average, and air pollution in Lima will decrease by virtue of the conversion of old fossil fuel power plants to the use of natural gas, the cleanest of the fossil fuels.

Besides Camisea fields, Peru's natural gas production include the Aguaytia gas field (Maple Gas) in central Peru, block X in the northwest region, and block Z-2B located off the northwest coast.

In September 2005, Ecuador's Ministry of Energy signed a Memorandum of Understanding with BPZ Energy by which Peru could export up to 0.3 trillion m^3 of natural gas to Ecuador over a fifteen year period. In 2004, BPZ Energy announced that it had reached agreements to send natural gas from its offshore block Z-1 to power plants in Peru and southern Ecuador. The project would initially supply 2.22 million m^3 per day of natural gas to three electricity generators in Arenilla, with an eventual extension to Guayaquil, both cities located in Ecuador. BPZ Energy also planned to construct a gas-fired power plant in Peru that would source natural gas from the block Z-1 fields. Analysts estimate that block Z-1 contains 3.90 billion m^3 of proven reserves (Clough, 2008).

The Camisea natural gas extraction and pipeline project is one of the most significant energy infrastructure projects in Latin American and the Caribbean region. Camisea is expected to make an important contribution to Peru's economic development, creating jobs and significantly increasing the country's standard of living. Camisea will also allow Peru to become one of the few Latin American and the Caribbean countries able to meet its own internal energy needs as well as export natural gas in the coming years.

b) The Aguaytia Project

The Aguaytia project includes development of Aguaytia gas field, the construction and operation of gas processing and LNG fractionation facilities, 299 km of natural gas and LNG pipelines, a 160 MW power plant, and a 392 km electric transmission line to the coast. The Aguaytia natural gas project was the first initiated under the current hydrocarbons law. Gas from Aguaytia fires a 160 MW power plant that feeds the north interconnected power grid. It also produces about 1 300 barrels per day of LPG and 2 500 barrels per day of gasoline. Aquaytia could increase production from its estimated 13.20 billion m^3 reserves but it remains unclear whether Peruvian electricity demand will warrant an increase of this level. Furthermore, the future of the Camisea project is relevant to Aguaytia. The project is operated by an independent management team and different international companies with shares in the project.

Plans of expanding the generation capacity of Aguaytia have been shelved mainly due to the increased supply of hydro and coal-based electricity into the Peruvian system. As a result, Aguaytia has been reinserting most of the natural gas and dispatching electricity only during the peak hours. Planned expansions of State hydro facilities are expected to further challenge Aguaytia development project.

Natural Gas Pipelines

According to the EIA, there are two pipelines carrying natural gas from the Camisea fields. The 540 km Camisea pipeline terminates within the Paracas National Reservation (San Martín) at the Pisco terminal. It passes through the Malvinas plant where LNG (propane and heavier liquids) are separated from natural gas. The pipeline has capacity of 13.50 million m^3 per day.

The second pipeline runs from Malvinas along the coast to Lima and Callao for distribution to residential and industrial consumers in Lima. LPG is exported through the Pisco terminal.

The construction of an additional natural gas pipeline from Camisea to supply Lima and other regions is expected to begin in 2013, after several delays. Demand for natural gas has increased sharply in Peru since its main Camisea fields went on-stream in mid-2004, while national pipeline infrastructure has lagged. The new pipeline is part of a commitment by the private consortium Transportadora de Gas Peruano to boost domestic gas supplies to 27.60 million m^3 per day by 2012. Other proposed plans include the Gasoducto Andino del Sur Gas Pipeline in southern Peru, which is moving closer to construction following intergovernmental talks between Peru and Brazil. In addition, negotiations are currently underway between Peru and Bolivia to provide natural gas via pipeline to Chile.

Electricity Generation

According to EIA sources, Peru had 7 270 MW of installed electricity generating capacity in 2008. It is expects that total capacity be expanded by around 70% between 2010 and 2020, due to investment in gas-fired and hydro power plants. Peru plans to begin exporting 6 GWh per year of electricity to Brazil, following a recent energy integration agreement.

A transmission line connecting Peru and Ecuador was built in 2003 but has rarely been used because the two countries have been unable to agree on a price for electricity.

Substantial private investment in gas-fired power plants has increased the share of electricity generated from natural gas following government incentives to decrease the impact of fluctuations in the hydro power supply. Plans to export electricity to Chilean mines from gas-fired power plants along the border have faced nationalist resistance due to territorial disputes.

Electricity consumption in Peru has increased from 15.8 billion kWh in 1998 to 29.3 billion kWh in 2008, nearly doubling as a result of consistent GDP growth, urbanization, and improvements to the electricity infrastructure. The national interconnected electricity system delivers 85% of the electricity generated in the country, with State-owned generators like Electroperu generating one-third of the nation's electricity, and managing distribution in the regions. The government plans to invest around US $2.2 billion to connect eight million Peruvians to the electricity grid by 2018. Industry and mining account for roughly half of electricity consumption in Peru, and industry and mining electricity plants account for 30% of Peru's generating capacity.

Looking Forward

With the start of natural gas production from the Camisea project, the Peruvian government has encouraged greater investment in gas-fired power plants as a way to reduce reliance upon hydroelectricity. Since production began in 2004, its output has grown by an average of 37% per year. Another major gas field is being explored in southern Peru at Madre de Dios, with some experts predicting that this field could be as large as Camisea field. Peru also produces natural gas in the largely offshore Talara Basin in northwest Peru and in December 2010 natural gas production began from a new exploration block in the Corvina offshore field. By that date, Peru's natural gas production was in excess of 28.32 million m^3 per day.

At the same time, the government is promoting the production of LNG in order to satisfy an increase of its energy needs in the coming years. Peru began construction on its first liquefied natural gas project in January 2007, and it became operational in June 2010. This plant at Pampa Melchorita is presently operating at its full capacity of 6.1 billion m^3 per year, with a second and possibly a third train being added within the next four to five years. In 2010, LNG cargoes were shipped to Canada, Europe, and Asia but the majority of its exports are expected to go to an LNG terminal in Manzanillo, Mexico, once it becomes operational in the last quarter of 2011 or beginning of 2012.

TRINIDAD AND TOBAGO

Natural Gas Production, Consumption, and Reserves

Trinidad and Tobago is the Caribbean's largest producer of oil and natural gas. The first major gas discovery in the country was made by the Amoco Energy Company of Trinidad and Tobago in 1968, on the southeastern coast of Trinidad. Both natural gas and oil exploration activities in Trinidad and Tobago have continued at a fast pace since the beginning of the 21st century. While crude oil production has increased slightly in the few past years, natural gas production in Trinidad and Tobago has increased dramatically. According to the 2008 BP Statistical Energy Survey, Trinidad and Tobago had, in 2007, proved natural gas reserves of 0.48 trillion m^3.

Natural gas production increased from 25 billion m^3 in 2004 to 39 billion m^3 in 2009, an increase of 56% in the whole period (average increase of 9.3% per year). The consumption of natural gas increased from 13 billion m^3 in 2004 to 21 billion m^3 in 2010, an increase of 62% in the whole period (average increase of 10.3% per year). One important increase in the production of gas natural occurred in the period, when it jumps from 28 billion m^3 in 2007 to 39 billion m^3 in 2008, an increase of 39.3%. Another important increase in the level of consumption occurred in 2007, when the consumption of natural gas jumped from 14 billion m^3 to 20 billion m^3 in 2008, an increase of 43%.

Natural gas production continues to expand and should meet the needs of new industrial plants coming on stream over the next few years, including iron, aluminum, ethylene, and propylene. The petrochemical sector includes plants producing methanol, ammonia, urea, and LNG. After steady growth in recent years, this sector more than any other felt the impact of a global economic slowdown in late 2008.

Trinidad and Tobago is one of the Latin American and Caribbean countries that have made a transition from an oil-based economy to one based on natural gas.

In 2007, the government of Trinidad and Tobago commissioned a consulting firm to do a study of the nation's natural gas reserves. Experts' opinion questioned the adequacy of the nation's natural gas reserves and this has fueled debate on whether or not the country has already found all of its natural gas reserves. The country is consuming natural gas reserves much faster than new reserves are found. Without any further new field discoveries, the country's proven reserves (both oil and natural gas) will be exhausted by the year 2025. Given that this sector is responsible for almost 80% of Trinidad and Tobago foreign revenue, it is surprising that public reaction has been until now negligible.

The industry viewpoint is that there is more natural gas still to be found. Energy experts believe that the sizes of fields yet to be discovered, are no larger than 0.02 trillion m^3. This is much less that the multi fields discovered in the past. On average, the country consumes 0.05 trillion m^3 of natural gas per year. Yet, for the past few years, new discoveries each year only add up to 0.02 trillion m^3, hence the declining reserves position. According to some experts' opinion, the country need to drill between 30 to 40 exploration wells each year but in 2007 and 2008 only a dozen wells were drilled, even though Trinidad is considered to be one of the top ten hydrocarbon producer countries in the world.

The Naturtal Gas Industry Development

Without doubt, Trinidad and Tobago's increased natural gas production has transformed the islands into one of the major natural gas development centers in the world. Besides LNG exports, Trinidad has a large petrochemical industry, with nine ammonia complexes, six methanol units, a urea plant, and an iron and steel complex. Trinidad and Tobago is the largest supplier of LNG to the United States, and one of the largest LNG exporters in the world.

Amoco currently provides 46% of all natural gas used in the country. Most production comes from five natural gas fields: Teak, Cassia, Banyan, Immortelle, and Flamboyant. The National Gas Company (NGC) was formed in 1975. Over the past years the NGC's gas suppliers have been Enron Gas, Oil Trinidad Limited, and the British Gas/Texaco Consortium. The government is promoting domestic consumption of natural gas in different sectors with the purpose of reducing the consumption of oil.

On April 1999, the LNG plant built in Point Fortin, belonging to the company Atlantic Liquefied Natural Gas began operations, with a production capacity of three million tons per year. It has in-port loading facilities for ships between 70 000 m^3 to 135 000 m^3 of capacity. Production is exported to the USA and Spain.

A second and third liquefying facility will supply LNG for Puerto Rico, Dominican Republic and the States of Maryland, North and South Carolina in the United States and, in the future, possibly for the northeastern market of Brazil.

Exports of LNG have facilitated this large increase in production. The country has benefited from a large amount of foreign investment into the sector, with BP Trinidad and Tobago (BPTT) leading these efforts. Other important players in the natural gas sector include British Gas and Chevron. In October 2009, BPTT brought the Savonette field on-stream, at a rate of 180 million m^3 per day.

The Atlantic LNG Company, a consortium led by BP, British Gas, and Repsol-YPF, operates four LNG trains at Point Fortin, on the south-western coast of Trinidad. The first LNG train was completed in March 1999, with subsequent trains completed in 2002, 2003, and 2006. The four trains have capacity to produce a combined 14.8 million metric tons of LNG per year (21.95 billion m^3 of re-gasified natural gas). There has been discussions between Atlantic Liquefied Natural Gas and the government of Trinidad and Tobago over the construction of a fifth and sixth train, though there are no firm plans as of yet to pursue these projects. Trinidad and Tobago also has a substantial petrochemical industry to further monetize natural gas reserves.

Over the next twenty years, natural gas will be used for domestic consumption and current LNG export commitments. Assuming that domestic demand grows by 5%, the reserve required to cover domestic consumption would be 0.02 trillion m^3, and 0.27 trillion m^3 would be needed for committed LNG exports. Taking into account the 83.9% yield of rich gas to marketable gas, an additional reserve of 0.12 trillion m^3 would be needed.

Export of Natural and Liquefied Natural Gas

It is important to know that about half of the country's natural gas production is converted into LNG at the Atlantic Liquefied Natural Gas facility in Trinidad, and then exported under long-term contracts and to the spot market. In 2008, Trinidad and Tobago exported 7.92 billion m^3 of natural gas to the United States, about 75% of total US LNG net imports but only 15% of total US natural gas supply. US LNG imports from Trinidad and Tobago, in 2008, were almost half the amount received in 2007, reflective of the general decline in total US LNG imports for that year. This trend continued in the first half of 2009, with US LNG imports from Trinidad and Tobago near 2008 levels. Sales of LNG cargos to European and Asian markets have helped to offset the decline in shipments to the US, along with the opening of several new regasification terminals in the Western Hemisphere in the last two years.

Electricity Generation

The country produced in 2010 a total of 7 662 MWh of electricity. The total amount of electricity produced using natural gas as fuel was 7 634 MWh, which represents 99.6% of the total electricity produced by the country in that year. The level of participation reached by natural gas in the energy mix of the country will continue to be almost the same during the coming years.

Looking Forward

According to several experts' opinion, it is expected a significant expansion in gas production due to the coming on stream of Atlantic Liquefied Natural Gas Trains 2 and 3 in 2003 and in 2004 respectively, as well as additional gas-based industrial development. For this reason, the use of natural gas for electricity generation and for export purpose will increase in the country in the coming years.

URUGUAY

Uruguay's energy supply system is rapidly changing because of ongoing energy market reforms, continued regional integration in the Mercosur free trade zone, and ongoing upgrades and modifications to existing energy supply facilities. The level of electric system integration with Argentina and Brazil will also play a significant role in natural gas demand. With electric integration, electricity exports are expected to increase substantially, driving up the demand for natural gas in the power sector.

At the present the energy situation of the country can be summarized as follows:

a) Strong dependence from oil for electricity generation. The consumption of petroleum double the global average:

b)   Scarce domestic sources in the energy grid (25%-40%);
c)   Several energy supplies crisis in recent years increasing the dependency of the country of regional suppliers;
d)   Delay in investment in infrastructure;
e)   Lack of energy efficiency culture;
f)   Hydro power source has been almost exploited completely. The remaining sites can be exploited only by small hydro power projects;
g)   There is a lack of local fossil fuel resources reserves;
h)   There is no availability of natural gas in the country;
i)   There is a vast potential among different renewable energy sources that can be used for electricity generation but these resources has not been exploited yet.

Natural Gas Production, Consumption, and Reserves

Uruguay has no proven natural gas reserves and, for this reason, all natural gas consumed should be imported. In 2008, around 70 million m^3 of natural gas was consumed in the country. A similar amount was imported. Although currently the market for natural gas in Uruguay is relatively small, it is expected to play a much more significant role in the future. Preliminary geological exploration suggests the possibility of significant natural gas reserves within the country's territorial waters. The Uruguayan government signed an agreement with Petrobras for further exploration of natural gas reserves in order to determine the volume and commercial viability of the potential natural gas deposits available in the country, which if confirmed would substantially alter the country's energy consumption matrix, eventually changing Uruguay from a net natural gas importer to natural gas exporter during the coming years.

In August 2008, the government made an appeal to the UN to extend its maritime border by 150 nautical miles, a move which coincided with the publication of data showing that the area contained significant natural gas and oil deposits. The current maritime border, fixed at 200 nautical miles from the Uruguayan coast, was ratified in the Río de la Plata treaty, signed between Uruguay and Argentina in 1973.

Natural gas imports in 2013 are forecast to be between 25% and 28% of primary energy needs. Results for the residential sector show that the overall market share of natural gas will reach around 24% by 2013 with a range up to 83%, depending on natural gas availability. Although natural gas will displace some residential electricity demand in areas where it is available, the overall demand is not expected to change significantly. Similar results are available for other sectors.

The role of natural gas in Uruguay's energy sector is expected to grow over the next few years. Approximately 850 MW of new gas-fired electricity generating capacity is expected to be installed in Uruguay over the next ten years. Present power plants using oil for the electricity generation are to be converted to dual use (oil and natural gas) in the future with the aim of increasing the participation of natural gas in the energy mix of the country.

Natural Gas Exploration

In June 2006, ANCAP announced that it had completed an appraisal of potential natural gas reserves in Uruguay's offshore Punta del Este Basin. According to the company, the basin contains between 0.03 trillion m^3 and 0.06 trillion m^3 of potential natural gas reserves, though there has not been any actual exploration of the area. ANCAP hoped to bring first production from the area on-stream by 2015.

February 2010 marked the entry of Petrobras into the Uruguayan energy sector. The company, in partnership with YPF and GALD Energia, signed a contract with ANCAP for the exploration and production of oil and natural gas on the Uruguayan continental shelf. The signing of the document concluded the Ronda Uruguay 2009 bidding process, brought forward by the Uruguayan government in July 2009 when the consortium presented the best bid for blocks 3 and 4 located in the south-southwest region of the Punta del Este Basin. Petrobras is the operator of block 4 situated 150 km off the coast at a depth of between 100 m and 200 m. Block 3, operated by Repsol-YPF, is located 300 km off the coast and at a depth of between 200 m and 1 500 m. The consortium has four years to complete studies and will decide if they will undertake drilling operations in the coming years. The commitments undertaken by the company in the bidding were the purchase of the existing 2D seismic records and the reprocessing of the data.

Argentina and Uruguay have received interest from thirty nine companies to build infrastructure for a floating LNG terminal, a project they are fast-tracking to start operations by the end of 2013.

The companies are preparing bids for a construction contract, which will be offered at an international tender later this year, according to the information made available by the Uruguay National Energy Department. The bidders are the main companies in the field of LNG. Argentina and Uruguay, in March 2011, gave the final go-ahead for the project, which involves installing about US $20 million in infrastructure for the terminal, and between US $120 and US $150 million in pipelines and other works for delivering supplies.

Natural Gas Pipelines

There are two natural gas pipelines connecting Uruguay to Argentina. The first, the CR. Federico Slinger (also known as Gasoducto del Litoral), runs 19 km from Colón in Argentina to Paysandu in western Uruguay. The US $8 million pipeline started to operate with a volume of 138 000 m^3 of natural gas a day supplying to a cement plant owned by ANCAP. The pipeline, constructed and operated by the company, began operations in November 1998 and has an operating capacity of 0.15 million m^3 per day. The second pipeline is the Gasoducto Cruz del Sur, also known as the Southern Cross pipeline. Operated by a consortium led by British Gas, the Gasoducto Cruz del Sur extends 208 km from Argentina's natural gas grid to Montevideo, and has a capacity of 5.40 million m^3 per day. The Gasoducto Cruz del Sur project also holds a concession for a possible 864 km extension of the pipeline to Porto Alegre in Brazil. The construction cost will be US $2.5 billion. Argentina's Techint handled the construction of the pipeline, while distribution will be handled by Sempra Energy of the USA and Union Fenosa of Spain. ANCAP has rights to a 45% stake in the distribution.

Substantive work began in March 2001. The main market is initially Montevideo. The natural gas will be supplied from Argentina's western Neuquen Basin and southern Austral Basin fields. This pipeline is part of a 1 089 km line from Buenos Aires in Argentina to Porto Alegre in southern Brazil, and represents a design-construction-operation concession agreement with Gasoducto Cruz del Sur, a consortium comprising British Gas (40%), Pan American Energy, itself a joint-venture between BP Amoco and Bridas Energy of Argentina (40%), and ANCAP (20%). Cruz del Sur pipeline provide energy to residential, industrial and commercial consumers, as well as to power plants.

According to the agreement, National Electric Power Generation and Transmission Administration will purchase natural gas from this pipeline for the next fifteen years. Other investments totaling approximately US $961 million will eventually extend the gas network throughout Uruguay. Another US $67 million pipeline was built by a Skanska-led consortium from Colonia to Montevideo. Overall, the Southern Cone's natural gas industry is poised for unprecedented growth that will limit these economies' exposure to the volatility of world's oil prices.

Presently, Gaz de France (GdF), through its subsidiary Gaseba, controls the gas distribution of greater Montevideo. In December 1999 the Conecta consortium, including Union Fenosa, Sempra Energy, and ANCAP, won a twenty year contract to distribute natural gas in Uruguay. The consortium's investment in the project over a five year period is expected to be in the US $150- US $200 million range, with plans to distribute natural gas to 770 000 potential customers outside of Montevideo.

Two companies, Gaseba and Conecta, are responsible for distributing natural gas in Uruguay. Gaseba distribute natural gas in Montevideo, whereas Conecta controls distribution in the rest of the country. Gaz de France owns a majority stake in Gaseba. Petrobras has the control of Conecta since it purchased a majority stake in the company from Spain's Union Fenosa in 2005.

Looking Forward

The following are the main actions that need to be implemented in order to enhance the energy sector in the country in the coming years:

a) Directive role of the State involving controlled participation of private actors;
b) Diversification of electric grid, including sources and suppliers, guaranteeing provision at reasonable costs, reducing dependency on oil imports, increasing the participation level of local sources of energy, fostering non-traditional renewable energies, improving local development, and encouraging the preservation of the environment;
c) Energy efficiency in all economy sectors;
d) Training different types of professionals and technicians for the energy sector;
e) Increase the financial resources available in order to ensure the adequate development of the energy sector;
f) Promote regional energy integration;
g) Energy access for the whole population.

It is foresee an investment of more than US $1 100 million during the coming years for the development of the natural gas sector in the country.

VENEZUELA

Energy Reform

In 1999, Venezuela adopted the Gas Hydrocarbons Law, which was intended to facilitate non-associated natural gas development and expand role of natural gas in Venezuela's energy sector.

This legislation allows private operators to own 100% of non-associated natural gas projects, in contrast to the ownership rules in the oil sector. It also mandates lower royalty and income tax rates on non-associated natural gas projects compared to oil projects. The Law gives PdVSA the right to purchase a 35% stake in any project that moves into commercial status.

Natural Gas Production, Consumption, and Reserves

According to *OGJ*, Venezuela had 5.37 trillion m^3 of proven natural gas reserves in 2011, an increase of 8% respect to 2010, the first largest natural gas reserves in the Latin American and the Caribbean region, and the second largest in the Western Hemisphere behind the United States. In 2009, the country produced 19.53 billion m^3 of natural gas, while consuming 21.42 billion m^3. In 2010, Venezuela occupied the 9th place within the world's list of countries with major natural gas proven reserves.

It is important to stress that Venezuela, with significant gas reserves, produces less gas than it consumes. Venezuela is presently not exporting gas.

Ninety percent of its reserves are natural gas associated with oil, which would justify optimizing jointly the production of oil and natural gas to meet domestic needs and exportable levels of both liquid hydrocarbons and natural gas. It is important to know that the petroleum industry consumes the majority of Venezuela's natural gas production, with the largest share of that consumption in the form of gas re-injection to aid crude oil extraction. Due to the declining output of mature oil fields, natural gas use for enhanced oil recovery has increased by more than 50% since 2005.

PdVSA produces the largest amount of natural gas in Venezuela, and it is also the largest natural gas distributor. A number of private companies also currently operate in Venezuela's gas sector. Participants with significant assets include Repsol-YPF, Chevron, and Statoil.

Currently, Venezuela is working to increase the production on non-associated natural gas, largely through the development of its offshore reserves. PdVSA has awarded exploration blocks in the Plataforma Deltana, Mariscal Sucre, and Blanquilla-Tortuga areas off of Venezuela's northeast coast, and in the Gulf of Venezuela, in the northwestern part of the country. Offshore exploration has yielded numerous successful finds, including Repsol-YPF and ENI's discovery of between 0.18 trillion m^3 and 0.24 trillion m^3 of recoverable natural gas in the Cardon IV block in the Gulf of Venezuela – one of the largest natural gas discoveries in the history of the county.

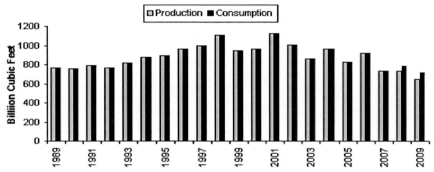

Source: Energy Information Administration.

Figure 101. Natural gas production and consumption in Venezuela during the period 1999-2009.

For Venezuela's offshore natural gas development to move forward in a meaningful way, international partners will need to play a central role in production. PdVSA does not have experience in producing non-associated natural gas – the company's most recent attempt at operating an offshore natural gas project resulted in the sinking of the Aban Pearl semi-submersible drilling rig in May 2011.

From Figure 101, the following can be stated: The production of natural gas increased from a little less than 800 billion m^3 in 1989 to around 1,100 billion m^3 in 1998; this represents an increase of 37.5%. The consumption followed the same trend. However, the production and consumption of natural gas started to decline during the period 1998 to 2009. In 2008 and 2009, the production of natural gas overpassed the consumption of this type of energy. Currently almost all natural gas produced by the country is used to increase the production of oil.

Liquefied Natural Gas

In recent years, Venezuela has improved its domestic natural gas transport network to allow greater domestic utilization and movement of natural gas production. The interconnection Centro Occidente system connects the central and western parts of the country, making natural gas more easily available for domestic consumers, and for re-injection into western oil fields. Upon its scheduled completion in 2011, the interconnection Centro Occidente will have a capacity of 147.25 billion m^3 per day. In 2008, the Antonio Ricaurte pipeline came online, connecting Venezuela with Colombia. Initially, the pipeline will allow Colombia to export natural gas to Venezuela, with contracted volumes ranging between 2.4 trillion m^3 per day and 4.5 billion m^3 per day. Current plans call for the flow of the pipeline to be reversed in 2012, with Venezuela exporting 4.2 billion m^3 per day of natural gas to Colombia.

In September 2008, Venezuela signed initial agreements to create three joint venture companies to pursue LNG projects along the northern coast of the country. Each project will consist of a separate liquefaction train with the capacity to export an estimated 3.04 trillion m^3 per year.

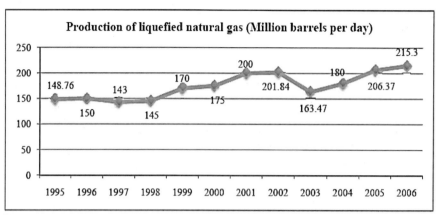

Source: EIA.

Figure 102. Production of liquefied natural gas in Venezuela during the period 1995-2006.

Although PdVSA signed contracts with a number of investors for these projects, it is not clear that adequate feedstock will be developed to meet their scheduled start date of 2014. According to EIA sources, in 2009 Venezuela produced 215.36 million barrels per day of LNG, an increase of 8% from the level reached in 2008, which represent 41.7% of the whole production of the region and 2.7% of the world's total.

According to Deutsche Montan Technologie GmbH, OLADE and CIEMAT (2005), the region's LNG exports are expected to grow rapidly over the next three decades, potentially reaching 90 109 m^3 in 2030. This would require more than US $15 billion in LNG liquefaction plants alone. Venezuela is one of the countries with enough natural gas reserves to become a major LNG exporter in the future[116].

From Figure 102, the following can be stated: The production of LNG increased from 148.7 million of barrels per day in 1995 to around 215.3 million barrels per day in 2008, an increase of 45% for the whole period. It is expected that this trend will continue in the coming years.

Import and Export of Natural Gas

In the past three years, Venezuela imported 3.63 billion of m^3 of natural gas, representing 4.7% of the total natural gas imported in the region. There are no exports of natural gas reported since 1980.

---

[116] Bolivia is also investigating using some of its reserves for an LNG plant to be constructed on the coast in Chile or in Peru in the future, which would allow exports to the USA or Mexico. Peruvian natural gas from the giant Camisea field might also be exported as LNG.

Electricity Generation

According to the ECLAC report for 2010 entitled "Preliminary Overview of the Economies of Latin America and the Caribbean 2010," Venezuela ranks 19th in the item related to development of the electricity industry. Venezuela shows a slow growth in this indicator in 2010 (17.3%), only above Dominican Republic and Haiti, which reported a decline, and Suriname, Guyana, Trinidad and Tobago, Colombia, and Uruguay, which reported slight expansions.

However, there are no public reports on the use of natural gas for the production of electricity in the country in 2010 and 2011.

Looking Forward

Venezuela should increase the participation of natural gas in electricity generation in the coming future, with the purpose of reducing the country's dependency from hydro power and oil. With this purpose, additional financial resources should be allocated by the government and the private sector in order to increase the use of natural gas for electricity generation in the coming future.

THE USE OF NATURAL GAS FOF ELECTRICITY GENERATION IN CENTRAL AMERICA AND OTHER CARIBBEAN COUNTRIES

Currently, Central America and the Caribbean sub-regions neither produce nor consume natural gas, with the exception of Trinidad and Tobago, Cuba, Costa Rica[117], and the Dominican Republic.

Nevertheless, in July 2006, Venezuela and Columbia began work on a natural gas pipeline that will connect the two countries. There are future plans to extend the completed pipeline from Cartagena in Colombia to Colón in Panama, for which, a final feasibility study is underway.

In December 1999, Guatemala and Mexico signed a protocol on construction of a natural gas pipeline connecting Jaltiplan de Morelos in southern Mexico to Puerto Quetzal in Guatemala. The pipeline eventually could be extended to the Honduran and Salvadoran borders, and possibly to Nicaragua and Costa Rica, as part of a wider Central American natural gas pipeline network.

In 2005, Mexico and countries within Central America signed the Cancun Declaration for implementing regional energy projects. One of those projects outlined in the declaration consisted of constructing a natural gas pipeline from various regasification plants in Mexico to different countries within the Central American region. The ECLAC Meso-American Energy Integration Program has been carried out a feasibility of a regional gas pipeline from Mexico through Central America to Colombia. The investment is over US $1.5 billion and

---

[117] Mallon Resources of the United States holds an onshore natural gas exploration concession in northeastern of Costa Rica.

could be financed by the IDB, the Central American Bank for Economic Integration, and those private companies that win the bids for the various components (storage and distribution infrastructure) in each of the countries in the region.

At the same time, it is important to stress that some countries within the Central American sub-region are investing in the natural gas sector with the purpose of reducing the current high dependence from oil forelectricity generation. For example, Nicaragua will invest US $17 million in three main areas: Improving service quality, enlarging distribution networks to reach more costumers, and reducing energy losses in order to provide a better service for over 700 000 clients.

On the other hand, NG Group Panama will construct gas fired electricity generating plant and a terminal to store LNG in Colón. The country will spend US $300 million on a LNG terminal and US $130 million on a gas-fired generating plant, according to government sources. The projects will help meet the country's growing energy demand, and reduce the use of liquid fuels for electricity generation. The LNG terminal will allow the country to receive, store, and then regasify LNG cargos in Colón, which is near the Atlantic entrance to the Panama Canal. The projects will take around five years to complete.

Guatemala called, in 2008, for bids to explore three areas in the Pacific Basin with a combined area of 1 406 674 hectares. The Ministry of Energy and Mines is optimist and expect that natural gas and oil will be found in these areas. The three projects - each involving an area of more than 400 000 hectares - will be undertaken jointly with El Salvador. Three other purely Guatemalan exploration projects are also on the drawing board - two in the northern province of Peten (Laguna Blanca and Cotzal) and one in Quiche (Piedras Blancas). Guatemala has proven natural gas reserves of 2.96 billion m^3, which is the largest natural gas reserve in Central America.

According to OLADE, the inclusion of two large power generation plants with a regional perspective could be a solution to the energy problems now facing countries in the Central American sub-region. Considering that building a natural gas pipeline through the region is presently not feasible, due to the lack of a potentially attractive market, OLADE feels that the most probable source of natural gas would be through liquefaction and maritime transportation, thus eliminating restrictions on free placement of plant proposals. In this way they could be located in such manner as to optimize load requirements and power flows, and take advantage of power interconnection characteristics, enabling better operational conditions. Electric energy would be provided to the SIEPAC line from these centers. Also, local gas pipelines would supply the major potential gas consumption markets in the industrial, transportation, commercial, and residential markets located within the area of influence of the point of supply. Point of entry locations should be defined taking the following factors into account:

a) Port installations for receiving LNG;
b) Operational advantages of the power interconnection system;
c) Favorable conditions for installing the re-gassing and thermoelectric power plants;
d) Optimal natural gas access to markets for other consumption sectors.

The LNG supply to Central America from the area of influence (Trinidad and Tobago and/or Venezuela), involves including new infrastructure in the area, which consists of investing in gas field development and expanding the capacity of the following facilities:

a) Natural gas liquefaction;
b) Storage;
c) In-port ship loading systems;
d) Methane tanker ships;
e) Re-gassing plants, the latter at one of the natural gas points of entry to the area.

Investments in liquefaction plant and ship building should take into account the capacity required to supply Central America and the Caribbean with LNG, making better use of available capacity.

In the Central America and the Caribbean sub-region, there is currently only one existing liquefaction LNG terminal operating from Trinidad and Tobago. Two regasification LNG terminals are located in the Dominican Republic and in Puerto Rico. In addition to these facilities, three LNG regasification terminal projects have been proposed or are under construction in the Bahamas, El Salvador, and Honduras. In addition, a joint LNG regasification project between Jamaica and Trinidad and Tobago has also been proposed. The two proposed LNG regasification terminal projects in the Bahamas, located on the Grand Bahamas Island and Ocean Cay Island, a man-made island, if approved, will connect with the natural gas network in Florida.

Chapter IV

THE CURRENT AND FUTURE ROLE OF COAL IN THE REGIONAL ELECTRICITY GENERATION

GENERAL OVERVIEW

Coal is the most frequent fossil fuel in the Earth and is the major fuel used for generating electricity worldwide. The 1973 world's average coal share of electricity production was, according to EIA sources 38.3%, which by 2006 had risen significantly to 41% and is expected to reach 44% by 2015. The EIA's growth estimate for annual coal generated electricity is expected to be 4.2% for the period 2005-2015.

There are proven coal reserves in more than 100 countries. With the speed of the present production of coal on our planet, it is possible to use it for more than 100 years, much longer than oil and natural gas.

Nevertheless, coal deposits are currently economical non-recoverable in many countries, like other important raw materials, because its price makes it difficult to be exploited economically, particularly for the electricity generation. This will possibly change in the next few years, if the price of oil and gas continue increasing.

The BP Statistic Report 2010 indicated that "world coal[118] consumption was flat in 2009, the weakest annual change since 1999. Elsewhere, consumption grew by 7.4%, near the historical average, with China accounting for 95% of the increase. Consumption fell in all regions, except in Asia-Pacific and the Middle East."

From Figure 103, the following can be stated: The use of coal for the electricity generation at world's level increased from 42.9% in 1973 to 65.6% in 2008; this represents an increase of 23.2% in the past thirty five years. The use of coal diminished in all sectors in the period under consideration.

---

[118] There are three different categories of coal: a) Bituminous (hard coal) coal contains 45%-86% carbon. Bituminous coal was formed under high heat and pressure. Bituminous coal is used to generate electricity, and is an important fuel and raw material for the steel and iron industries; b) Sub-bituminous coal has a lower heating value than bituminous coal. Sub-bituminous coal typically contains 35%-45% carbon; and c) Lignite (brown coal) is the lowest rank of coal with the lowest energy content. Lignite coal deposits tend to be relatively young coal deposits that were not subjected to extreme heat or pressure, containing 25%-35% carbon. Lignite is crumbly and has high moisture content. Lignite is mainly burned at power plants to generate electricity.

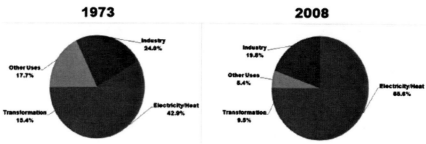

Source: IEA.

Figure 103. World's consumption of coal.

According to the IEO (2009) report, total recoverable reserves of coal around the world are estimated at 929 billion tons (2008)[119]. Historically, estimates of world's recoverable coal reserves, although relatively stable, have declined gradually from 1,145 billion tons in 1991, to 1,083 billion tons in 2000, and 929 billion tons in 2006 (World Energy Council, 2007). In 2009, the world's coal reserves dropped further to 826 billion tons, a decrease of 11% in comparison with 2006.

The most recent assessment of world's coal reserves includes a substantial downward adjustment for India from 102 billion tons in 2003 to 62 billion tons in 2006 attributable to better data, which permitted the estimation of recoverable coal reserves as compared with previous estimates of in-place coal reserves.

In 2010, Latin America has proven recoverable coal reserves of 16 billion tons representing between 1.6% and 2% of the world's coal reserves. According to BP Statistic report 2010, Brazil has 7.06 billion of tons of coal, representing the highest coal reserves in the region, followed by Colombia with 6.82 billion of tons, Mexico with 1.2 billion tons, and Venezuela with 0.48 billion tons (see Table 58). Recoverable coal reserves in Central and South America, excluding Brazil, are the following: Hard coal: 8.5 billion tons; Sub-bituminous: 2.2 billion tons, and lignite: 0.1 billion tons.

Central and South America consumed 0.9 quadrillion Btu of coal in 2007. Brazil, with the world's ninth-largest steel production in 2007, accounted for 51% of the region's coal demand, and Chile, Colombia, Argentina, and Peru accounted for most of the remainder. Coal consumption in Central and South America is expect to increases by 0.8 quadrillion Btu from 2007 to 2035, with most of the increase in Brazil, primarily for coke manufacture and electricity generation. Brazil's steel companies currently plan to expand production capacity by a substantial amount over the mid-term to meet increasing domestic and international demand for steel. Overall, South America's imports of coking coal - driven primarily by demand in Brazil - grow from about 0.4 quadrillion Btu in 2008 to 1.1 quadrillion Btu in 2035; this represents an increase of 175%. Brazil and Chile account for most of the increase in thermal coal imports to South America through 2035.

According to OLADE sources, during the period 1999-2008, the major consumers of coal were Brazil, followed by Mexico, Chile, Peru, and Argentina (see Table 57).

---

[119] According to the World Coal Institute, proven coal reserves are sufficient to sustain production at current levels for at least the next 130 years. Oil and gas reserves are around 41 and 63 years, respectively.

Table 57. Coal demand during the period 1999-2008

COAL – DOMESTIC DEMAND (kt)

Países/ Countries	1999	2000	2001	2002	2003	2004	2005	2006	2007	2008
ARGENTINA	1,485	1,234	1,086	1,173	922	1,008	937	574	921	921
BARBADOS	0	0	0	0	0	0	0	0	0	0
BOLIVIA	0	0	0	0	0	0	0	0	0	0
BRASIL / BRAZIL	24,715	25,975	25,365	23,778	23,650	26,518	26,189	26,061	27,773	27,042
CHILE	5,939	4,589	3,601	3,629	3,470	4,769	4,428	4,918	5,837	5,837
COLOMBIA	3,945	4,251	4,367	3,637	4,235	3,144	4,172	2,644	3,697	4,351
COSTA RICA	0	0	42	49	70	60	60	2	21	22
CUBA	14	15	13	13	14	14	13	22	14	18
ECUADOR	0	0	0	0	0	0	0	0	0	0
EL SALVADOR	0	0	0	0	0	0	0	0	0	0
GRENADA	0	0	0	0	0	0	0	0	0	0
GUATEMALA	15	215	356	390	366	425	409	428	448	451
GUYANA	0	0	0	0	0	0	0	0	0	0
HAITI	0	0	0	0	0	0	0	0	0	0
HONDURAS	56	135	123	141	169	177	241	59	64	105
JAMAICA	29	53	53	88	85	93	59	15	15	15
MEXICO	11,922	12,458	13,142	14,214	12,334	14,783	18,931	18,928	18,363	14,471
NICARAGUA	0	0	0	0	0	0	0	0	0	0
PANAMA	60	60	0	0	0	0	0	0	0	0
PARAGUAY	0	0	0	0	0	0	0	0	0	0
PERU	438	679	596	910	889	925	1,069	818	1,134	1,179
REP.DOM. / DOM. REP.	5	93	203	233	1,057	777	476	704	728	763
SURINAME	0	0	0	0	0	0	0	0	0	0
TRINIDAD & TOBAGO	0	0	0	0	0	0	0	0	0	0
URUGUAY	1	1	1	1	1	1	1	2	2	2
VENEZUELA	50	181	67	25	58	0	51	60	62	62
ALBC / LABC	48,673	49,938	49,018	48,281	47,320	52,694	57,036	55,235	59,075	55,239

2.1.6 CARBÓN MINERAL – DEMANDA INTERNA POR SUBREGIONES (kt)

COAL –DOMESTIC DEMAND BY SUB-REGIONS (kt)

Sub – regiones / Sub-regions	1999	2000	2001	2002	2003	2004	2005	2006	2007	2008
México	11,922	12,458	13,142	14,214	12,334	14,783	18,931	18,928	18,363	14,471
América Central / Central America	131	410	521	579	605	663	710	490	532	578
Caribe / Caribbean	49	160	269	335	1,156	884	547	741	757	795
Región Andina / Andean Region	4,432	5,110	5,031	4,572	5,183	4,069	5,293	3,522	4,893	5,592
Brasil / Brazil	24,715	25,975	25,365	23,778	23,650	26,518	26,189	26,061	27,773	27,042
Cono Sur / Southern Cone	7,425	5,824	4,668	4,803	4,393	5,778	5,367	5,494	6,760	6,760
ALBC / LABC	48,673	49,938	49,018	48,281	47,320	52,694	57,036	55,235	59,075	55,239

Source: OLADE.

South America will remain the world's third-largest coal-exporting region in 2035, primarily as a result of continued increases in exports from Colombia as expected. The government of Colombia expects that the coal production reach 160 million tons by 2019, up from about 72.1 million tons in 2009, an increase of 122% (12.2% average annual increase for the whole period).

The expansion will require sizable investments in mine capacity, rail infrastructure, and port capacity. Colombia is the only Latin American and the Caribbean country included in the world's top ten coal producers.

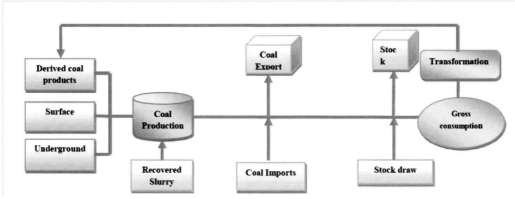

Source: Author design.

Figure 104. Simplified flow chart for coal.

In the specific case of the Andean countries, coal's consumption is concentrated in Colombia and Peru (13% of South American total). A slight increase in consumption of this fuel is expected in Peru and a higher increase in Colombia in the coming years. The largest coal's reserves in the Andean region are in Colombia, Venezuela, and Peru, accounting for 41% of the total South American coal's reserves.

In the specific case of the Southern Cone, Chile and Argentina both have little coal's reserves. Chile uses coal in thermal power plants for electricity generation; 90% of coal is imported from Australia, Indonesia and Colombia. Argentina uses local coal in steelmaking and to a lesser extent in supplementing hydro power generation (World Energy Council, 2008).

Source: BP Statistic Report 2010.

Figure 105. Map of world's coal reserves.

Table 58. Energy proven coal reserves at end 2009 (Million tons)

Rank	Country	Anthracite And bitumous	Sub-bitumous And lignite	Total	Percent of world's total
10.	Brazil	-	7 059	7 059	0.85%
11.	Colombia	6 434	380	6 814	0.82%
22.	Mexico	860	351	1 211	0.15%
28.	Venezuela	479	-	479	0.06%
	World	411 321	414 680	826 001	100%

Source: World Energy Council.

Table 59. Coal proven reserves during the period 1999-2008

COAL+ PROVEN RESERVES LA&C (Mt)

Países / Countries	1999	2000	2001	2002	2003	2004	2005	2006	2007	2008
ARGENTINA	424	424	424	424	423	423	423	423	423	423
BARBADOS	0	0	0	0	0	0	0	0	0	0
BOLIVIA	0	0	0	0	0	0	0	0	0	0
BRASIL / BRAZIL	32,370	32,364	32,358	32,353	32,348	32,342	32,336	32,330	32,324	32,319
CHILE	166	166	166	166	165	165	155	155	155	155
COLOMBIA	6,693	6,655	6,611	6,571	6,522	6,522	6,611	6,885	6,871	6,798
COSTA RICA	33	33	33	33	33	33	33	33	33	33
CUBA	0	0	0	0	0	0	0	0	0	0
ECUADOR	22	22	22	22	22	22	22	22	22	22
EL SALVADOR	0	0	0	0	0	0	0	0	0	0
GRENADA	0	0	0	0	0	0	0	0	0	0
GUATEMALA	0	0	0	0	0	0	0	0	0	0
GUYANA	0	0	0	0	0	0	0	0	0	0
HAITI	9	9	9	9	9	9	9	9	9	0
HONDURAS	21	21	0	0	0	0	0	0	0	0
JAMAICA	333	333	333	333	333	333	333	333	333	333
MEXICO	1,848	1,848	1,848	1,848	1,838	1,838	1,211	1,211	1,211	1,226
NICARAGUA	0	0	0	0	0	0	0	0	0	0
PANAMA	1	1	1	1	1	1	139	119	119	119
PARAGUAY	0	0	0	0	0	0	0	0	0	0
PERU	58	58	59	59	59	59	50	50	50	50
REP.DOM. / DOM. REP.	0	0	0	0	0	0	0	0	0	0
SURINAME	0	0	0	0	0	0	0	0	0	0
TRINIDAD & TOBAGO	0	0	0	0	0	0	0	0	0	0
URUGUAY	0	0	0	0	0	0	0	0	0	0
VENEZUELA	1,309	1,303	1,295	1,295	1,288	1,461	1,454	1,447	1,447	1,439
AL&C /LA&C	43,287	43,236	43,150	43,113	43,041	43,208	42,755	43,016	42,996	42,916

2.1.2 CARBÓN MINERAL-RESERVAS PROBADAS POR SUB-REGIONES (Mt)
COAL+ PROVEN RESERVES BY SUB- REGIONS (Mt)

Sub - regiones / Sub-regions	1999	2000	2001	2002	2003	2004	2005	2006	2007	2008
Mexico	1,848	1,848	1,848	1,848	1,838	1,838	1,211	1,211	1,211	1,226
América Central / Central America	55	55	34	34	34	34	152	152	152	152
Caribe / Caribbean	342	342	342	342	342	342	342	342	342	333
Región Andina / Andean Region	8,082	8,038	7,987	7,947	7,891	8,063	8,137	8,404	8,390	8,308
Brasil / Brazil	32,370	32,364	32,358	32,353	32,348	32,342	32,336	32,330	32,324	32,319
Cono Sur / Southern Cone	590	590	590	590	588	588	578	578	578	578
AL&C /LA&C	43,287	43,236	43,150	43,113	43,041	43,208	42,755	43,016	42,996	42,916

Source: OLADE.

Table 60. Coal demand forecasts (ton)

	2004	2013	2018
Southern Cone	5.8	7.8	9.2
Andean Community	4.4	6.1	7.2
Brazil	39.1	46.4	51.6
Total	49.3	60.2	68

Source: World Energy Council, Brazilian data, and OLADE.

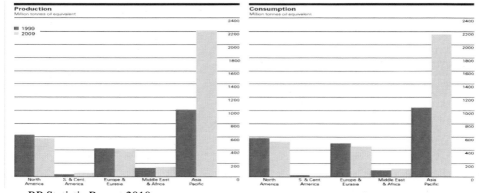

Source: BP Statistic Report 2010.

Figure 106. Latin American and the Caribbean coal production and consumption in 2009.

Table 61. Coal production during the period 1999-2008

COAL-PRODUCTION LA&C (kt)

Países/ Countries	1999	2000	2001	2002	2003	2004	2005	2006	2007	2,008
ARGENTINA	336	259	186	97	89	42	41	360	379	379
BARBADOS	0	0	0	0	0	0	0	0	0	0
BOLIVIA	0	0	0	0	0	0	0	0	0	0
BRASIL / BRAZIL	4,422	5,426	4,536	4,149	3,784	4,471	5,164	4,755	4,884	4,739
CHILE	485	366	576	637	576	576	163	396	243	243
COLOMBIA	32,754	38,142	43,441	39,532	50,028	51,693	59,064	65,596	69,902	73,502
COSTA RICA	0	0	0	0	0	0	0	0	0	0
CUBA	0	0	0	0	0	0	0	0	0	0
ECUADOR	0	0	0	0	0	0	0	0	0	0
EL SALVADOR	0	0	0	0	0	0	0	0	0	0
GRENADA	0	0	0	0	0	0	0	0	0	0
GUATEMALA	0	0	0	0	0	0	0	0	0	0
GUYANA	0	0	0	0	0	0	0	0	0	0
HAITI	0	0	0	0	0	0	0	0	0	0
HONDURAS	0	0	0	0	0	0	0	0	0	0
JAMAICA	0	0	0	0	0	0	0	0	0	0
MEXICO	10,379	11,415	11,656	10,967	6,586	9,562	10,387	11,094	12,081	11,080
NICARAGUA	0	0	0	0	0	0	0	0	0	0
PANAMA	0	0	0	0	0	0	0	0	0	0
PARAGUAY	0	0	0	0	0	0	0	0	0	0
PERU	22	17	19	22	16	16	43	107	112	115
REP.DOM. / DON. REP.	0	0	0	0	0	0	0	0	0	0
SURINAME	0	0	0	0	0	0	0	0	0	0
TRINIDAD & TOBAGO	0	0	0	0	0	0	0	0	0	0
URUGUAY	0	0	0	0	0	0	0	0	0	0
VENEZUELA	6,979	7,885	7,585	7,369	6,613	6,555	7,195	7,871	7,647	7,647
AL&C /LA&C	55,376	63,509	66,000	62,773	67,692	74,918	82,656	90,178	95,247	97,706

2.1.4 CARBÓN MINERAL-PRODUCCIÓN POR SUBREGIONES (kt)
COAL-PRODUCTION BY SUB- REGIONS (kt)

Subregiones / Sub-regiones	1999	2000	2001	2002	2003	2004	2005	2006	2007	2,008
Mexico	10,379	11,415	11,656	10,967	6,586	9,562	10,387	11,094	12,081	11,080
América Central / Central America	0	0	0	0	0	0	0	0	0	0
Caribe / Caribbean	0	0	0	0	0	0	0	0	0	0
Región Andina / Andean Region	39,755	46,043	51,045	46,923	56,657	60,265	66,301	73,574	77,660	81,265
Brasil / Brazil	4,422	5,426	4,536	4,149	3,784	4,471	5,164	4,755	4,884	4,739
Cono Sur / Southern Cone	821	625	762	734	665	618	205	756	621	621
AL&C /LA&C	55,376	63,509	66,000	62,773	67,692	74,918	82,656	90,178	95,247	97,706

Source: OLADE.

From Figure 106, the following can be stated: Around 2% of the coal's world reserves in 2009 are located in the Latin American and the Caribbean region. This percentage could increase to 5% in the coming years.

It is important to know that fifteen countries in the Latin American and the Caribbean region have no coal's reserves. These countries are the following: Barbados, Bolivia, Cuba, Dominican Republic, El Salvador, Grenada, Guatemala, Guyana, Honduras, Nicaragua, Paraguay, Suriname Trinidad and Tobago, and Uruguay. Colombia and Venezuela, in the Latin American and the Caribbean region, are among the top four exporters of steam coal in 2007. South America is one of the regions expected to expand their international coal trade by 2030.

Brazil's steel companies currently plan to expand production capacity by a substantial amount over the mid-term to meet increasing domestic and international demand for steel (Pregnaca, 2008). Brazil's steelmaking capacity is projected to more than double by 2018; this represents an increase to 88 million tons from 37 million tons consumed in 2007 (Walters, 2007). With rich reserves of iron ore but no coking grade coal, Brazil's steel industry will need to imports more coking coal from Australia, Canada, the USA, and Southern Africa in order to satisfy it coking coal needs.

Expansion projects on Colombia's Caribbean coast include a coal terminal at the port of Cienaga, and an expanded river-to-port terminal at Barranquilla, each with an annual capacity of about 0.9 quadrillion Btu (Argus Coal Transportation Report, 2009). About 42% of coal production in the region is exported to the EU and USA.

However, with the depletion of oil and natural gas reserves in the future, coal may gain a more preferential position in the energy power sector in the coming years. Some coal-fired power plants can be found in Colombia, Chile, Brazil, Dominican Republic, and Mexico.

Table 62. World coal flows by importing and exporting regions, Reference case 2007, 2015 and 2030 (Quadrillion Btu)

Exporters		Importer Steam 2007		
	Europe	Asia	Americas	Total
South America	1.00	0.00	0.89	1.90
Total	4.46	8.56	1.57	14.69
		2015		
South America	1.79	0.00	0.97	2.76
Total	5.1	10.03	1.49	16.94
		2030		
South America	2.15	0.38	1.43	3.95
Total	4.87	12.90	2.12	19.88

Note: 1 metric ton = 22 877 388 Btu.
Source: IEO (2009).

Table 63. Coal import during the period 1999-2008

COAL-IMPORT LA&C (kt)

Paises/ Countries	1999	2000	2001	2002	2003	2004	2005	2006	2007	2008
ARGENTINA	1,134	975	969	1,008	846	941	959	311	606	606
BARBADOS	0	0	0	0	0	0	0	0	0	0
BOLIVIA	0	0	0	0	0	0	0	0	0	0
BRASIL / BRAZIL	19,618	20,328	19,968	19,987	19,946	21,638	20,937	20,612	22,868	22,358
CHILE	5,043	4,402	2,834	2,963	2,905	4,193	4,264	4,525	5,859	5,859
COLOMBIA	0	0	0	1,501	0	3	3	3	0	0
COSTA RICA	0	0	42	49	70	60	60	2	21	22
CUBA	23	22	13	26	14	22	21	22	14	18
ECUADOR	0	0	0	0	0	0	0	0	0	0
EL SALVADOR	0	0	0	0	0	0	0	0	0	0
GRENADA	0	0	0	0	0	0	0	0	0	0
GUATEMALA	15	215	390	378	430	370	408	268	464	477
GUYANA	0	0	0	0	0	0	0	0	0	0
HAITI	0	0	0	0	0	0	0	0	0	0
HONDURAS	96	135	123	169	169	177	241	61	64	104
JAMAICA	29	53	53	88	85	93	60	28	28	28
MEXICO	2,085	2,195	2,583	5,187	6,423	5,249	9,193	9,609	6,946	5,502
NICARAGUA	0	0	0	0	0	0	0	0	0	0
PANAMA	60	60	0	0	0	0	0	0	0	0
PARAGUAY	0	0	0	0	0	0	0	0	0	0
PERU	425	625	467	812	741	771	921	753	922	959
RER.DOM. / DOM. REP.	5	93	203	233	1,057	777	476	704	728	763
SURINAME	0	0	0	0	0	0	0	0	0	0
TRINIDAD & TOBAGO	0	0	0	0	0	0	0	0	0	0
URUGUAY	1	1	1	1	1	1	1	2	2	2
VENEZUELA	0	0	0	0	0	0	0	98	0	0
AL&C /LA&C	28,535	29,103	27,647	32,402	32,686	34,294	37,543	36,997	38,523	36,698

2.1.8 CARBÓN MINERAL-IMPORTACIÓN POR SUBREGIONES (kt)
COAL-IMPORT BY SUB- REGIONS (kt)

Subregiones / Sub-regions	1999	2000	2001	2002	2003	2004	2005	2006	2007	2008
Mexico	2,085	2,195	2,583	5,187	6,423	5,249	9,193	9,609	6,946	5,502
América Central / Central America	171	410	555	596	669	607	709	331	549	602
Caribe / Caribbean	57	167	269	348	1,156	892	557	754	770	808
Región Andina / Andean Region	425	625	467	2,313	741	773	924	853	923	960
Brasil / Brazil	19,618	20,328	19,968	19,987	19,946	21,638	20,937	20,612	22,868	22,358
Cono Sur / Southern Cone	6,178	5,377	3,805	3,972	3,751	5,135	5,224	4,839	6,468	6,468
AL&C /LA&C	28,535	29,103	27,647	32,402	32,686	34,294	37,543	36,997	38,523	36,698

Source: OLADE.

From Table 63, the following can be stated: In 2007, the major importer of steam coal was Europe, followed by the USA. The same pattern is foreseen for 2015. However, in 2030 it is foreseeable that South America will export steam coal to Asia for the first time in the history.

According to public data, in the Latin American and the Caribbean region, coal actually only plays a minor role as energy source for electricity production. However, the development of novel and more environmentally friendly coal technologies, called "Clean Coal Technologies", have change somehow the perception that coal is a "dirty and old-fashioned fuel for use in poorer countries", and that the use of coal for electricity generation due to its high-ash content reduces the efficiency of generating units, accelerates the deterioration of equipment, and brings about adverse social, economic and ecological effects. Designed to enhance both the efficiency and the environmental acceptability of coal extraction, preparation and use, these new technologies are believed capable of bringing coal back into business.

This is because the environmental concerns with coal are associated with the ways in which coal is used rather than with coal itself. Although some clean coal technologies are still at the research and development stage, they are enjoying growing interest worldwide, including in the Latin American and the Caribbean region. With the use of new technologies, the world's consumption of coal is expected to increase from 25% to 28%, in 2030. However, the main increase will take place mainly in Australia, China, India, Indonesia, North America, and Latin America.

For this reason, coal is projected to provide larger shares of the total energy used for electricity generation worldwide in 2030 than in 2004. The coal's energy share is expected to increases, at world level, from 41% now to 45% in 2030; this represents an increase of 4%.

It is important to note that co-combustion of coal actually is of minor importance for the Latin American and the Caribbean countries as there are only a few coal-fired power plants available in the region. However, co-combustion may gain importance when the number of coal-fired power plants increases in the medium-to-long-term future, and if a proper technology can be used to reduce CO_2 emissions.

The situation of the coal sector in a selected group of countries is briefly presented in the following paragraphs.

ARGENTINA

Coal Production, Consumption, and Reserves

Argentina has very limited coal resources and, for this reason, coal is not a major component of the country's fuel mix. With only 470 million short tons of recoverable coal reserves, the country produced 0.05 million short tons during the period 2004-2006. In 2009, Argentina produced 0.181 million short tons and consumed 1.44 million of short tons, an increase of 60% in comparison to 2004.

To satisfy this level of consumption, the country imported 1.263 million of short tons in 2009, around 0.5 million short tons less than in 2008. According to EIA sources, in 2008 the coal reserves increased up to 551.16 million of short tons, representing an increase of 17% in comparison to 2004. In 2009, Argentina imported 1.26 million short tons from Australia, the United States, and South Africa.

Almost 99% of Argentina's coal reserves are located mainly in two sites: Pico Quemado mine in Rio Negro province (estimated reserves 750 million tons; currently not in operation), and Rio Turbio mine in Santa Cruz province (estimated reserves: 750 million tons). Before 2002, Yacimientos Carboníferos Fiscales, previously a government agency that was privatized in the early 1990s, continued to operate the Rio Turbio mine, which produces sub-bituminous coal. Some of the produced coal is consumed on-site with the remainder being sent to Buenos Aires province for power generation at San Nicolas power plant.

Table 64. Coal production in Argentina in 2008 and 2009 (Million short tons)

	Argentina 2008	Central and South America	World	Rank	Argentina 2009
Production	0.121	98	7 505	57	0.181
Consumption	1.943	45	7 346	58	1.444
Net export/import (-)	-1.727	49	--	34	-1.263

Source: EIA.

Electricity Generation

In 2009, the total production of electricity in Argentina was 115 081 MWh, out of which 2 494 MWh was produced using coal as a fuel; this represents 2% of the total. This percentage shows that coal is not an important fuel for electricity generation in the country, and this situation will not change significantly in the coming years.

Looking Forward

Of the total power plants in Argentina that rely on fossil fuels for electricity generation, only one plant, San Nicolas in Santa Fe province, uses coal for this specific purpose. There are no concrete plans approved by the government to increase the participation of coal for electricity generation in the coming years.

BRAZIL

Energy Reform

On April 2002, Brazilian Congress approved Law 10,438 which introduced a mechanism that fosters the diversification of Brazil's electric power generation matrix. This mechanism, called "Energy Development Account", permits that all electric power consumers of interconnected systems, except Brazil's northern region, contribute to a fund that will foster electricity generation through renewable energy sources, clean coal, and the implementation of gas pipelines in regions that have none.

The Law allows Brazil to count on an additional 3 000 MW generated with coal as fuel but using clean coal technologies. Allows also that, at the first stage up to the year 2006, around 3 000 MW should be produced using different renewable energy sources and, at a second stage in the next twenty years, these sources should meet 10% of Brazil's electricity consumption.

Coal Production, Consumption, and Reserves

According to the 2010 BP Statistical Energy Survey, Brazil had at the end of 2009 coal reserves of 7 059 million short tons, representing 46% of Brazilian fossil fuel reserves. In 2009, Brazil produced 6.9 million short tons, representing 0.07% of the total production in the region, and ranking 32th in the list of world's coal producers. The percentage of coal production in Brazil in comparison with the total world production is very small (0.09%). Brazil had in 2009 a coal consumption of 25.4 million short tons, representing 54% of the coal regional consumption, 0.3 % of the world's total, and ranking 27th in the list of world's coal consumers (see Table 65). Brazil is the largest South American consumer of coal.

Table 65. Production and consumption of coal in Brazil in 2008 and 2009
(Million short tons)

	Brazil 2008	Central and South America	World	Rank	Brazil 2009
Production	7.288	98	7 505	32	6.854
Consumption	24.610	45	7 346	27	25.364
Net export/import (-)	-18.893	49	--	11	-18.493

Source: EIA.

In spite of the Brazil's coal reserves, the coal industry does not constitute a large part of the country's mineral industry. It is in fact Latin America's largest coal consumer based on its well-developed steel industry but an import part of the coal consumed in this industry is imported. Coal is purchased mainly from the USA, Australia, China, Canada, and South Africa.

Brazil's leading coal producer is Copelmi Mineraçao. The company holds the concession of more than 3 billion short tons of coal in several areas of the State of Rio Grande do Sul, and currently achieves a production of more than 2 million short tons of raw coal per annum, generating more than 1 million tons of product per annum through its mining operations.

Import of Coal

In 2009, the country import 18.5 million short tons, ranking 11th in the list of world's top coal importing countries (see Table 65).

Brazil is attempting to reverse its status as a net importer of coal in the coming years. According to available reports, Brazil's Banco Nacional de Desenvolvimento Economico e Social (BNDES) is developing a plan to expand the country's coal industry. BNDES hopes that the proposed program will make Brazil self-sufficient in coal in this decade, and eventually a net exporter of coal in the future.

Coal Exploitation

Coal mined in Brazil was initially used in railroad and waterway transport, as well as in the production of gas for public illumination. Throughout the past decades and currently coal is also used in electricity generation, in the metallurgic industry, for producing metallurgic coke, and for generating heat for the chemical, cement and paper, ceramic, and metal industries.

In Brazil, the main incentive to develop the coal industry, starting with the mines existing in the southern region[120], was that in the past the State metallurgic industry used to be obliged to employ national mineral coal[121].

Economic coal mining for the purpose of energy started in Brazil upon the installation of the Charqueadas power plant and the thermoelectric power plant of Candiota, south of the State of Rio Grande do Sul; it was later consolidated when the thermal park of Jorge Lacerda was installed.

Coal as an input for generating electric began with the diversification of the electrical sector's energy matrix. It reduced the vulnerability of hydroelectric systems and contributed to optimizing energy supply. The use of coal in the energy matrix is considered important since it allows a greater diversification of sources, and provides less exchange risks and less risk of price changes in commodities such as oil and natural gas. Additionally, the nationalization index of equipment for coal-driven power plants is larger than of gas-driven power plants, providing more benefits in terms of income and job opportunities in the Brazilian industry.

Coal is a domestic macroeconomic input with no weight in the balance of payments, permitting Brazil's foreign resources to be used in the acquisition of goods that improve the competitiveness of Brazilian products in international trade. Aside from the potential domestic importance, the use of coal contributes to reduce dependence on external sources for energy, which is growing due to electrical interconnections and imported natural gas. In addition, coal provides long-term stability since coal reserves are known and available.

As a result of the publication of Law 10,438, which creates incentives for a program of diversification of Brazil's energy matrix, including national mineral coal provided it is based on a clean technology, the discussion of a program for new coal-driven thermoelectric power plants with a minimum capacity of 2 000 MW to be implemented with private capital is now in its final stage.

However, Brazil's principal and largest national mine, the Candiota, is not greatly washable. It is therefore exclusively used in thermoelectric power plants in the vicinity of the mine. Its ash content is 53%, its sulfur content 1.5%, and its humidity is up to 18%. On the other hand, coal processing through washing causes environmental problems by generating major quantities of liquid and solid residues. Therefore, large investments in preserving the environment are required.

---

[120] In Brazil, coal is found in its southern States: Rio Grande do Sul, Santa Catarina and Paraná. Its use for electricity generation is also concentrated in these States.

[121] This requirement is no longer in force.

Electricity Generation

The country has in 2011 an installed electricity capacity of 100 GWh, and produced in 2009 a total of 461 GWh. The electricity consumption in 2009 was 421 GWh; this represents 91% of the total electricity generated by the country in that year. The electricity production from coal sources in Brazil in 2009 was 10 114 MWh, representing only 2.3% of the total electricity generated in the country in that year.

Table 66. Main coal mines in Brazil

State	Mine	Resources (Million tons)
Parana	Cambui	44
	Sapopema	45
	Outros	14
Santa Catarina	Barro Bronco	1 045
	Bonito	1 601
	Pre- Bonito	414
	Others	289
Rio Grande du Sul	Candiota	12 275
	Leão	2 439
	Charqueadas	2 993
	Irui/Capane	2 688
	Morungava	3 128
	Santa Terezinha/ Torres	5 068
	Others	207
Total		32 250

Source: Informativo Annual da Industria Carbonifera DPNM/99.

Looking Forward

There are eight coal power plants operating in the country with a capacity of 1 414 MW, and two under construction with a capacity of 70 MW. In the next fifteen to twenty years, it is expected that the use of hydro power plants for electricity generation will continue to play a decisive role, with emphasis on thermal efficiency gains, and not in the construction of new power plants.

Transition should therefore be smooth for full operation of the market mechanisms in a competitive economy. During this interval, the best use of the abundant hydric resources Brazil has the fortune to dispose of is assured, and there is a chance that the coal mining industry in the south of the country will take a new lease on life. For reasons of environment and location, the new hydroelectric plants in Brazil will have a lower water storage capacity and that, in order to allow more energy sold, confirms the thesis of the need for flexible thermoelectric plants.

The main impact in the use of coal power plants for electricity generation in the country during the coming years can be summarized as follows:

a) An increase in national production amounting to US $ 0.7 million impacting directly on the economy of the States of Rio Grande do Sul, Paraná, and Santa Catarina in the south of Brazil;

b) The attraction of industries that use by-products as inputs for the production of cement, fertilizers, steam, etc., leading to the development of integrated projects of major social-economic impact;

c) The possibility of supplying approximately 60% of the national ammonium sulphate market, 85% of which is currently supplied by an imported product;

d) The possibility to create around 14 000 new direct and indirect jobs;

e) The new coal-driven-electric power technologies is intended to introduce in Brazil, the so called "clean coal technologies", greatly reduce environmental emissions that are therefore perfectly compatible with the strict standards of Brazil's environmental legislation.

f) Increase in tax collection.

COLOMBIA

Privatization of the Coal Sector

In 2001, the Colombian government sold off the State-run coal company Carbones de Colombia (Carbocol). This sale was one of the IMF requirements for obtaining a US $2.7 billion loan package; the purchaser was a group headed up by UK's Billiton and Anglo American, and Switzerland's Glencore, which is the largest coal producer in Colombia.

The sale netted US $384 million for the government, but critics have claimed that the price was too low. Carbocol now has a 50% equity interest in the Cerrejon Zona Norte (CZN) coal mine, with the other half owned by Intercor, an Exxon-Mobil subsidiary. The CNZ is the largest coal mine in Latin America and the largest open-cast coal mine in the world. CZN, which consists of an integrated mine, railroad, and coastal export terminal, exported over 30 million short tons of coal in 2009. Drummond operates the second-largest coal mine in Colombia, La Loma, also an integrated mine-railway-port project, producing about 20 million short tons per year.

In 2009, Drummond ships its first coal exports from the El Descanso project, which could reach production of 20 million short tons by 2010-2011. Glencore operates the Jagua and Prodeco coal mines, with total production capacity of about eight million short tons per year. Carbocol and Intercor hold the right to operate CZN until 2033. Colombia completed the privatization of its coal sector in 2004 with the closing of Minercol, a former State-owned coal company.

Another major coal mine in Colombia is the Pribbenow mine, located near La Loma in Cesar department, which has estimated reserves in excess of 534 million tons of high Btu, low-ash and low sulfur coal. The mine is operated by the US based company Drummond Ltd.

The company is expected to increase its cumulative capital investment in the coal industry in Colombia to US $1 billion. This additional expenditure would increase its output in 100% annually. The Colombian government has awarded a twenty five year contract for a value of US $12.5 million to operate the Patilla coal mine on the Guajira peninsula to Carbocol. The mine has 71.65 million short tons of proven reserves of high quality coal, and yearly output is between 3.04 million short tons and 4.41 million short tons.

Coal Production, Consumption, and Reserves

The country has the second-largest coal reserves in South America, slightly behind Brazil, with most of those reserves concentrated in the Guajira peninsula in the north and the Andean foothills, which is home to the Cerrejon Zona Norte mine.

According to the BP Statistical Review of World Energy (2010), Colombia had at the end of 2009 coal reserves of 6 814 million short tons, 0.82% of the world's total. Colombia had in 2009 a coal production of 72.1 million short tons, 1.37% of the world's total, and a coal consumption of 6.69 million short tons or 9.3% of the total production of that year[122]. In 2010, the coal production was 82.78 million short tons, a 15% increase from 2009 but below the government's target of 90 million short tons for 2010, reportedly due to unusually heavy rains in the last months of the year. Colombia's total coal export for 2010 was 68.14 million short tons. According to government plans, coal production should reach 160 million short tons in 2020; this represents an increase of 93% in comparison to the production of 2010.

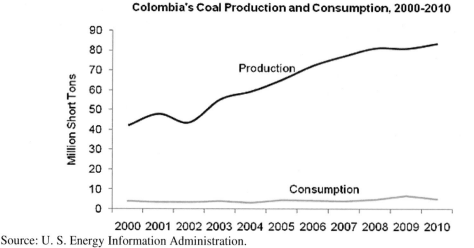

Source: U. S. Energy Information Administration.

Figure 107. Colombia's coal production and consumption during the period 2000-2010.

It is important to know that coal reserves consist of high-quality bituminous coal and a small quantity of metallurgical coal. The coal is relatively clean and has sculpture content about 0.7% in average. Nevertheless, the weakest limb of the coal chain is still the

---

[122] Colombian coal production, which is exclusively carried out by private companies, has nearly doubled since 2000.

infrastructure. In spite of many improvements during the past years it is yet not possible for the most export companies to use their conveyor capacity completely.

It is likely that Colombia's coal production will continue to increase in coming years, as exploration and profitable developments continue throughout the north and interior of the country. Colombia's coal consumption is very low, leaving most of the country's production available for export (see Figure 107).

Coal Basins

Colombia has seven coal basins, whereof the Guajira and Cesar departments near of the coast are economically the most interesting areas. The largest coal reserves are situated on the peninsula of Guajira. Reasons for the beginning of coal mining activities in Colombia gave the offer shortage released by the second oil crisis in 1979/1980 and the situation at the steam coal world market during this period. At that time, the American mineral oil group Exxon together with the Colombian State enterprise Carbocol decided to starts the common development of the deposit El Cerrejón North on the peninsula of Guajira[123]. The deposit is divided in four zones:

a) North Zone: Originated as a joint-venture between Carbocol and Intercor. The cooperation began in 1977 as a research project; in 1980 the construction project began and the production started in 1986;

b) Central Zone: In production since 1981;

c) South Zone: This zone still is in exploration;

d) The Oreganal Zone: The zone was decided at the beginning between Carbones del Caribe and the Colombia's State. Most of the mining concessions have validity for thirty years.

La Loma is the second biggest coal deposit of Colombia. Already in the 1980's, the US group Drummond acquired the rights the mining of Mina Pribbenow/La Loma. The development starts in the 1990's. The coal of Mina Pribbenow owns a good coal quality, which has an ash content of 7.7 % and the sculpture content amounts to 0.61%. The reserves are about 450 million tons.

La Jagua is the third biggest coal deposit of Colombia and is in the Cesar department. The reserves amount to about 258.3 million tons. The coal quality is good, the ash content is about 5.32% and the sculpture has about 0.62%. The other coal basins are located in Cesar, Cundinamarca, Boyaca, and Santander departments.

More than 90% of the coal contracts are long-term contracts. During the past years, Colombia has developed to an important global exporter. The country exported in 2007 about 70 million metric tons of coal.

---

[123] El Cerrejón is the biggest open coal cast mine of the world. The reserves of the deposit amount to approximately 950 million tons of coal and are located to 100 m depth, 2 000 million tons to 200 m depth, and 3 000 million tons to 300 m depth.

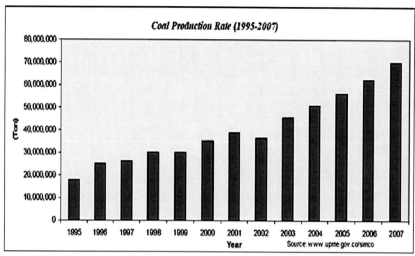

Note: 1 mt = 1.10231 short tons.

Figure 108. Colombia's coal production in metric tons during the period 1995-2007.

From Figure 108, the following can be stated: Coal production increased each year since 2002, transforming the country in one the biggest coal producer and exporter country in the world. The richest coal deposits are distributed well over the northern and western regions of Colombia; however, the biggest export operations limit themselves to the Guajira and Cesar departments in the north of the country.

Coal Exports and Investment in Port Infrastructure

Coal plays a significant but not major role in Colombia's energy picture from the standpoint of electricity generation. Most of the coal mined in Colombia (almost 90%) is exported; coal is Colombia's third leading export and the country is, at the same time, Latin America's leading coal exporter. Currently, most Colombian coal exports go to Europe, North America, and other countries in Latin America, as the vast majority of Colombia's coal producing and exporting infrastructure is located on the Caribbean coast. Coal is an important part of the Colombian economy; in 2009, coal represented about one-quarter of total export earnings, and mining taxes and royalties paid to the Colombian government exceeded   US $1 billion. During the first nine months of 2009, the USA imported 13.6 million short tons of coal from Colombia, about 80% of total US coal imports.

Some of the non-integrated coal mines in Colombia export their production via the Venezuelan ports of La Cieba and Maracaibo. In order to sustain the rise in coal exports, Colombia will need to invest in transportation infrastructure to remove potential production bottlenecks. In May 2006, former President Uribe announced plans to build a US $300 million export terminal near Santa Marta. The facility will have special measures to reduce the spreading of coal dust in the nearby area, a popular tourist destination. Drummond also has plans to install a second rail line at its La Loma complex.

Drummond is now producing from its El Descanso mine, and it expects ultimately to attain export production of 40 million tons per year through 2032[124]. The El Hatillo mine is planning to increase production from 1.8 million tons to 4.5 million tons by 2011; this represents an increase of 150%.

Increasing coal transportation infrastructure is also a concern for Colombia. There is a proposal to build a tunnel that would expedite coal transportation via truck to Colombia's Pacific Ocean port of Buenaventura when it is completed in 2013. Another planned infrastructure project, the Carare railway, now appears to be at risk because the government has decided not to provide financial support for the project, which was intended to facilitate coal transport from central Colombia to the Caribbean coast. Other expansion projects on Colombia's Caribbean coast appear to be on track, including a coal terminal at the port of Cienaga, Puerto Nuevo, ultimately handling 66 million short tons per year, roughly one-half of which would be available by 2013.

Brazil's MPX is planning a coal export terminal along the Colombia's Atlantic seaboard with a capacity of 20 million short tons per year. An expanded river-to-port terminal at Barranquilla, Colombia, with an annual capacity of about 39 million short tons, is also planned.

It is important to single out that many of Colombia's port expansions are carrying out on the Caribbean coast near the eastward opening of the Panama Canal. The Canal expansion should enhance opportunities for coal exports from both the United States and South America traveling westward to Asian markets. The so-called "post-panamax" vessels, which are capable of holding about 20% more than current panamax vessels, will be able to transit the Canal. Because many ports may not be able to accommodate the larger vessels without dredging, however, some opportunities could be limited at least in the near future (IEO, 2010).

The coal industry in Colombia is aggressively seeking to expand its current exports by 2011 to greater than 80 million short tons.

From Figure 109, the following can be stated: In 2010, Europe is the first destiny of the Colombia's coal export with 48% of the total, followed by the USA with 17%, Latin America and the Caribbean with 14%, China with 7%, and other Asian countries with 6%.

From Figure 110, can be stated the following: Colombia is the only Latin American and the Caribbean country within the five top coal exporter countries in 2008, with 81 million short tons. According to media reports, Colombia began in 2009 exporting sizable quantities of coal to Asian markets, especially China. According to Global Trade Information Services, Asia's share of Colombian coal exports grew from less than 1% in 2009 to 12.7% in 2010.

A combination of higher prices in Asia, lower freight costs, and falling exports to the United States, created spurred this expansion into Asian markets. Both, the expansion of the Panama Canal[125] and Chinese-backed transportation infrastructure projects, could facilitate greater exports of Colombian coal to Asia in the future.

---

[124] Drummond has stated that its Colombian mines could contain up to 0.0622 trillion m^3 of coal bed methane (CBM), which is a gaseous hydrocarbon that occurs along with coal reserves. It is similar to natural gas and can be transported and used in similar ways. Drummond has signed contracts with Ecopetrol to extract CBM from both the La Loma and El Descanso mines. CBM has the potential to dramatically increase Colombia's proven natural gas reserves, facilitate greater domestic production, and potentially allow additional exports to neighboring countries.

[125] The expansion begun in 2008 and it is expected to be completed by 2015.

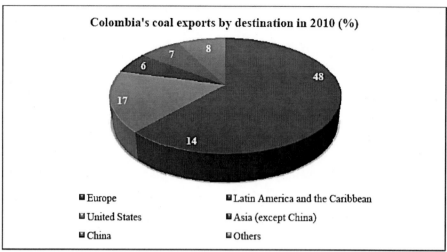

Source: EIA.

Figure 109. Colombia's coal exports by regions.

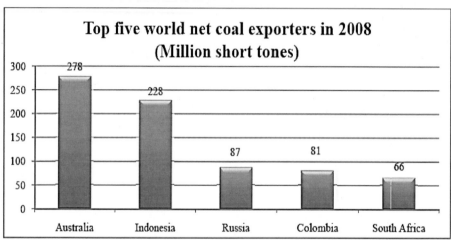

Source: EIA.

Figure 110. Top five world net coal exporters (2008).

Electricity Generation

The country produced 55 314 MWh and consumed 43 328 MWh of electricity in 2009, an increase of 13% in comparison to 2004. The production of electricity using coal as a fuel was 3 493 MWh, which represent only 6.03% of the total electricity produced in that year. This percentage is almost the same than in 2000, and will not increase significantly in the coming years.

Looking Forward

According to BMI, Colombia will increase its electricity consumption per capita around 15% between 2010 and 2014. The country's power consumption is expected to increase from an estimated 42 TWh in 2010 to 51 TWh by the end of the forecast period.

Between 2010 and 2019, BMI are forecasting an increase in Colombian electricity generation of 39.1%, which is above average for the Latin America region. This equates to 17.6% in the period 2014-2019, down from 18.2% in the period 2010-2014. Primary energy demand growth is set to ease from 18.8% in the period 2010-2014 to 15.9% during the period 2014- 2019, representing 37.6% for the entire forecast period. An increase of 20% in hydro power use during the period 2010-2019 is one key element of generation growth. Thermal power generation is forecast to rise by 47% between 2010 and 2019.

On the other hand, according to EIO (2010), the government of Colombia expects the nation's coal production to reach 160 million tons by 2019, up from about 87 million tons in 2008 (BN Mining News, 2009). The expansion will require sizable investments in mine capacity, rail infrastructure, and port capacity. Drummond is now producing from its El Descanso mine, and it expects ultimately to attain export production of 40 million tons per year through 2032 (Muse, 2009). According to Tex Energy Report (2009) and Argus Coal Transportation Report (2009), the El Hatillo mine is planning to increase production from 1.8 million tons to 4.5 million tons by 2011.

Finally, it is important to stress the following: Due to the current status of the infrastructure of the coal transportation sector, the government is considering a proposal to build a tunnel that would expedite coal transportation via truck to Colombia's Pacific Ocean port of Buenaventura when it is completed in 2013. Another planned infrastructure project, the Carare railway, now appears to be at risk because the government has decided not to provide financial support for the project (Argus Coal Transportation Report, 2009), which was intended to facilitate coal transport from central Colombia to the Caribbean coast. Other expansion projects on Colombia's Caribbean coast appear to be on track, including a coal terminal at the port of Cienaga, Puerto Nuevo, ultimately handling 66 million tons per year, roughly one-half of which would be available by 2013 (South American Business Information, 2009).

Brazil's MPX is planning a coal export terminal along the Colombia's Atlantic seaboard with a capacity of 20 million tons per year (Marketwire, 2010). An expanded river-to-port terminal at Barranquilla, Colombia, with an annual capacity of about 39 million tons, is also planned (Argus Coal Transportation Report, 2009).

Despite significant improvements in the security situation in the country, Colombia's electricity sector continues to face serious supply and financial challenges due to lack of investment, security risks, and power theft. Repeated attacks on electricity infrastructure increase the risk of blackouts and raise cost of operation for the electricity sector. However, service quality in Colombia, as measured by service interruptions, is much lower than the average for the Latin American and the Caribbean region. In 2005, the average number of interruptions per subscriber was 185.7, far above the regional average of 13 interruptions. The duration of interruptions per subscriber was 66 hours, also far above the regional average of 14 hours.

CHILE

Energy Reform

Chile represents the world's longest running comprehensive electricity reform in the post-World War II period. The reform was led by the 1982 Electricity Act, which is still the most important law regulating the organization of the electricity sector in the country. The reform was designed based on the UK's model. It started, in 1981, with vertical and horizontal unbundling of generation, transmission, and distribution. According to Pollitt (2004), the reform is widely regarded as a successful example of electricity reform in a developing country and has been used as a model for other privatizations in Latin America and around the world. The electric market in the country is a free market.

The Energy National Commission has a relevant role in the surveillance and regulation of the energy sector. Nevertheless, the legal framework provides a system by virtue of which the operation of the generation plants is ruled by the generation, transmission, and distribution companies that fulfill the legal requirements. For such purpose, the Law provides for an interconnected operation of the system. In fact, the above-mentioned companies integrate the Economic Load Dispatch Centre, which determines which generation plants can inject electricity to the system based upon generation costs, allowing such companies to inject their electricity and power to the extent that they operate at the lowest marginal cost of the system. With respect to the transmission system, considering the shape of the country (a narrow strip of land), the same has been evolved as a natural monopoly. Nevertheless, the Law, considering the public policy principle of guaranteeing supply to the population, has provided a right to access to the system. By virtue of such access rights, third parties have the right to inject or withdraw energy from the transmission system (Nuñez and Muñoz, 2008).

In the period 1970-73, the government had undertaken a process of nationalization of many large companies, including utilities and banks. By 1974, inflation, high fuel prices and price controls had led to large losses and lack of investment in electric utilities, which were then under public ownership. The subsequent governments decided to reorganize the sector through the introduction of economic discipline. By the end of the 1990s, foreign firms had gained majority ownership of the Chilean electricity system (Pollitt, 2004).

Coal Production, Consumption, and Reserves

According to EIA sources, Chile has recoverable coal reserves of 170.86 million short tons in 2008, and produced 7.5 million short tons, an increase of 5.88% respect to 2007. In 2009, the country produced 7.7 million short tons, an increase of 3% respect to 2008. The coal consumption in 2008 was 7.2 million short tons, which represent an increase of 15.1% respect to 2007. In 2009, the coal consumption was almost the same than in 2008 (see Table 67 and Figure 111).

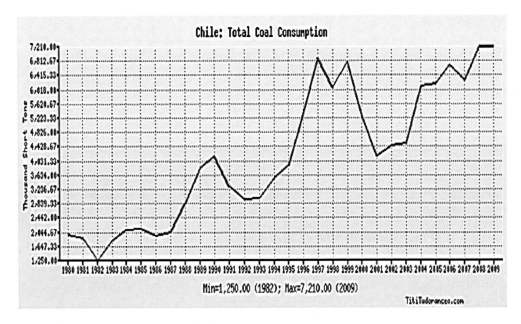

Figure 111. Total coal consumption in Chile.

Table 67. Coal consumption in Chile during the period 2000-2009 (Million short tons)

Year	Chile	Change percent	Chile, percent of Central and South America consumption	Chile, percent of world consumption
2000	5.294	-21.929%	14.376%	0.105%
2001	4.162	-21.383%	12.047%	0.081%
2002	4.433	6.511%	12.903%	0.084%
2003	4.517	1.895%	12.245%	0.079%
2004	6.109	35.245%	15.524%	0.098%
2005	6.152	0.704%	15.282%	0.095%
2006	6.674	8.485%	16.214%	0.099%
2007	6.255	-6.278%	14.551%	0.089%
2008	7.203	15.156%	14.201%	0.100%
2009	7.210	0.097%	N/A	N/A

Source: Titi Tudorancea.

The level of coal consumption has tended to fluctuate, as the power sector, the country's largest coal consumer, uses the fuel largely as a backup to hydro power. In this role, it is possible that coal consumption will rise rapidly in coming years, especially if the unreliability of natural gas imports from Argentina continues. Chile's potential in the coal sector remains great with five projects scheduled for completion in the next five years, generating 3 500 MW.

Import of Coal

The EIA estimates indicate that in 2009 Chile imported 680 000 short tons of steaming coal from the US, which accounted for the bulk of US coal exported to South America.

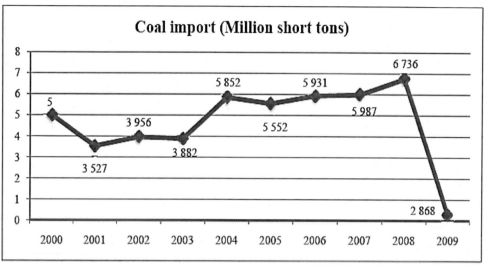

Source: Titi Tudorance.

Figure 112. Import of coal in Chile during the period 2000-2009.

From Figure 112, the following can be stated: The import of coal by Chile increased systematically during the period 2001-2009 from 3.527 million short tons in 2001 to 6.736 million short tons in 2008. However, in 2009 the import of coal dropped to 286 803 short tons, almost 96% with respect to the level reached in 2008.

Coal Exploitation

Domestic coal production is located in the Lota/Coronel area and in the extreme south on Tierra del Fuego. The country has two mines operated by Empresa Nacional del Carbon and La Compañía Carbonífera San Pedro de Catamutun, respectively.

Due to the Argentina natural gas supply reduction in the past years, coal-fired power plants have begun to receive renewed attention. Chile has two existing coal-fired power plants, the 340 MW Ventanas and the Guacolda power plants.

In early 2006, Guacolda (majority-owned by AES) received environmental approval for a 200 MW addition at the facility. AES also received environmental approval in August 2006 for a 250 MW expansion at the Ventanas power plant. Other companies that have stated interest in building new coal-fired capacity include BHP Billiton (300 MW), Endesa (350 MW), and Suez (400 MW).

Coal Investment

The high levels of investment that have been attained since 1982 have enabled the expansion of the central interconnected system from 2 713 MW to 6 991 MW (4.1% per year), and of the northern interconnected system from 428 MW up to 3 634 MW between 1982 and 2004, an increase of 749% (Pollitt, 2004).

In January 2011, it was reported that 48% of the power projects to be inaugurated in Chile between 2011 and 2014 will use coal as the main fuel. More than US $28.5 billion will be invested in coal-fired power plants in the country through 2014. This includes the construction of the US $400 million, 350 MW Santa Maria coal-fired power plant, owned by Colbun SA, and the Bocamina II power plant. Both plants are expected to become operational before 2012.

Table 68. Coal mines in exploitation in Chile

Company	Mine	Region	Tons mined in 2007 in short ton
Empresa Nacional del Carbón S.A. (ENACAR)	Trongol coal mine near Curanilahue, and plant at Lota	Region VIII	100 000
Carbonífera Victoria de Lebu S.A. (99.9% owned by ENACAR)	La Fortuna coal mine near Lebu	Region VIII	Not available
Inmobiliaria e. Inversiones Valle Hermoso Ltd.	Santa Fe 2 coal mine near Curanilahue,	Region VIII	Not available
Chabunco S.A.	Bish coal mine, Magallanes	Region XII	600 000

Source: US Geological Survey.

The 20 MW Calle power plant is located eight kilometers from Valdivia city. This project is valued at US $4.8 million.

Although coal is cheap and obtaining it is not a complicated process, several projects, including the Barrancones and Castilla thermal power plants, have faced difficulties related to obtaining environmental permits. The 700 MW Castilla coal-fired power plant is currently awaiting environmental permits to start construction. The owner, MPX Energia SA (Brazil), plans to invest US $750 million to supply the Atacama region with electricity. The plant will have two coal-fired supercritical boilers to drive two 350 MW steam turbines. On the other hand, the 540 MW Barrancones project obtained the environmental permits but Chilean President Sebastián Piñera decided to abort the construction of the coal-fired power facility.

Electricity Generation

In 2008, the country generated 56.3 TWh of electricity. Around 6% of the total electricity generation of the region was generated using coal as fuel. During the period 1973-2008, the participation of coal as fuel in electricity generation increased from 14% in 1973 to 23.6% in 2008; this represents an increase of 69% in thirty five years (an average of 2% per year) (see Figure 113).

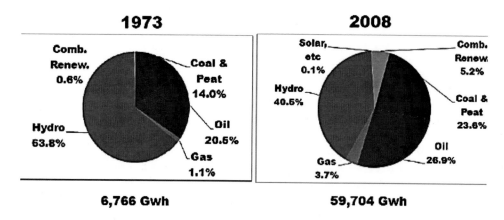

Electricity generation up almost 8 times, with coal share up 70 percent
Source: IEA.

Figure 113. Coal participation in the country electricity generation during the period 1973-2008.

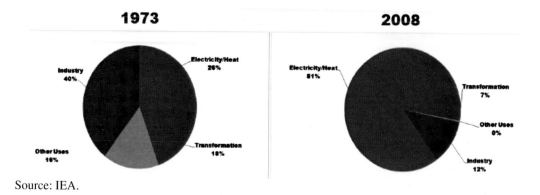

Source: IEA.

Figure 114. Chile use of coal in 1973 and 2008.

From Figure 114, the following can be stated: In 1973, the use of coal for the production of electricity and heat represented 26% of the total (14% for electricity generation and 12% for heating); in 2008, this percentage increased up to 81% (23.6% for the electricity generation, an increase of 9.6% respect to 1973); this respresents an increase of 55% respect to 1973. The participation of coal in the industry dropped from 40% in 1973 to 12% in 2008.

Looking Forward

In July 2010, the Minera Isla Reisco company - a joint venture between Chilean fuel distributor and forest company conglomerate Copec and the shipping company Ultramar - announced that its new Mina Invierno coal mine, in the country's Southern Region X11, would replace "close to 30% of coal imports." Along with reserves in Rio Eduardo and Elena, the three sites are believed to host more than 1 billion tons of coal (estimated at 1 302 million tons in 2010). The largest of these deposits lies in the Bío-Bío region.

In January 2011, it was announced by government officials that 48% of the power projects to be inaugurated in Chile between 2011 and 2014 will use coal as the main fuel. More than US $13.5 billion will be invested in coal-fired power plants in the country through 2014.

In March 2010, Endesa stated that it projected that there would be "9 400 MW of new capacity during next ten years" in Chile and that "3 300 MW are already under construction". Of the new supply, Endesa projected that coal would account for 38% of the new capacity.

In Feb. 2011, Chile's environment regulator approved MPX Energia SA's proposed US $4.4 billion coal-fired power plant project in northern Chile. MPX plans to build the largest coal-fired power plant in Chile. The Castilla coal-fired power plant will be built on the Pacific Coast 700 kilometers north of Santiago and will provide 2 100 MW of energy to Chile's central power grid.

Finally it is important to stick out the following: A new coal-fired power plant was built in Mejillones, on the Pacific Ocean. The power plant use circulating fluidized bed technology, which will enable the burning of biomass and other fuels for the generation of electricity. The power plant went online in 2010. This project, along with the LNG import and regasification terminal in Mejillones, and the Horniots thermoelectric power plant, will contribute decisively to fuel security and diversity on the electricity network. That enhanced security will benefit residential customers as well as mining, industrial, and services activities in Chile's Norte Grande region.

MEXICO

The Energy Reform

The structure of Mexican mining changed deeply with the 1961 Mining Code, which in essence placed the control of resources in Mexican hands, through purchase of international, mainly American, interests such as the mining properties of American Smelting and Refining Company. The 1975 Mining Code limited foreign interests to a maximum 34% of total capital in coal, as well as in sulfur, among other essentially non-metallic mining products. In 1983, approximately 25% of coal production was controlled by the government and the remaining 75% by private capital, mostly Mexican.

Nevertheless, the new 1992 Mexican Mining Law, following a generally liberal international trend, permits 100% control of coal mining properties (as well as sulfur, phosphate, and other deposits) not only by private Mexican interests but also by foreign mining companies as well, subject to a standard and more facilitated concessionary process.

Coal Production, Consumption, and Reserves

According to Dr. Wallace from the UNAM, the first known economic coal production in Mexico was initiated in 1884 near Sabinas in Coahuila State. Later, continued production on a small scale together with imports serviced the railroads and towards the latter years of the 19th century, the nascent metallurgical and steel industries, mostly located in northern

Mexico, required increasing amounts of coal. Although the interest in coal suffered from the rapid development and production of oil in the early years of the 20th century, particularly affecting coal's use in electricity generation, it remained an indispensable input for steel and the mining-metallurgical industry. Nevertheless, even during the period of growth 1902-1910, total coal production only summed a little over 10 million metric tons, and even in 1920, when Mexico's northern neighbor was extracting 600 million metric tons per year, Mexico was not able to surpass the 1.3 million metric tons it had produced in 1910. The Mexican Revolution (1910-1917) caused an abrupt and ongoing decline in overall economic activity, as evidenced in the case of coal also by a total production of only about four million metric tons during the period 1911-1921. This stagnation was not much improved upon during the next two decades during which total coal production was about 12 million metric tons, mostly of the coking variety.

Mexico has a coal reserves of 1,211 billion short tons in 2009, which represent 0.15% of world's total coal reserves. Out of this total, about 860 million tons is bituminous coal with minor quantities metamorphosed to anthracite, and 351 million tons is sub-bituminous. The majority of the coal reserves are in the State of Coahuila, in the northeastern part of the country. The proved reserves/production ratio at the end of 2007 was estimated to be about 99 years.

Table 69. Production and consumption of coal in Mexico in 2008 and 2009 (Million short tons)

	Mexico 2008	North America	World	Rank	Mexico 2009
Production	12.652	1 259	7 505	26	11.627
Consumption	16.710	1 199	7 346	31	19.890
Net export/import (-)	-5.068	53	--	27	-6.852

Source: EIA.

Nevertheless, after many decades of virtual stagnation or low growth, beginning in 1983 Mexican coal production increased significantly to 5.5 million tons and, with minor fluctuations, reached 11.3 million tons in 2000, after which it leveled off. Of the 11.5 million tons produced in 2006, 83% was sub-bituminous thermal coal destined for electricity power plants and the rest, coking coal, mostly for the iron and steel industry. But even with the respectable increase of domestic production, the total amount was not enough to satisfy total coal demand, particularly for sub-bituminous coal demanded by the CFE, whose growing interest in coal-fired electricity power plants apparently is due to a prudent skepticism regarding future PEMEX oil and gas production (Martin-Amouroux, 2008). For example, in 2006 national production of approximately 11.5 million tons minus stock changes (-2.3 million tons) was far short of satisfying demand (16.9 million tons), thus requiring imports of 7.6 million tons of coal. The CFE absorbed 14.7 million tons of total supply (87%).

Mexico produced 12.7 million short tons in 2008 and 11.6 million short tons in 2009, a reduction of 9% respect to 2008. The coal consumption in 2008 was 16.7 million short tons and, in 2009 it was 19.8 million short tons, representing an increase of 19% in comparison with 2008. Most coal consumption is for electricity generation, followed by steel-making. In 2008, the import of coal reached 5.1 million short tons and in 2009 was 6.9 million short tons, an increase of 31% respect to 2008.

The most important coal producer in Mexico until recently was Mission Energy through the purchase of government owned Minera Carbonífera Río Escondido (MICARE) but this group apparently withdrew from most of its widespread international interests, including MICARE in 2004, which is now a 100% subsidiary of Altos Hornos de Mexico, itself controlled by Grupo Acerero del Norte. Other important mining companies are Minera Monclova, a 98% owned subsidiary of Altos Hornos de Mexico and Carbonífera de San Patricio (a 100% private Mexican firm). Minera Carbonífera Río Escondido, basically a thermal coal producer, and Minera Monclova, the principal producer of metallurgical coal, together produced about 82% of the nation's coal in 2007. Hidalgo Mining International, headquartered in New York, with 300 million tons of coal reserves in northern Mexico, has been the object of a purchase offer by Consolidated Mining and Mineral. Minera Monclova operated four underground mines and two open pit mines in 2007, while Minera Carbonífera Río Escondido has one producing open pit mine and two underground mines. All are located in the Sabinas Basin.

Coal Exploration

Coal provides only about 4% of Mexico's total energy requirements. The major coal mines are:

a) Mimosa and the Palau coal mines located in Coahuila State, which combined produced approximately three million tons. The coal from the mines is processed at the Muzquiz washing plant at Palau, and the coking plant at Monclova. The mines are operated by Minera Monclova, S.A. a wholly owned subsidiary of Altos Hornos de México, S.A.;

b) The Progreso coal mine in Coahuila State which produced approximately 1.3 million tons. The mine is owned by the privately owned company Carbonífera de San Patricio S.A.;

c) The Nueva Rosita coal mine produced approximately 1.5 million tons. The mine is owned by Industrial Minera México S.A., a 90% owned subsidiary of Grupo Mexico;

d) The Mina I and II coal mines at Nava and the Tajo I coal mine at Piedras have a combined output of 6.5 million tons. The mines are wholly owned subsidiaries of Altos Hornos de Mexico.

Mission Energy's production comes from the Sabinas and Fuentes-Rio Escondido Basins in Coahuila State. Operations there are comprised of two open pits and three underground mines with reserves of 208.5 million tons. Domestic supplies are augmented by a small volume of imports from the United States, Canada, and Colombia. Both hard coal and brown coal are consumed in Mexico. Hard coal is used by coke ovens in industrial operations, while consumption of brown coal is devoted entirely to electricity generation.

Although traces of coal have been detected in numerous States, there are three locally important coal regions. The most important is the Sabinas Basin and Fuentes-Rio Escondido of north-central Coahuila State, including a small contiguous area of Nuevo Leon, covering approximately 12 000 km. The Sabinas Basin (the source of mostly coking coal of lower ash content than thermal coal) and Fuentes-Rio Escondido (mostly thermal coal) produce more than 90% of Mexican coal.

The next most important region, though vastly inferior, is found in the northwest portion of Oaxaca, where seams varying from a few centimeters to three meters are estimated to contain not much more than 30 million tons (Corona et al, 2006). The third field, located south of Hermosillo in Sonora is also of low estimated reserves (85 million tons) (Martin-Amouroux, 2008).

Electricity Generation

The country generated 245.52 billion kWh in 2009, which represent a decrease of 2% respect to 2008. Conventional thermal generation represents the overwhelming majority of Mexico's electricity generation, though the mix from these sources is gradually shifting from oil products to natural gas.

According to SENER, of total Mexican electricity generation in 2006, coal was responsible for 12.7%. Nevertheless, regarding the total installed public service capacity, the electric generating plants using coal accounted for only 9.2% in 2007. It is expected an increase in the use of coal for the generation of electricity in the coming years, due to a foreseen reduction in the production of oil and the desire of the government to reduce the country's high reliance on natural gas.

Looking Forward

According to Dr. Wallace from the UNAM, there is a major difference regarding the demand forecasts for the use of coal in the electricity generating industry versus the iron and steel industry. To satisfy primary energy demand, total demand for coal is expected to grow at about 4.2% annually to 2030. The expected increase in coal's share is largely due to the government's desire to diversify fuel usage in electricity generation and, thereby, reduce the country's high reliance on natural gas. Electricity generation is projected to be about 505 TWh by 2030, of which amount 59% will be provided by gas, 19% by coal, 10% by oil, 7% by hydro and 3% by nuclear plus renewable energy sources.

VENEZUELA

Coal Production, Consumption, and Reserves

According to the BP Statistical Review of World Energy (2010), Venezuela had, at the end of 2009, coal reserves of 479 million short tons and recoverable coal reserves of approximately 528 million short tons, most of which is bituminous. Venezuela had in 2006, a coal production of 8.1 million short tons. In 2008, the coal production was 8.4 million short tons, an increase of 4% in comparison to 2006. In 2009, the coal production was 9.7 million short tons (an increase of 15% in comparison to 2008), ranking 30th in the list of world's coal producers. Most coal production is exported, mainly to the USA and Europe. In 2008, the consumption of coal was 0.1 million short tons and in 2009 it was 0.35 million short tons; this represents an increase of 218%, ranking 91th in the list of world's coal consumers. Venezuela exports 9.35 million short tons in 2009.

Coal use in Venezuela is mainly limited to the use of coking coal in small local foundries in the Andes region, and in other small-scale industry elsewhere. There is a small level of production from the Andes region that generally comprising small underground mines producing coking coal for local consumption, and also in the northeastern region of the country. In 2002, a tender was invited for development of coal deposits in Anzoátegui State, in the northeastern part of the country, and another tender process was commenced for development of concessions in Falcon State, in the west of the country but in neither case has significant development progressed due to different causes.

Coal Exploitation

The majority of Venezuela's coal mines are located in the Guasaré Basin near the Colombian border. Fortunately, the favorable location of the coal field to deep-water ports as well as good coal quality, make Venezuela's coal highly favorable to foreign investment. Production is dominated by Carbozulia, which is owned by PdVSA. The company operates in joint ventures with a number of foreign companies, such as Shell, Ruhrkohle, and Inter-American Coal.

Table 70. Coal production and consumption in Venezuela in 2008 and 2009
(Millions of short tons)

	Venezuela 2008	Central and South America	World	Rank	Venezuela 2009
Production	8.429	98	7 505	30	9.692
Consumption	0.113	45	7 346	91	0.347
Net export/import (-)	8.128	49	--	100	9.345

Source: EIA.

Anglo Coal acquired a 24.9% interest in Carbones del Guasaré that owns and operates the Paso Diablo mine in the State of Zulia, in northern Venezuela. Paso Diablo is one of Venezuela's largest coal mines and has reserves estimated at 180 million short tons.

There are also a number of additional coal blocks in the Zulia region that are said to be under evaluation and permitting. The most imminent for development and production is Las Carmelitas, situated in the Guajira coal area, west of Maracaibo, which will be operated by Complejo Siderúrgico del Lago CA, a subsidiary of Tomen America, which already owns the coal export port of Palmarejo on Lake Maracaibo.

Carbones de la Guajira is the second-largest coal producer and operates Mina Norte with production capacity of around 1.5 million short tons in 2003 compared to 1.4 million short tons in 2002, an increase of 7%. Carbones de la Guajira is a joint venture between Carbozulia and Interamerican Coal Inc. The Paso Diablo and Mina Norte operations each truck their coal over 100 km to independent port facilities on Lake Maracaibo, in each case requiring barge transfer and floating cranes for loading in the main shipping channel of the lake.

Current government plans call for opening the sector up further to private operators, extending concessions to forty years, and improving tax laws. Several foreign companies have been awarded contracts to manage Venezuelan coal mines.

Electricity Generation

Coal is not used in Venezuela for electricity generation.

Chapter V

CONCLUSION

One of the main problems that the world is facing is how to satisfy the increase in electricity demand using all available energy sources in the most efficient manner and without increasing CO_2 emission.

The preparation of a national energy policy, in which priorities and preferences are identified, should be one of the main governmental responsibilities. Every country's energy mix should involve a range of national preferences and priorities in order to satisfy the foreseable increase in electricity demand without affecting the climate. These national policies and strategies should balance between expected energy shortages, environmental quality, energy security, energy cost, public attitudes, safety and security, and production and service capabilities.

Relevant national energy authorities and the representatives of the energy industry must take all of these elements into account when formulating an energy policy and strategy for the development of the energy sector in the future.

The provision of adequate and reliable energy services at an affordable cost in a secure and environmentally benign manner and in conformity with social and economic development needs is an essential element of sustainable development. Energy is vital for eradicating poverty, improving human welfare and raising living standards. However, most current patterns of energy supply and use are considered unsustainable. Many areas of the world have no reliable and secure energy supplies, and hence no energy services, which limits their economic development. In other areas, environmental degradation from energy production and use inhibits sustainable development.

Adequate and affordable energy services have been critical to economic development and the transition from subsistence agricultural economies to modern industrial and service-oriented societies. Energy is central to improved social and economic well-being, and is indispensable for industrial and commercial wealth generation. But, however, essential it may be for economic and social development, energy is only a means to an end. The end is a sustainable economy and a clean environment, high living standards, prosperity, and good health.

In 2009, the installed electrical generation capacity of the Latin America and the Caribbean region was, according to British Petroleum (2010), of 1 082.3 TWh, a decrease of 4% respect to 2008. The consumption was, according to EIA (2010), of 873.51 TWh; this represents 80.7% of the total production.

According Business Monitor International sources, Latin American and the Caribbean power generation assumption for 2010 was 1 198 TWh, an increase of 11% over 2008 and the forecast for 2014 is 1 359 TWh, representing an increase of 13.5% between 2010 and 2014. The BMI report forecast for 2010 Latin American thermal power generation to reach 445 TWh[126], accounting for 37.1% of the total electricity supplied in the region. The BMI forecast for 2014 is 480 TWh, implying 8% growth between 2010 and 2014.

According to IEO (2010), world's net electricity generation increases by 87% in the reference case, from 18.8 trillion kWh in 2007 to 25 trillion kWh in 2020 and to 35.2 trillion kWh in 2035. Although the recession slowed the growth in electricity demand in 2008 and 2009, it is expected that growth will returns to pre-recession rates by 2015. In general, in the industrialized world, where electricity markets are well established and consumption patterns are mature, the growth of electricity demand is slower than in other countries, where a large amount of potential demand remains unmet. In the reference case, total net generation in this last group of countries increases by 3.3% per year on average, as compared with 1.1% per year in the industrialized nations.

In the Latin America and the Caribbean region, the majority of the installed capacity of electricity belongs to the public sector (92% of the total), and the rest were private and auto-generators. In the list of top 15 countries with the highest electricity generation capacity only Brazil (9th) and Mexico (15th) are included.

According to historical data, the power sector in Latin America and the Caribbean has experienced steady growth since the 1970s. The regional electricity production grew at an average rate of 5.9% per year between 1970 and 2005, compared to the worldwide average over the period of 4.3%; this means an increase of 1.6% over the world average. Six countries of the region account for 84% of total electricity production in the Latin American and the Caribbean region. Brazil is the largest electricity producer (35.7% of the total), followed by Mexico (20.8%), Argentina (9.4%), Venezuela (9%), Colombia (4.6%), Paraguay (4.5%), and Chile (4.4%). Paraguay is a significant producer through its share of production from the gigantic Itaipú hydro power plant is sold to Brazil.

It is important to stress, regarding the mix of primary fuels, the following: The mix of primary fuels used to generate electricity has changed a great deal over the past four decades on a worldwide basis. Coal continues to be the fuel most widely used for electricity generation, except for the Latin American and the Caribbean region, although generation from nuclear power increased rapidly from the 1970s through the 1980s, and natural-gas-fired generation grew rapidly in the 1980s and 1990s.

The use of oil for electricity generation has been declining since the mid-1970s, when the oil embargo by Arab producers in 1973-1974 and the Iranian Revolution in 1979 caused oil's prices to increase to levels much higher than those for other fuels. Although world's oil prices contracted strongly at the end of 2008 and into 2009, the high prices recorded in 2012 combined with concerns about the environmental consequences of greenhouse gas emissions and the level of oil's reserves, renewed interest in the development of alternatives to fossil fuels—specifically, nuclear power and renewable energy sources.

Natural gas has become increasingly important for electricity production globally, and particularly in Latin American and the Caribbean region over the last twenty years, gaining ground at the expense of oil and hydroelectric sources. As can be noted, the share of

---

[126] A decrease of 2% respect to 2008.

electricity produced from oil in the world's generation mix declined from 11% in 1985 to only 6% in 2005 and this trend will continue in the future. The use of nuclear energy for electricity generation is expected to increases from about 2.6 trillion kWh in 2007 to a projected 3.6 trillion kWh in 2020, and then to 4.5 trillion kWh in 2035. However, this projection could be significantly reduced as result of the nuclear accident in the Fukushima nuclear power plant occurred in March 2011 and by the adoption of a nuclear phase-out policy by a group of countries.

The rapid increase in world energy prices from 2003 to 2012, combined with concerns about the environmental consequences of greenhouse gas emissions, has led to renewed interest in alternatives to fossil fuels - particularly, nuclear power and renewable energy resources. As a result, long-term prospects continue to improve for generation from both nuclear and renewable energy sources - supported by government incentives and by higher fossil fuel prices. From 2007 to 2035, world renewable energy use for electricity generation is expected to grow by an average of 3% per year, and the renewable share of world electricity generation is expected to increases from 18% in 2007 to 23% in 2035.

It is important to stress that higher future prices for fossil fuels make nuclear power economically competitive with electricity generation from coal, natural gas, and liquid fuels, despite the relatively high capital costs associated to the construcution of nuclear power plants. Moreover, higher capacity utilization rates have been reported for many existing nuclear facilities, and the projection anticipates that several nuclear power plants in North America, Europe and Asia will be granted extensions to their operating lives. However, the final number of nuclear power reactors that their operating lives will be extended is, at this stage, unknown as result of the negative reaction of some governments to authorize this extension after the nuclear accident in the Fukushima nuclear power plant. The projection for nuclear electricity generation in 2030 is 9% higher than the projection published in last year's IEO but this increase could be much lower as a consequence of the nuclear accident in the Fukushima nuclear power plant.

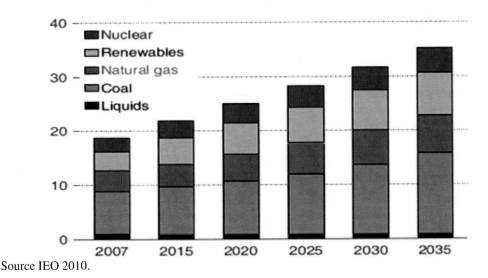

Source IEO 2010.

Figure 115. World net electricity generation by fuel during the period 2007-2035 (Trillion kWh).

Based on the IEO (2009) report, the impact of the recession on electricity consumption is likely to be felt most strongly in the industrial sector, as manufacturing slows as a result of lower demand for manufactured products. Demand in the residential sector is less sensitive to changing economic conditions than the industrial sector, because people generally continue to consume electricity for space heating and cooling, cooking, refrigeration, and hot water heating even in a recession.

In the Latin American and the Caribbean region with oil trading at more than US $100 per barrel in 2012, natural gas in short supply, and a new wave of droughts threatening hydroelectricity production, several countries of the region are once again facing the possibility of energy shortages. Argentina, Brazil, Chile, Ecuador, and Venezuela are under particular pressure to ensure that overstretched electricity and gas supplies could meet an increase electricity demand during the coming months and years. In contrast to shortages in the past, which were blamed on short-term factors, many analysts now believe that energy scarcity will be a long-term problem. The two fundamental reasons are the demand driven by sustained economic growth in emerging economies, and the difficulty of obtaining new sources of fossil fuels. The Latin American and the Caribbean countries exemplify both trends.

In the specific case of the Andean zone, electricity consumption increased 30% between 1994 and 2004 reaching 168 TWh in the last year of the period. In 2007, around 25% of the installed capacity in South America was in the Andean countries. Demand in the Andean zone has been rising by 3.3% a year. In this group of countries electricity generation is diverse, namely hydro, coal, gas, oil for thermal generation, and alternative sources such as wind and solar energy. The expected increase in thermal power generation will also lead to an increase in the consumption of oil, natural gas, and coal particularly in Peru. New hydro power plants and renewable energy sources will also be used to meet this expected increase.

At the beginning of the 1990s, the electricity system of the Andean countries was in a critical situation, caused by the lack of resources to guarantee the necessary investments to increase the supply and assure the upkeep of the existing infrastructure. Due to this situation, several Andean countries began reorganization of their electricity systems. In general, they tried to separate the State's roles, in order to allow the private sector to act as entrepreneur and foster investments, while the government was restricted to the role of policy maker and regulator. In Peru, Bolivia, and Ecuador, regulatory agencies were created but linked to certain established Ministries. In Colombia, an independent regulatory agency was created, supervised by the government, while the task of defining policies was assigned to the Administration. Only Venezuela, now outside the Andean group, did not make any substantial change to the structure of its electric system.

As a result of implemented changes, the Andean zone, except Venezuela, adopted some ways to trade energy with the obligatory participation by market players. Generally, that meant the creation of wholesale electricity markets. The common motivation was to create competition in the electricity system in order to improve an infrastructure that is not in a position to meet the growing demand for electricity, to attract foreign investments, and to allow expansion of the installed energy capacity.

Decision 536 "General Framework for Sub-Regional Interconnection of Electric Power Systems and Intra-community Exchange of Electricity", approved in December 2002, gave the community a legal framework for promoting the development of the electricity theme among member countries.

It is foreseen that the energy demand in Latin American and the Caribbean region will increase 75% by 2030, requesting an investments of US $1,600 billion in the next decade alone in order to support this increase. The region will require a 50% increase in its energy installed capacity; this represents more than 90 GW to satisfy the foreseable energy demand in the coming years.

Summing up the following can be stated:

1. By 2030, with a modest rate of economic growth, the region's demand for electricity would reach nearly 2 500 TWh, up from around 1 150 TWh in 2008; this represents an increase of 117.4%. Electricity demand in Brazil would more than double to around 1 090 TWh. A total of 239 GW of new electricity generation capacity would be needed to match demand at regional level, with Brazil adding about 97 GW, the Southern Cone 45 GW, Mexico 44 GW, the Andean Zone 30 GW, Central America 15 GW, and the Caribbean 7 GW;

2. Hydro and natural gas would provide the majority of additional power capacity. Although the share of hydro will continue to decline, the combined share of hydro and natural gas will be higher. There would continue to be a decline in the use of oil and a slight increase in the use nuclear energy for electricity generation (concentrated in Argentina, Brazil, and Mexico) despite the Fukushima nuclear accident, and the increase in the use non-hydro renewables for electricity generation;

3. The high degree of fuel and generation technology diversity in the Southern Cone would become even more dynamic over the period, with the region adding sizeable generating capacity for hydro, natural gas, coal, and nuclear energy in the specific case of Argentina and Brazil;

4. In Central America, fuel oil, coal, and natural gas would together account for about 45% of additional capacity;

5. In the Caribbean sub-region, the generation mix would continue to be largely fossil fuel-dependent, with gas accounting for 43% of the additional capacity to be installed and coal 23%;

6. The investment in new generation capacity is estimated to be about US $430 billion between 2008 and 2030. Investments by country and sub-region would be: Brazil US $182 billion, the Southern Cone US $78 billion, the Andean Community of Nations US $58 billion, Central America US $25 billion, and the Caribbean US $9 billion;

7. CO_2 emissions from electricity generation in Latin America and the Caribbean would more than double between 2008 and 2030 as a result of the decline in hydroelectricity and an increase in fossil fuels.

BIBLIOGRAPHY

[1]   Activities and Prospects In Coal Exporting and Importing Countries (2009); *Tex Energy Report* (September 7, 2009).

[2]   A Review of the Power Sector in Latin America and the Caribbean, *Evolution in the Market and Investment Opportunities for CFTs* (2005); Deutsche Montan Technologie GmbH Essen, Germany; OLADE, Latin American Energy Organization, Quito, Ecuador; and CIEMAT, Madrid, Spain; March 2005.

[3]   Alhajji, A. and Maris, T.L. (2003); *The Future of Cuba's Energy Sector*; Chapter 8, Economic Transitions, web.gc.cuny.edu/dept/bildn/publications/documents/Ahajjiand Maris8.pd; 2003.

[4]   Altomonte, H.; Coviello, M. and Lutz, W.F. (2003); Energías Renovables y Eficiencia Energética en América Latina y el Caribe. *Restricciones y Perspectivas*; ECLAC; Santiago de Chile; Chile; 2003.

[5]   Alves Ferreira, Pedro Jobim (2002); *On the Efficiency of the Argentinean Electricity Wholesale Market;* Department of Economics, University of Chicago, Chicago, USA; 2002.

[6]   *An Energy Overview of Chile* (2002); U.S. Department of Energy, Office of Fossil Energy, Washington DC, USA; 2002.

[7]   *Anuario Estadístico de Cuba* 2003 (2004); Statistic National Office; Havana, Cuba; 2004.

[8]   Arrastia Avila, Mario Alberto (2008); *Distributed Generation in Cuba: part of a transition towards a new energy paradigm;* Centre of Information Management and Energy Development; Co-generation and On-Site Power Production; Havana, Cuba; November–December 2008.

[9]   Arriagada, G. (2006); *Petro politics in Latin America: A Review of Energy Policy and Regional Relations;* Inter-American Dialogue; Washington D.C., USA; December 2006.

[10] Assessment of Undiscovered Oil and Gas Resources of the North Cuba Basin (2005); *World Assessment of Oil and Gas Fact Sheet;* US Geological Survey; USA; 2005.

[11] Bacon, R.W. and Besant-Jones, J. (2002); Global Electric Power Reform, Privatization and Liberalization of the Electric Power Industry in Developing Countries; *Energy and Mining Sector Board Discussion Paper No. 2;* World Bank; Washington, DC., USA; June 2002.

[12] Belt, Juan A. B. (2009); *The Electric Power Sector in Cuba: Potential Ways to Increase Efficiency and Sustainability*; U.S. Agency for International Development; USA; 2009.

[13] *Brazil: A Country Profile on Sustainable Energy Development* (2006); Jointly sponsored by the IAEA- International Atomic Energy Agency, COPPE—Graduate School of Engineering (Federal University of Rio de Janeiro), CENBIO—Brazilian Reference Centre on Biomass (University of São Paulo) and United Nations Department of Economic and Social Affairs; IAEA, Vienna; Austria; STI/PUB/1247; August 2006.

[14] British Petroleum Statistical Review of World Energy (2009); *BP Statistical Review of World Energy;* London, UK; 2009.

[15] British Petroleum Statistical Review of World Energy (2010); BP Statistical Review of World Energy; London, UK; June 2010.

[16] Brito Castillo, Jorge (2007); Using Natural Gas to Produce Electricity; Mipymes Magazine July - August 2006. Inter-American Entrepreneurial Federation (FIE); 2007.

[17] Caribbean Regional Electricity Generation, Interconnection, and Fuels Supply Strategy (2010); *Final Report*; Nexant; World Bank; 2010.

[18] Clemente, Jude (2008); *Energy Security in Mexico: Problems and Implications*; San Diego State University; California; USA; 2008.

[19] Clough, Langdon D. (2007); "Energy profile of Ecuador." In: *Encyclopedia of Earth*. Eds. Cutler J. Cleveland; Energy Information Administration, Environmental Information Coalition, National Council for Science and the Environment; 2007.

[20] Clough, Langdon D. (2008): Energy Profile of Peru (2008); In: *Encyclopedia of Earth*. Eds. Cutler J. Cleveland; Energy Information Administration (Content source); Washington, D.C.: Environmental Information Coalition, National Council for Science and the Environment; Washington, D.C.; USA; 2008.

[21] CNE (Comisión Nacional de Energía), *Estadísticas-Electricidad*; http://www.cne.cl/electricidad/f_sector.html.

[22] *Colombia: Ausenco Gets Engineering Contract for Puerto Nuevo* (2009); South American Business Information; December, 2009.

[23] Colombia Energy Data, Statistics and Analysis - Oil, Gas, Electricity and Coal (2010); *Colombia Country Analysis Briefs*; Energy Information Administration; USA; 2010.

[24] Colombia: Country energy profiles (2009). In Energy Information Administration, *World Energy Overview*: 1996-2006; US DOE; USA; EIA web site: http://www.eia.doe.gov/iea/; 2009.

[25] Colombia Moves Ahead on Port Expansions (2008); *Argus Coal Transportation Report,* Vol. 28, No. 4; January, 2008.

[26] Colombia Suspends Coal Rail Project (2010); *Argus Coal Transportation Report*, Vol. 98, No. 8; February, 2010).

[27] Commission on Sustainable Development, *Report of the ninth session* (2001); E/CN.17/2001/19; United Nations, New York; USA; 2001.

[28] Corona-Esquivel, Rodolfo et al (2006); Geología, estructura y composición de los principales yacimientos de carbón mineral en México; *Boletín de la Sociedad Geológica Mexicana,* Tomo LVIII, Núm. 1; 2006.

[29] Cuba: A Country Profile on Sustainable Energy Development (2008); *A report Jointly Sponsored by the International Atomic Energy Agency*, The Centro de Gestión de la

Información y Desarrollo de la Energía and the United Nations Department of Economic and Social Affairs; Vienna, Austria; 2008.

[30] De Martino Jannuzzi, Gilberto (2004); Power sector reforms in Brazil and its impacts on energy efficiency and research and development activities; Universidade Estadual de Campinas, Campinas São Paulo, Brazil; International Energy Initiative: Latin America; *Energy Discussion paper No. 2.62-01/04*; 2004.

[31] Delaveau, Gonzalo and Zavala, MARCOs (2010); *The International Comparative Legal Guide to Gas Regulation*; Published by Global Legal Group in association with Ashurst LLP; Chapter 9, Chile; Guerrero, Olivos, Novoa y Errázuriz Ltda; 2010.

[32] Delgado, G.C. (2004); *Cuba y la Geopolítica Petrolera Imperial en el Golfo de México;* Rebelión; Mexico City, Mexico; 2004.

[33] Dussan, M. (1996); *Electric Power Sector Reform in Latin America and the Caribbean;* Inter-American Development Bank; Washington D.C., USA; 1996.

[34] Echeverry, Juan Carlos; Navas, Jaime and Navas, Veronica (2008); Oil *in Colombia: history, regulation and macroeconomic impact*; Universidad de los Andes; Colombia; 2008.

[35] Ecuador Country Analysis Brief (2009); *Energy Information Administration, Department of Energy;* Washington DC, USA; 2009.

[36] Ecuador Country Analysis Brief (2010); *Energy Information Administration, Department of Energy;* Washington DC, USA; 2010.

[37] Ellsworth, Chris and Gibbs, Eric (2004); Brazil's Natural Gas Industry: Missed Opportunities on the Road to Liberalizing Markets; *Critical Issues in Brazil's Energy Sector;* The James A. Baker III Institute for Public Policy of Rice University with the support of the BP Foundation; March 2004.

[38] *Energy indicators for sustainable development: Country Studies on Brazil, Cuba, Lithuania Mexico, Russian Federation, Slovakia and Thailand* (2007); International Atomic Energy Agency and the United Nations Department of Economic and Social Affair; February 2007.

[39] Energy profile of Ecuador (2007); *Energy Information Administration*, Department of Energy; Washington DC, USA; 2007.

[40] Energy profile of Mexico (2009); *Encyclopedia of Earth, Environmental Information Coalition*, National Council for Science and the Environment; Washington, D.C., USA; http://www.eoearth.org/article/Energy profile of Mexico; 2009.

[41] Goldwyn, David (2006); Energy Security in Latin America: The Challenge to US Influence; *Testimony of before the Senate Foreign Relations Committee*; Washington DC, USA; June 2006.

[42] Government Aims To Have Coal Production of Chile, Peru by 2019 (2009); Colombia," *BN Mining News*; (2009).

[43] Hammons, T.J. (2001); Electricity Restructuring in Latin America Systems with Significant Hydro Generation; University of Glasgow, Glasgow, UK; *Rev. Energ. Ren. Power Engineering;* 2001.

[44] Huiskamp, Han (2007); *Investing in Sustainable Energy Security*: Ecuador, the Netherlands and Kyoto; Quito, Ecuador; 2007.

[45] IJHD (2010); World Atlas and Industry Guide. *International Journal of Hydro power and Dams*; Wallington, Surrey, UK; 2010.

[46] *International Energy Outlook 2007;* Energy Information Administration, DOE/EIA-0484 (2007); Washington, DC, USA; 2007.

[47] *International Energy Outlook 2008;* Energy Information Administration, DOE/EIA-0484 (2008); Washington, DC, USA; September 2008.

[48] *International Energy Outlook 2009;* Energy Information Administration, DOE/EIA-0484 (2009), Office of Integrated Analysis and Forecasting, U.S. Department of Energy; Washington, DC 20585; May 2009.

[49] *International Energy Outlook 2010;* Energy Information Administration, DOE/EIA-0484 (2010); Washington, DC, USA; September 2010.

[50] Isbell, P. (2009); *Energy for the Western Hemisphere: Revisiting Latin America's Energy Scene before the 5th Summit of the Americas*; Elcano Royal Institute; 2009.

[51] Landau, George D. (2007); *Brazil and Latin America's Energy Crisis*; Energy Security: An Agenda of Global Challenges; Institute for Security Studies; European Union, EUISS Annual Conference on Effective Multilateralism: Engaging with the new global players, Paris, France; 22-23 November 2007.

[52] Lamm, M. (2009); *Energy Policy in Latin America: A Crossroads of Environmentalism, Indigenous Rights and Development*; Americas; September 2009.

[53] López, I. and Pérez, D. (2000); *Comportamiento de las emisiones de gases de efecto invernadero en el sector eléctrico durante 1990–1999*; Encuentro Nacional de Aplicaciones Nucleares (Proc. Conf. Rio de Janeiro, 2000), ABEN, Rio de Janeiro, Brazil; 2000.

[54] Lynch, Richard (2003); An *Energy Overview of Argentina;* U.S. Department of Energy, Office of Fossil Energy; Washington, D.C., USA; 2003.

[55] Lynch, Richard (2003 a); An *Energy Overview of Colombia;* U.S. Department of Energy, Office of Fossil Energy Washington, D.C., USA; 2003.

[56] Lynch, Richard (2003 b); An *Energy Overview of Mexico;* U.S. Department of Energy, Office of Fossil Energy Washington, D.C., USA; 2003.

[57] Martin-Amouroux, Jean-Marie (2008); *Charbon, Les métamorphoses d'une industrie*; Ëditions TECHNIP; Paris, France; 2008.

[58] *Brazilian Energy Balance 2004* (2005); Ministry of Mines and Energy; Brasilia, Brazil; www.mme.gov.br; (2005).

[59] *Memories 2004* (2005); Despacho Nacional de Carga, UNE, Basic Industry Ministry; Havana, Cuba; 2005.

[60] Mendonça, A. and Dahl, C. (1999); *The Brazilian electrical system reform*; Energy Policy 27 2; 1999.

[61] MINAE (2003); *IV Plan nacional de energía 2002-2016*; Ministerio del Ambiente y Energía, Dirección Sectorial de Energía; Costa Rica; 2003.

[62] Morales Pedraza, J. (2008); *The Current Situation and the Perspectives of the Energy Sector in the European Region*, Chapter 1 of the book titled "Energy in Europe: Economics, Policy and Strategy"; Nova Science Publisher; New York, USA; 2008.

[63] Muse, T. (2009); Drummond Shifts First Exports From El Descanso; *Platts International Coal Report*, Vol. 16,

[64] Issue 924; June 2009.

[65] *MPX Secures Logistics Solution to Integrated Mining System in Colombia Through Acquisition of Strategic Site to Build Port* (2010); Marketwire; January, 2010.

[66] National Electricity Regulatory Agency (ANEEL) (2005); Banco de Geração; Brasilia, Brazil, www.ANEEL.gov.br; (2005).

[67] Oficina Nacional de Estadísticas (Statistics National Office, ONE 2003b), Estadísticas Energéticas 2001, Havana, Cuba; 2003.

[68] Perczyk, Daniel; *Coal Industry Situation in Argentina;* Instituto Torcuato Di Tella; www.globalmethane.org/documents/partners_argentina_coal_update.pdf.

[69] Peru 2009; The Renewable Energy and Energy Efficiency Partnership (REEEP); www.reeep.org/index.php?id=9353andtext=policyandspecial=viewitemandcid; 2009.

[70] Pollitt, Michael (2004); *Electricity Reform in Chile. Lesson for Developing Countries;* Center for Energy and Environmental Policy Research (CEEPR), University of Cambridge, UK; 2004.

[71] Poveda, M. (2004); *Competence of the energy markets: An evaluation of the restructuring of the energy markets in Latin America and the Caribbean;* OLADE, ACDI-CIDA; University of Calgary; December 2004.

[72] Poveda, M. (2007); *Energy efficiency: an unexploited resource;* OLADE; August 2007.

[73] Pregnaca, R. (2008); *Can Brazil Live Up to Its Steel Powerhouse Billing?;* American Metal Market, web site amm.com/2008-08-21_16-39-54. html; and Brazil Steel Sector Sees Output Up 135 pct. by 2018; Reuters (January 29, 2008), web site www.reuters.com/article/companyNews/idUSN2941534820080129; 2008.

[74] *Preliminary Overview of the Economics of Latin America and the Caribbean 2010* (2010); ECLAC; United Nations; Santiago de Chile; Chile; 2010.

[75] *Regional Energy Integration in Latin America and the Caribbean* (2008); World Energy Council; London; United Kingdom; 2008.

[76] Ruiz Caro, A. (2008); *Energy Integration and Security in Latin America and the Caribbean*; Latin American Centre for Social Equality (CLAES) and the Development; Economy, Ecology, and Equity; Montevideo, Uruguay; July 14-15, 2005. Original paper was presented in this event; 2008.

[77] Ruiz B.J, and Rodríguez-Padilla V. (2006); Renewable energy sources in the Colombian energy policy, analysis and perspectives; *Energy Policy* 34; 2006.

[78] *SENER: Informe de Labores 2005*; Comisión Nacional para el Ahorro de Energía (CONAE); Mexico; 2006.

[79] *Survey of Energy Sources* (2007); World Energy Council, 21st Edition; London, UK; September 2007.

[80] Szklo, A.; Tavares, M.; Barboza, J. (2004); *Existing Brazilian Refineries Production Profile Evolution;* Technical report prepared for IBP Seminar on Brazil's Refinery Expansion up to 2015 presented at COPPE/UFRJ; Rio de Janeiro, Brazil; 2004.

[81] Talwani, Manik (2011); *Oil and gas; Geology, production rates and reserves*: *The future of oil in Mexico*; James Baker III Institute for Public Policy, Rice University and the Mexican studies program at Nuffield College, Oxford University; UK; April 2011.

[82] Tarta, Ramona; Storry, Mark and Cushing, Oliver (2009); Chile Plans for Growth with "All the Options" Energy Mix; *A special report from Global Business Reports and Power;* November 1, 2009.

[83] Tolmasquim, M.; Szklo, A. and Machado, G. (2002); Ministry of Mines and Energy (MME), Plano de Longo Prazo: Projeção da Matriz 2022 — *Sumario Executivo*, MME Press, Brasilia (2002).

[84] Vargas, R. (2007); *Energy Security in Mexico: An Evaluation in the Light of St. Petersburg;* Friedrich Ebert Stiftung, Briefing Paper; Berlin, Germany; 10, July 2007.

[85] Vignolo, Mario and Monzón, Pablo; *Deregulating the electricity sector;* Facultad de Ingeniería, UDELAR, Montevideo, Uruguay; iie.fing.edu.uy/investigación/grupos/syspot/IASTED.pdf.

[86] Viscidi, Lisa (2010); Colombia's Energy Renaissance; *A Working Paper of the Americas Society*/Council of the Americas Energy Action Group; America society/Council of the Americas; Published by Americas Society and Council of the Americas Washington D.C., USA; December 2010.

[87] Wallace, Robert B.; *Coal in Mexico;* http://www.economia.unam.mx/publicaciones/econinforma/pdfs/359/brucelish.pdf.

[88] Walters, J. (2007); Links Mine and Port Expansions; *Argus Coal Transportation Report,* Vol. 26, No. 23; November 6, 2007.

[89] *World Energy Assessment: Energy and the Challenge of Sustainability* (2000); United Nations Development Program (UNDP), United Nations Department of Economic and Social Affairs (UNDESA) and World Energy Council (WEC); 2000.

[90] *World Energy Investment Outlook 2003* (2003); International Energy Agency and the Organization for Economic Co-operation and Development; Paris, France; 2003.

[91] Yepez- García, Rigoberto Ariel; Johnson, Todd M, and Andres, Luis Alberto (2010); *Meeting the Electricity Supply/Demand Balance in Latin America and the Caribbean;* World Bank; September 2010.

ABOUT THE AUTHOR

Jorge Morales Pedraza currently works as a Consultant on International Affairs and possess degrees on Mathematic and on Economic Sciences. Formerly he was a Cuban Ambassador for more than 25 years. In the 1980s, Morales Pedraza was appointed as Ambassador and Permanent Representative of Cuba to the IAEA (International Atomic Energy Agency) and in the 1990s gained the same title with the OPCW (Organization for the Prohibition of Chemical Weapons). In addition he was invited university professor in Mathematics Science and Invited Professor for International Relations in the Diplomatic Academy of Cuba. Thoughtout the 1990s and into the 2000s Morales Pedraza worked for the IAEA as Senior Manager in the Director's office. Over the past years he was involved in the preparation, as author and coauthor, of more than 45 articles published by international publishers houses, including the IAEA, as well as several chapters for various books focusing on the peaceful uses of nuclear energy, renewable and conventional energy, the use of the radition for the sterilization of tissues, tissue banking, financial investment, among other topics. During this period he also authored three books and was invited editor for international journals. Morales Pedraza is member of the Editorial Team of an international specialized journal.

INDEX

C

F

G

H

181, 183, 187, 188, 189, 190, 204, 206, 212, 223, 227, 239, 244, 265, 271, 292, 300
hydroelectric power, 27, 51, 72, 74, 77, 106, 261
hydrogen, 9, 97, 116, 271
hydrological conditions, 50, 218
hyperinflation, 243

I

identification, 6
ideology, 136
IEA, 11, 24, 37, 97, 220, 222, 308, 330
illumination, 317
image, 12, 43
IMF, 71, 319
imitation, 189
impact assessment, 16, 91, 154
imported products, 184
imports, 2, 4, 25, 35, 74, 79, 80, 99, 101, 102, 106, 107, 108, 110, 113, 124, 127, 129, 130, 155, 158, 159, 160, 162, 163, 164, 168, 170, 175, 176, 177, 182, 184, 190, 194, 197, 201, 208, 216, 218, 220, 239, 247, 248, 252, 256, 258, 260, 261, 262, 272, 273, 274, 276, 277, 279, 282, 284, 285, 287, 296, 297, 299, 308, 312, 322, 327, 330, 331, 332, 333
improvements, 13, 19, 45, 46, 158, 293, 321, 325
income, 8, 13, 70, 145, 182, 188, 206, 244, 300, 317
income tax, 300
independence, 43, 188, 217, 275, 277
India, 2, 35, 92, 104, 165, 166, 236, 308, 314
individuals, 289
Indonesia, 214, 253, 286, 310, 314
industrial policy, 21
industrial sectors, 23, 80, 102, 174
industrialization, 48, 130
industrialized countries, 5, 44, 49
industries, 6, 51, 82, 154, 158, 194, 280, 286, 307, 317, 319, 331
ineffectiveness, 9
inefficiency, 25, 174
inertia, 196
inflation, 7, 135, 326
infrastructure, 3, 8, 19, 25, 30, 35, 36, 37, 38, 47, 50, 51, 52, 53, 62, 77, 79, 80, 84, 86, 89, 94, 109, 110, 121, 131, 136, 137, 149, 158, 159, 160, 161, 166, 178, 195, 197, 201, 203, 204, 231, 240, 249, 259, 260, 262, 275, 278, 281, 286, 290, 291, 292, 293, 297, 298, 304, 305, 309, 321, 322, 323, 325, 340
injury, iv
insecurity, 174
inspections, 281

institutions, 42, 43, 63, 71, 76, 84, 91, 158, 159, 206, 254, 277
integration, 6, 7, 9, 14, 32, 37, 63, 69, 71, 72, 73, 74, 75, 76, 77, 78, 79, 83, 84, 85, 86, 89, 90, 111, 124, 133, 179, 226, 237, 238, 240, 253, 262, 268, 274, 277, 293, 296, 299
Inter-American Development Bank, 345
interference, 7, 8, 37, 106
International Atomic Energy Agency, 344, 345, 349
International Energy Agency, 44, 211, 348
international financial institutions, 84
International Monetary Fund, 71
international standards, 26, 31, 57, 116, 138, 157, 160, 204, 215, 219
international trade, 110, 317
intervention, 13
investment capital, 223
investments, 7, 12, 16, 19, 20, 21, 22, 23, 32, 33, 41, 44, 47, 51, 52, 53, 54, 55, 62, 65, 71, 72, 75, 76, 80, 82, 84, 90, 108, 114, 125, 128, 135, 136, 152, 155, 159, 160, 167, 176, 178, 188, 210, 212, 219, 221, 222, 225, 237, 240, 241, 244, 251, 266, 271, 275, 276, 284, 299, 309, 317, 325, 340, 341
investors, 15, 30, 31, 32, 51, 54, 72, 87, 89, 126, 127, 130, 131, 139, 141, 220, 265, 288, 302
ions, 254
Iran, 60, 102, 105, 214, 221
Iraq, 102, 105
iron, 294, 295, 307, 312, 332, 334
islands, 109, 111, 215, 295
Israel, 105
issues, 6, 18, 23, 82, 137, 183, 215, 221, 241, 268
Italy, 137, 259

J

Jamaica, 15, 70, 83, 88, 229, 232, 305
Japan, vii, 60, 61, 190, 259
joint stock company, 264
joint ventures, 108, 149, 222, 286, 335

K

kerosene, 26, 121
Korea, 185, 210, 259
Kuwait, 102
Kyoto Protocol, 6, 17

L

labeling, 19

M

N

O

P

S

U

V

W